W9-DHT-651

NORTH AMERICAN TREES

North American TREES

(Exclusive of Mexico and Tropical United States)

RICHARD J. PRESTON, JR.

Dean, School of Forestry
North Carolina State College

*A handbook
designed for field use,
with plates and
distribution maps*

582.16
P

The Iowa State University Press, *Ames,* Iowa

Learning Resource Center
Wawasee High School
Syracuse, Indiana

WITHDRAWN

© 1948, 1961 The Iowa State University Press
All rights reserved. Printed in the U.S.A.

First edition, 1948
  Second printing, 1950

Second edition, 1961
  Second printing, 1962
  Third printing, 1965
  Fourth printing, 1967

Library of Congress Catalog Card Number: 60–16604

TO MY WIFE
BERNICE BOYNTON PRESTON

PREFACE

Ever increasing numbers of people are becoming interested in the trees and forests of North America. Regional manuals of our native trees are available for the different sections of the United States and Canada, but no simple yet complete up-to-date field manual for the entire area has been available.

This manual covers the trees of North America with the exception of Mexico and the tropical species found in the southern fringe of the United States. Care has been taken to include all tree species native to this area (except for the 162 species of hawthorn and 20 usually shrubby willows which, for the most part, can only be distinguished by specialists), as well as naturalized or commonly planted exotic species.

In all, 135 genera containing 568 species are treated. Drawings showing descriptive characters, distribution maps, and concise descriptions of botanical and silvical characters have been included for 232 species of trees which are either of importance or general interest, while an additional 336 less important species are either briefly described or included in the complete keys.

North American Trees has been designed to meet the needs of an interested nontechnical public, as well as those of students and scientists. The terminology has been kept as simple as possible without sacrificing scientific accuracy. Basic information on characters and techniques used in identifying trees appears in the introduction, and a comprehensive glossary defines necessary technical terms that might not be generally understood. It is believed that anyone interested in knowing how to identify the native trees will find this manual understandable and easily used.

The nomenclature of woody plants follows the 1944 revision of the United States Forest Service check list. Inasmuch as this revision follows the International Rules of botanical nomenclature, rather than the American Rules followed by earlier authors, there have been numerous changes in tree names from earlier manuals.

There are 160 full page plates containing drawings of 232

species. Sixty-nine of these drawings are original, the work of Bruce Eastman or Robert Lorenz. The remaining drawings were taken, with permission, from the following sources:

1. United States Forest Service. Publications of Sudworth and Timber Pines of the South. All of the drawings of conifers except those on pages 8, 16, 20, 32, 54, 66, 80, and 108; also the drawings on pages 158, 170, 172, 184, 186, 210, 236, 300, 316, 332, 340, 350, 352, 356, and 370. The map showing Forest Regions also was secured from the United States Forest Service.

2. Otis, *Michigan Trees*. The drawings on pages 16, 20, 54, 66, 108, 122, 132, 136, 140, 142, 144, 148, 150, 152, 162, 164, 166, 168, 180, 190, 192, 196, 198, 216, 218, 222, 226, 228, 234, 238, 242, 246, 248, 250, 260, 262, 264, 272, 274, 276, 282, 286, 296, 298, 302, 306, 318, 326, 330, 346, 348, 350, 352, 360, and 366.

3. Illick, *Pennsylvania Trees*. The drawings on pages 240, 288, 290, 310, 322, 334, 336, 340, and 356.

4. Hanzlik, *Trees and Forests of Western United States*. The drawings on pages 8 and 80.

Both the author and publisher wish to thank the individuals and organizations involved for permission to make use of these drawings.

RICHARD J. PRESTON, JR.

August, 1948

PREFACE TO SECOND EDITION

This edition follows, with the exception of *Pseudotsuga taxifolia* for the scientific name for Douglas-fir, the scientific and common names appearing in the USDA Agriculture Handbook No. 41, *Check List of Native and Naturalized Trees of the United States 1953*. This has resulted in numerous changes in nomenclature and accepted species. Keys have been revised and other corrections made. Drawings for 12 plates were re-drawn in whole or in part by Tom Olive.

RICHARD J. PRESTON, JR.

April, 1960

TABLE OF CONTENTS

PREFACE... vii

INTRODUCTION

    Natural Relationship of Trees........................ xi

    Forest Regions of North America..................... xiii

    Tree Characters..................................... xvi

KEY TO THE GENERA................................. xxiii

HANDBOOK OF NORTH AMERICAN TREES.....1 to 371

GLOSSARY... 373

INDEX... 383

INTRODUCTION

NATURAL RELATIONSHIP OF TREES

Trees, with the exception of tropical tree ferns, belong to one of two major plant groups: the forms with naked seeds commonly subtended by a scale being known as Gymnosperms, and the forms which contain an ovary which encloses the ovules being known as Angiosperms.

Two of the four orders of Gymnosperms contain trees which grow in temperate climates, and by far the most important of these are the cone-bearing trees such as the pines, spruces, and cedars which are known as conifers (*Coniferales*). The members of this group have distinctive needle-like, linear, or scalelike leaves and are often known as either evergreens (in spite of the fact that some shed their needles annually) or softwoods (although several have hard dense wood). Fifteen genera of conifers containing 95 species are native to North America. These, together with 8 exotic species, are treated in the first 118 pages of this book.

The other order of Gymnosperms present in tree form in the region covered by this text is represented by a single surviving species, the ginkgo or maidenhair tree (*Ginkgo biloba* L.) of China. This interesting tree is extensively planted through all but the coldest parts of the United States and is remarkably free from disease or inspects and very tolerant of city smoke. Ginkgo forms a slender, spire-like tree (Fig. 1) with fan-shaped, fern-like, deciduous leaves which are borne either spirally on the twigs or at the ends of spur-like shoots. The flowers are dioecious and of interest botanically because of the free-swimming antherozoids. The fruit is orange-yellow to green, about one inch in diameter, and resembles a plum with its fleshy, ill-smelling, outer pulp enclosing a large, edible, silvery pit.

The Angiosperms likewise divide into two groups—the Monocotyledons and the Dicotyledons. The first of these is represented in this text by one palm, three palmettos, and seven yuccas. These monocotyledonous plants are characterized by parallel major veins in the leaf, flower parts in threes or sixes, and fibrovascular bundles which are scattered through the stem.

GINKGO. MAIDENHAIR TREE

Fig. 1—(*a*) Winter twig, x ½; (*b*) leaf, x ½; (*c*) staminate flowering branchlet, x ½; (*d*) staminate flower, enlarged; **(*e*) pistillate** flower, enlarged; (*f*) fruit, x 1.

While trees in this group are important in the tropics, they are of little use in the temperate zones.

The Dicotyledons contain our most common and widespread trees such as the oaks, maples, and elms, and they are frequently referred to as broadleaf trees or hardwoods. They differ from the Monocotyledons in having prominent branched (pinnate or palmate) major veins in the leaves, floral parts usually in fours or fives, and fibrovascular bundles disposed in a ring around a pith. While most of the dicotyledonous trees are deciduous (drop their leaves each fall), many are evergreen and have leaves which persist for two or more years. In this text 116 genera of Dicotyledons are covered, including 160 species for which drawings, maps, and concise descriptions have been prepared, and 293 species which are either briefly described or included in the complete keys.

FOREST REGIONS OF NORTH AMERICA

As a result of differing conditions of moisture, temperature, and soil, the forests may vary from one section of the country to another, both in the species of trees present and in the type or character of the forest. In North America six broad, natural forest regions can be easily recognized. Two are restricted to the eastern part, two to the western part, and two regions are transcontinental. These regions are treated in the sections immediately following. Foresters generally subdivide these six major regions into a larger number.

Within each region there are several smaller natural associations or "forest types." These types are usually defined and named by one or more dominating tree species, such as the oak-hickory type in the Central Hardwoods region, or the lodgepole pine type in the Rocky Mountain region. More than 150 such forest types are recognized in the United States alone. Each of the regions will be briefly described, together with the important species found in the regions. The principal forest types for the United States are shown on the Forest Service map in the frontispiece.

TROPICAL FOREST REGION

In southern Florida and extreme southern Texas, Arizona, and California are forests made up largely of tropical species. While unimportant, this small area of tropical forest contains many interesting botanical forms. The tropical forest in Florida and Texas is humid in character and is the northern-most range for many species typical of the deep tropics. In Arizona and California, on the other hand, it is a desert climate with largely endemic species.

SOUTHERN FOREST REGION

This region covers the coastal area from Maryland to Texas, extending north along the river bottoms into Missouri, Arkansas, and Oklahoma. The area is characterized by abundant rainfall and mild temperatures, and it is one of the most important timber producing areas on the continent. The seven species of pine are found largely on the uplands or flatlands, while baldcypress, Atlantic white-cedar, and numerous hardwoods are typical of the extensive swamps and bottomlands. Among the important hardwoods are the sweetgum, tupelo gums, numerous oaks and hickories, beech, river birch, and several ashes and elms.

CENTRAL HARDWOOD FOREST REGION

There has been a greater decrease in the amount of forested land in this region than in any other, due to the large percentage of fertile agricultural land. There still remain, however, large quantities of high-grade hardwood lumber. This region embraces the central portion of the eastern United States, with the exception of the Appalachian Mountains, and extends into southern Canada. It is characterized by a very large number of species and many types. The climate is humid and generally moderate. Oaks are the dominant species in this region with hickories, ashes, elms, maples, gum, beech, yellow-poplar, walnut, cottonwood, sycamore, and dogwood also important.

NORTHERN FOREST REGION

This is by all odds the largest of the forest regions, extending from Georgia north along the Appalachian Mountains to New York, New England, and the northern portions of the Lake States in the United States, and north in Canada to the limits of tree growth. In Canada this region is transcontinental, extending in a continuous belt across the northern limits of the Great Plains and through the interior of Alaska. The southeastern part of this region is characterized by highly valuable timber species such as white, red, and jack pine, hemlock, red and white spruce, birches, beech, basswood, maples, and red oak. The northern transcontinental portion of this region is enormous in extent, but is largely composed of small-sized trees of white and black spruce, balsam fir, larch, paper birch, aspen, balsam poplar, and willows.

ROCKY MOUNTAIN FOREST REGION

This region, vast in extent, is spread over the mountains and high plateaus of the western interior from Mexico into northern Canada, where it merges with the Northern Forest region. It is bordered on the east by the Great Plains and on the west by the Pacific Coast forest. The forests are not continuous in this region, but are limited to the more humid higher areas which are interspersed between large treeless stretches occupying the arid lowlands.

The forests characteristically are grouped in conspicuous life zones or belts determined by the moisture, temperature, and topography. These zones tend to increase in altitude as they become more remote from polar regions, so that trees typical of the Northern Forest in northern Canada at elevations of a few hundred feet above sea level might be found at elevations of 8,000 feet in Montana, 10,500 feet in Colorado, and 12,500 feet in Arizona. In the higher, colder, and more humid belt, often called the Canadian zone, are dense forests of Engelmann spruce, alpine fir, western white and lodgepole pine, aspen and balsam poplar, and many other species closely resembling those found in the Northern Forest. Below this belt, in the transition zone, the characteristic tree is ponderosa pine, together with less important species such as western larch, Douglas-fir, various oaks, narrowleaf cottonwood, and water birch. This zone is warmer and drier, being intermediate between the humid Canadian zone and the arid Sonoran zone. The Sonoran zone is semi-tropical in nature and ranges from the high plains and foothills in the south to low plains and valleys further north. It is typified by pinyon-juniper forests, broad-leaved cottonwoods, mesquite, and numerous other shrubby tree species.

PACIFIC COAST FOREST REGION

Many highly important trees of very large size and growing in dense stands characterize this region, which contains the major portion of our remaining saw timber. This region, bounded on the east by the Rocky Mountain Forest, includes the Pacific Coast states plus the coastal portions of British Columbia and Alaska. Numerous forest types are recognized which include one or more of such species as the coast redwood, Douglas-fir, ponderosa pine, sugar pine, Jeffrey pine, western hemlock, true firs, cedars, spruces, cypresses, red alder, maples, myrtle, and oaks. While some of the southern portions of this region are dry, the great part of the coastal forests lies in a zone of heavy rainfall. The largest trees in the world (giant sequoia), the tallest trees in the world (redwood with a maximum height of 364 feet), and the most important timber species in the world (Douglas-fir) are found in this region.

TREE CHARACTERS

A brief discussion of the structural and silvical characters, an understanding of which is necessary in identifying trees, is presented here to aid students without previous botanical training.

Definition of a tree. There is no clear-cut line of demarcation between a tree and a shrub, and it is often impossible to place a plant definitely in one group or the other. Frequently a species treelike under favorable environmental conditions will be shrublike over most of its range. In general, height, form, and diameter must be taken into account in determining the classification of a doubtful form. In this manual, a tree is defined as a woody plant having one well-defined stem, a more or less definitely formed crown, and attaining a minimum height of fifteen to twenty feet and a diameter of not less than two inches.

Terminology. While appearing cumbersome to the beginner, the use of technical terms in describing characters is often necessary for a concise, accurate description. These technical terms have been avoided wherever their omission did not impair the meaning of the passage, and a glossary explaining all technical terms used has been included. The student should familiarize himself with the more commonly used terms early in his study of the trees.

Name. Most species of trees have been given one or many common names which usually describe some character of the tree and are easily learned by students. Unfortunately, these common names have many limitations. Some are merely local, others apply to two or more entirely different species, and some apply to trees belonging to different genera. Because of this, while common names may be useful and convenient, it is essential that each species of tree have a definite, individual name that can be accepted throughout the world and which cannot be applied to any other species.

Botanists and scientists as a whole have agreed that these scientific names should be in Latin, as this is a dead language and not subject to change. Botanists have further agreed that the name of a tree should consist of three parts: a generic name referring the species to the group to which it belongs and which is capitalized; a specific epithet referring to the single species and beginning with a small letter; and the full or abbreviated name of the authority or person first describing

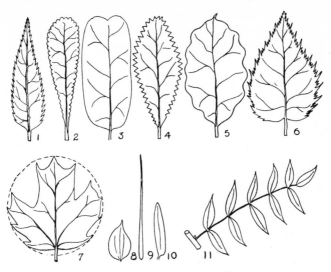

Fig. 2—LEAF PATTERNS

Leaf Shapes

1-Lanceolate.   2-Oblanceolate.   3-Oblong.   4-Elliptical.   5-Oval.
6-Ovate.   7-Orbicular.   8-Scale-like.   9-Acicular.   10-Linear.

Leaf Margins

1-Serrate.   2-Crenate.   3-Entire.   4-Dentate.   5-Sinuate.   6-Doubly
serrate.   7-Lobed.

Leaf Apices

1-Acuminate.   2-Rounded.   3-Emarginate.   4-Obtuse.   5-Mucronate.
6-Acute.

Leaf Bases

1-Obtuse.   2-Cuneate.   3-Rounded.   4-Acute.   5-Rounded.   6-Cor-
date.   7-Truncate.

Leaf Types

1 to 10-Simple leaves.   11-Pinnately compound leaf.

the plant. Thus, the scientific name of ponderosa pine is *Pinus ponderosa* Laws. When a variety of a species is recognized, the varietal name follows the specific name, so in the case of Arizona pine, a southern variety of ponderosa pine, the scientific name is *Pinus ponderosa* var. *arizonica* (Engelm.) Shaw. When the names of two authorities are given, one appearing in parentheses, it indicates that the species was first described by the authority

Fig. 3—FLOWER STRUCTURE

Perfect Flower   Flowers of Pine

1-Peduncle. 2-Receptacle. 3-Sepal (Calyx). 4-Petal (Corolla). 5-Stamen; a-Anther, b-Filament. 6-Pistil; a-Stigma, b-Style, c-Ovary, d-Ovule. 7-Staminate conelet. 8 and 9-Stamen, or pollen-bearing scale, showing side and lower surfaces. 10-Pistillate conelet. 11 and 12-Pistillate scale showing inner and outer surfaces respectively; a-Ovule, b-Bract.

indicated in the parentheses, but in a different group of the same rank, or in a different rank, and that the second author was the one that had effected the change. This is the case with the western hemlock, *Tsuga heterophylla* (Raf.) Sarg. In this work the nomenclature accepted by the United States Forest Service (as set forth in the revised Check List of 1953) has been followed.

Habit. This refers to the general appearance of a tree, usually as seen from a distance. The size; appearance and form of the trunk; shape, density, and size of crown; the number, size, and direction of growth of the branches, are all factors helpful in distinguishing trees. In the conifers there is typically a trunk that extends to the tip of the tree without dividing (*excurrent*), while most of the hardwoods have the trunk breaking up into several large branches (*deliquescent*). Both the crown and branches may vary greatly in the same species, depending upon whether the tree is growing in the open or in a dense stand where it is shaded on the sides by its neighbors.

Leaves. Since leaves display characteristic patterns, they are probably the most useful organs in identifying trees (Fig. 2). Leaves consist of an expanded portion or *blade*, a supporting stalk or *petiole*, and small leaflike or scaly structures (*stipules*)

Fig. 4—TYPES OF INFLORESCENCES

1-Ament. 2-Spike. 3-Raceme. 4-Panicle. 5-Umbel. 6-Corymb.

attached in pairs at the base of the petiole. Leaves having no stipules are termed *exstipulate*, and those without petioles are called *sessile*. Those species which are evergreen can be identified by their leaves throughout the year, while species which shed their leaves annually (*deciduous*) must be identified by other characters during the winter months. Leaves may be arranged *alternately* (with one leaf attached to the twig at a certain point), *oppositely* (where two leaves emerge at opposite sides from the same place on a twig) *whorled* (where more than two leaves emerge from one point of the twig), or *fascicled* (where a number of leaves emerge in a cluster or bundle). They may be *simple* and consist of a single blade or expanded portion, or *compound* and made up of several individual leaflets. If the leaflets in a compound leaf are arranged along each side of a common axis (*rachis*), the leaf is said to be *pinnately compound*, while if the leaflets all arise from the apex of the petiole, the leaf is termed *palmately compound*. Other characters used in identification are the shapes and types of margin, apex, and base. Texture, color, and the surface, whether smooth or hairy, are also useful characters.

Flowers. All trees have flowers, although frequently they are small and inconspicuous. These are the reproductive organs by means of which the species is perpetuated. Floral characters are the most accurate means of identifying many trees (Fig. 3), although they are little used in the field because they bloom for so short a period. Flowers vary greatly in form, structure, and size. A *complete* flower (Fig. 3) is made up usually of leaflike *sepals* (*calyx*), often brightly colored *petals* (*corolla*), *stamens* (the male organs which bear the *pollen* in saclike *anthers*), and a *pistil* (the female organ consisting of a terminal *stigma* which catches the pollen, a *style*, and an *ovary*). The ovary may consist of one or more compartments (*cells*) and contain one to many *ovules* which later mature into seeds.

If the ovary is inserted on top of the other flower parts it is *superior*, while if it appears below the origin of sepals, petals, and stamens it is *inferior*. Flowers may be *perfect* (contain both stamens and pistil) or *imperfect* (contain one sex but not the other). Plants having imperfect flowers are termed either *monoecious* (both sexes present in different flowers on the same plant) or *dioecious* (each sex borne on a different plant). When the only functioning sex

Fig. 5—(Left) Winter Twig of Black Walnut. (*a*) terminal bud; (*b*) lateral bud; (*c*) leaf scar; (*d*) bundle scars; (*e*) pith.
(Right) Winter Twig of Red Mulberry. (*a*) tip scar; (*b*) lateral bud; (*c*) leaf scar; (*d*) stipule scars.

organs in an imperfect flower are stamens the flower is termed *staminate*, while one in which the pistil is the active organ is *pistillate*. Plants which bear some perfect and some imperfect flowers are termed *polygamous*. Flowers may appear singly or in clusters (*inflorescences*, Fig. 4). In Gymnosperms the pistil is replaced by a seed-bearing scale which does not enclose the seed.

Fruit. While varying greatly in type and appearance, fruits are very useful in identification. The different kinds of fruits are pictured and discussed in the text and defined in the glossary. The seeds included in the fruit contain the embryonic plant. To the layman these are generally of secondary utility in identification.

Twigs. The color, stoutness, central pith, or surface coverings and markings may be very useful in identifying trees, especially during the winter months (Fig. 5). As buds, stipules, and leaves fall off they leave scars on the twig which are frequently characteristic. Buds are conspicuous on most twigs and helpful in identification. The shape, size, color, number of scales, arrangement, and the presence or absence of terminal bud are important diagnostic characters.

Bark. The appearance of bark, while varying greatly with age and environment, is often a helpful character in identification. Color and thickness of the bark, whether it is furrowed, scaly, or smooth, and its taste, are commonly helpful features.

Wood. The characters of the wood of trees form a separate means of identification which is more technical and difficult than the use of external characters. In this manual only the outstanding wood characters are given, such as the weight, color, and arrangement of large pores (whether *ring-porous* in a definite ringlike zone, or *diffuse-porous* and scattered throughout the wood). A statement as to importance and the uses of the woods is also included.

Silvical characters. The tolerance, sites, associates, reproduction, enemies, roots, life zones, and altitudinal distributions of species are often helpful in identification, and have been included wherever possible.

In identifying trees it must be remembered that characters are variable and often overlap with those of closely related trees. Wherever possible, identification should not be based on a single character, but on as many as are available.

KEY TO THE GENERA

BASED LARGELY ON LEAF CHARACTERS

1. Seeds not in an ovary; flowers unisexual; leaves fan-shaped, linear, needle-like, or scalelike...................................GYMNOSPERMS, (see A, page xxiii).
1. Seeds borne in a closed ovary which at maturity becomes the fruit................................ANGIOSPERMS, (see 2).
  2. Leaves narrow with parallel veins; flower parts in 3's or 6's; stems without central pith or annual layers of wood; embryo with a single cotyledon.....................................MONOCOTYLEDONS, (see B, page xxiv).
  2. Leaves generally broad or rarely wanting, with netted veins; flower parts usually in 4's or 5's; stems with pith and annual layers of wood; embryo with two cotyledons.....................................DICOTYLEDONS, (see C, page xxiv).

A. GYMNOSPERMS

1. Leaves fan-shaped with numerous fine veins radiating from the petiole, deciduous; twigs with spur shoots; fruit a drupelike seed...................................GINKGO, p. xii.
1. Leaves linear, needle-shaped, or scalelike, with 1 vein, usually persistent...................................CONIFERS, 2.
  2. Leaves needle-shaped, in fascicles of 1–5, each fascicle enclosed at base by a sheath...................................PINUS, p. 2.
  2. Leaves single, linear or scalelike...................................3
3. Leaves mostly linear; leaves and fruit scales spirally arranged..4
3. Leaves mostly scalelike; leaves and fruit scales opposite......12
  4. Fruit a woody or papery cone composed of seed-bearing scales...................................5
  4. Fruit a single seed partially or wholly surrounded by a fleshy aril...................................11
5. Cone scales thin, terminally attached; seed terminally winged, 2 to each scale...................................6
5. Cone scales peltate; seed laterally winged, 2 to many per scale. 10
  6. Leaves deciduous; twigs with spur shoots.....LARIX, p. 42.
  6. Leaves persistent; twigs without spur shoots...................................7
7. Base of leaves persistent on twigs as peglike projections (sterigmata)...................................8
7. Leaves not leaving peglike bases on twig upon falling.........9
  8. Leaves sessile, 4-angled or flattened.........PICEA, p. 48.
  8. Leaves stalked, flat or rounded in cross section. TSUGA, p. 64.
9. Leaves sessile; cones erect, the scales deciduous from the axis at maturity; buds rounded, resinous (except in *A. bracteata*).....................................ABIES, p. 72.

9. Leaves narrowed at base into stalk; cones pendent with distinctive exserted bracts; buds pointed, non-resinous..............
................................PSEUDOTSUGA, p. 63.
10. Leaves deciduous (persistent in the tropical *T. mucronatum*); 2 seeds under each scale; southeastern. TAXODIUM, p. 93.
10. Leaves persistent; 2–9 seeds under each scale; Pacific Coast
..................................SEQUOIA, pp. 89, 91.
11. Leaves ½–1 inch long; fruit a seed partially enclosed in a scarlet aril, maturing in 1 year.....................TAXUS, p. 119.
11. Leaves 1–3½ inches long; fruit a drupelike seed enclosed in a green or purple, fleshy covering; maturing in 2 years.........
....TORREYA, p. 117.
12. Cone berry-like; leaves scalelike or awl-shaped, both types usually present; seed wingless........JUNIPERUS, p. 106.
12. Cone woody or leathery; leaves scalelike; seed winged....13
13. Cones globose with peltate scales, 2–20 seeds per scale.......14
13. Cones oblong, thin-scaled, 2–3 seeds per scale...............15
14. Cone woody, over ½ inch across, of 6–12 scales; 6–20 seeds per scale.........................CUPRESSUS, p. 98.
14. Cone leathery, ¼–½ inch across, of 4–8 scales; 2–5 seeds per scale...................CHAMAECYPARIS, p. 98.
15. Cones ¾–1½ inches long, 6-scaled; Far West...............
....LIBOCEDRUS, p. 95.
15. Cones ⅓–½ inch long, 8–12 scaled...........THUJA, p. 97.

B. MONOCOTYLEDONS
LEAVES WITH PARALLEL VEINS, ALTERNATE, SIMPLE, AND PERSISTENT

1. Leaves lanceolate and long; fruit a large capsule. YUCCA, p. 369.
1. Leaves fan-shaped, large; fruit a drupelike berry.............2
2. Leaf stalks armed with spines; southwestern...............
....WASHINGTONIA, p. 371.
2. Leaf stalks unarmed; southeastern.........SABAL, p. 371.

C. DICOTYLEDONS
LEAVES WITH NETTED VEINS OR RARELY ABSENT

a. Leaves and buds opposite
 b. Leaves compound............................I, p. xxv
 b. Leaves simple...............................II, p. xxv
a. Leaves and buds alternate
 c. Leaves compound...........................III, p. xxvi
 c. Leaves simple
  d. Leaves persistent........................IV, p. xxvi
  d. Leaves deciduous........................V, p. xxviii

I. LEAVES OPPOSITE, COMPOUND, AND DECIDUOUS

1. Leaves palmately compound; fruit a capsule. AESCULUS, p. 308.
1. Leaves pinnately compound or 3-foliate....................2
   2. Leaflets entire or finely toothed; fruit a samara............
   ....FRAXINUS, p. 342.
   2. Leaflets deeply and sharply toothed......................3
3. Flowers yellow, showy; fruit a linear capsule 4–8 inches long; southwestern...........................TECOMA, p. 363.
3. Flowers small; fruit a double samara or drupe..............4
   4. Fruit a double samara in racemes; terminal bud present with one pair of outer scales.........ACER NEGUNDO, p. 307.
   4. Fruit a small drupe in dense clusters; terminal bud absent, lateral scaly......................SAMBUCUS, p. 365.

II. LEAVES OPPOSITE AND SIMPLE

1. Leaves persistent, entire, thick; fruit a drupe; southeastern coastal plain......................OSMANTHUS, p. 357.
1. Leaves deciduous, not leathery...........................2
   2. Leaves palmately lobed; fruit a double samara. ACER, p. 294.
   2. Leaves not lobed, fruit not a double samara..............3
3. Leaves entire...4
3. Leaves toothed...10
   4. Leaves heart-shaped, 5–12 inches long..................5
   4. Leaves linear to ovate, less than 5 inches long............6
5. Leaves 6–20 inches long, densely hairy below; flowers purple; capsule leathery, ovoid, 1–2 inches long. . PAULOWNIA, p. 361.
5. Leaves 8–12 inches long, slightly hairy below; flowers white; capsule linear, 8–20 inches long............CATALPA, p. 361.
   6. Leaves linear to lanceolate; fruit a linear capsule 7–12 inches long; southwestern..................CHILOPSIS, p. 359.
   6. Leaves suborbicular to elliptic..........................7
7. Stipules present and persistent; terminal bud absent, lateral minute; fruit a head of nutlike capsules.....................
...............................CEPHALANTHUS, p. 363.
7. Stipules absent; terminal bud present; fruit not a capsule.....8
   8. Fruit a samara with terminal wing; southwestern...........
   ....FRAXINUS ANOMALA, p. 345.
   8. Fruit a drupe..9
9. Leaves with arcuate venation; flowers small in heads; leaf scars with 3 bundle traces.....................CORNUS, p. 331.
9. Leaves with pinnate venation; flowers white in panicles; leaf scar with single bundle trace........CHIONANTHUS, p. 357.
   10. Buds enclosed by 2 large, valvate scales; fruit a drupe; petioles grooved..................VIBURNUM, p. 367.
   10. Buds many-scaled; petioles round in cross section........11
11. Leaves closely and finely serrate; lateral buds solitary; fruit a capsule in scarlet aril...............EUONYMUS, p. 293.

11. Leaves remotely and finely serrate; lateral buds several, super-posed; fruit a drupe..................FORESTIERA, p. 357.

III. LEAVES ALTERNATE AND COMPOUND

1. Fruit a legume; leaves 1 to many pinnate....................
.........................LEGUMINOSAE (key to), p. 267.
1. Fruit not a legume...2
   2. Leaves persistent; fruit a small drupe....................3
   2. Leaves deciduous..4
3. Leaflets spatulate, ¼ inch long; Texas......PISTACIA, p. 309.
3. Leaflets lanceolate, 2–3 inches long; southeastern coastal plain..
....................SAPINDUS MARGINATUS, p. 313.
   4. Twigs armed with spines.................................5
   4. Twigs unarmed..6
5. Leaves doubly pinnate; fruit a berry........ARALIA, p. 323.
5. Leaves once pinnate; fruit a capsule.ZANTHOXYLUM, p. 285.
   6. Leaves doubly pinnate; fruit a drupe...................7
   6. Leaves once pinnate....................................8
7. Leaflets 1–2 inches long; drupe yellow, ½–¾ inches..........
....MELIA, p. 287.
7. Leaflets ¼ inch long; drupe red, ¼ inch long...............
....BURSERA, p. 287.
   8. Leaves 3-foliate; fruit a winged samara....PTELEA, p. 285.
   8. Leaves 5 to many foliate..............................9
9. Pith conspicuously chambered; fruit a nutlike drupe with an indehiscent husk.......................JUGLANS, p. 134.
9. Pith solid; fruit not as above............................10
   10. Leaves 1½–4 feet long; leaflets with glands on coarse teeth; fruit a samara with twisted wing.....AILANTHUS, p. 287.
   10. Leaves smaller or leaflets without glands..............11
11. Stipules or stipular scars present; leaflets sharply serrate; buds resinous; fruit a pome....................SORBUS, p. 249.
11. Stipules absent; buds not resinous; fruit not a pome........12
   12. Leaflets entire; fruit a yellow berry....SAPINDUS, p. 313.
   12. Leaflets toothed (rarely entire in Rhus)................13
13. Buds large; fruit a nutlike drupe............CARYA, p. 138.
13. Buds small; fruit berry-like or capsular...................14
   14. Juice milky; fruit a berry-like drupe........RHUS, p. 289.
   14. Juice watery; fruit a capsule; southwestern.............
....................................UNGNADIA, p. 313.

IV. LEAVES ALTERNATE, SIMPLE, AND PERSISTENT

1. Leaves lobed...2
1. Leaves entire or toothed..................................4
   2. Leaves ⅓–½ inch long; fruit a long-tipped achene; South-west...COWANIA, p. 258.

2. Leaves 1 inch or longer...............................3

3. Leaves leathery; fruit an acorn...QUERCUS (in part), p. 174.

3. Leaves thick; fruit a hairy capsule; Southwest................
..........................FREMONTODENDRON, p. 321.

    4. Lower surface of leaves conspicuously dotted with scales or glands....................................5

    4. Lower surface of leaf without scales or glands............8

5. Leaves covered with yellow scales below; fruit a bur; West Coast............................CASTANOPSIS, p. 171.

5. Leaves glandular-dotted below; fruit a capsule or drupe.......6

    6. Leaves oblanceolate to oblong, 2–4 inches long, aromatic; fruit a wax covered drupe..............MYRICA, p. 135.

    6. Leaves lanceolate, 1½–2 inches long, non-aromatic; southeastern coastal plain.................................7

7. Fruit a 2–4 winged, indehiscent capsule...CLIFTONIA, p. 293.

7. Fruit a dehiscent, oblong capsule............LYONIA, p. 333.

    8. Fruit a linear achene tipped with a long, hairy style; western ....CERCOCARPUS, p. 255.

    8. Fruit not as above....................................9

9. Fruit an acorn in a cup; leaves leathery...................10

9. Fruit not an acorn..11

    10. Fruit cup scaly; leaves not woolly below.................
...............................QUERCUS (in part), p. 174.

    10. Fruit cup spiny; leaves woolly below; Pacific Coast........
..............................LITHOCARPUS, p. 173.

11. Leaves entire (rarely toothed on vigorous shoots)............12

11. Leaves toothed..23

    12. Leaves aromatic, 2–5 inches long; fruit a drupe.........13

    12. Leaves not aromatic.................................14

13. Calyx lobes persistent under fruit; southeastern................
....PERSEA, p. 239.

13. Calyx deciduous; California and Oregon.....................
..............................UMBELLULARIA, p. 237.

    14. Sap milky; fruit a multiple; Florida........FICUS, p. 229.

    14. Sap watery; fruit simple or aggregate..................15

15. Leaves red-woolly below, 5–8 inches long; flowers 6–8 inches across; fruit an aggregate of follicles........................
.....................MAGNOLIA GRANDIFLORA, p. 233.

15. Leaves not red-woolly; flowers smaller; fruit simple..........16

    16. Flowers showy; fruit a glandular-hispid, 5-celled capsule; southeastern....................................17

    16. Flowers small, white or green; fruit fleshy or a small, 2-celled capsule.....................................18

17. Leaves 3–4 inches long, flat, elliptic-lanceolate; twigs slender; fruit less than ¼ inch long.................KALMIA, p. 335.

17. Leaves 4–12 inches long, revolute, oblong; twigs stout; fruit ½ inch long...................RHODODENDRON, p. 335.

18. Twigs spiny or spinescent; fruit a drupe.................19
18. Twigs not spiny or spinescent........................20

19. Leaves 1–3 inches long; drupe black, ½ inch long............
....BUMELIA, p. 339.
19. Leaves ½–¾ inch long; drupe red, ⅕ inch long.............
......................................CONDALIA, p. 317.
   20. Fruit a 2-celled capsule ⅛ inch long; leaves oblong, 2–3
       inches long; southeastern coast.........CYRILLA, p. 293.
   20. Fruit a fleshy drupe or berry........................21
21. Stipules or their scars present; fruit red to brown..ILEX, p. 291.
21. Stipules or their scars absent..........................22
   22. Fruit black, lustrous; southeastern...VACCINIUM, p. 337.
   22. Fruit orange, glandular coated; Far West..............
       ....ARBUTUS, p. 333.
23. Leaves 3-nerved from base, 1–1½ inches long; flowers in corymbs;
    fruit a dry 3-lobed drupe; California....CEANOTHUS, p. 317.
23. Leaves with pinnate veins; flowers and fruit not as above.....24
   24. Stipules absent; southeastern coastal plain.............25
   24. Stipules or their scars present........................26
25. Leaves 1–2½ inches long, entire or obscurely toothed; flowers
    small, white; fruit a berry ¼ inch long..VACCINIUM, p. 337.
25. Leaves 3–6 inches long, finely or remotely toothed; flowers showy,
    2½ inches across; fruit a capsule.........GORDONIA, p. 323.
   26. Leaves narrowly lanceolate; fruit a woody capsule ¼ inch
       long; southwestern..............VAUQUELINIA, p. 245.
   26. Leaves broader; fruit a drupe or pome.................27
27. Fruit an obovoid pome ⅓ inch long; California.............
    ....PHOTINIA, p. 258.
27. Fruit a drupe; flowers and fruit not in panicles.............28
   28. Twigs spinescent; terminal bud absent; leaves 1–1½ inches
       long, mostly suborbicular with glandular spiny teeth;
       southwestern..............RHAMNUS CROCEA, p. 317.
   28. Twigs not spinescent; terminal bud present; leaves 1–4
       inches long, lanceolate to ovate......................29
29. Fruit ¼ inch long; flowers in cymes or solitary; leaf scar with
    single bundle trace..........................ILEX, p. 291.
29. Fruit ½–⅔ inch long; flowers in racemes; leaf scars with 3 or
    more bundle traces..............PRUNUS (in part), p. 257.

V. LEAVES ALTERNATE, SIMPLE, AND DECIDUOUS

A. LEAVES SCALELIKE, INCONSPICUOUS, OR WANTING
   (p. xxviii)
B. LEAVES LOBED (p. xxix)
C. LEAVES ENTIRE (p. xxix)
D. LEAVES TOOTHED (p. xxxi)

A. LEAVES SCALELIKE, INCONSPICUOUS, OR WANTING

1. Plants succulent (Cacti), with clustered spines...............2
1. Plants treelike, woody....................................3

   2. Branches columnar; seed dark...........CEREUS, p. 324.
   2. Branches jointed; seed pale.............OPUNTIA, p. 325.
3. Leaves scalelike, feathery; fruit a capsule...TAMARIX, p. 308.
3. Trees appearing leafless; southwestern......................4
   4. Twigs with black, cushion-like processes..CANOTIA, p. 293.
   4. Twigs without cushion-like processes....................5
5. Twigs with lateral spines; fruit a legume.......DALEA, p. 266.
5. Twigs terminating in a spine; fruit a berry...................
   ....KOEBERLINIA, p. 321.

B. LEAVES LOBED

1. Leaves 4-lobed; bud large with valvate scales; fruit an aggregate
   of samaras......................LIRIODENDRON, p. 235.
1. Leaves not 4-lobed; bud scales not valvate..................2
   2. Leaves entire or 1–2 lobed, all types usually present; aromatic;
     fruit a blue drupe on red stalk........SASSAFRAS, p. 239.
   2. Leaves more than 2-lobed, not strongly aromatic..........3
3. Leaves palmately 3–7 lobed; fruit in multiple heads..........4
3. Leaves not palmately 3–7 lobed; fruit not in heads...........5
   4. Leaves finely toothed; terminal bud scaly; twigs with corky
     wings; fruit of capsules...........LIQUIDAMBAR, p. 241.
   4. Leaves coarsely toothed; terminal bud absent, lateral enclosed
     in enlarged leaf petiole; fruit of achenes; bark characteristically
     mottled...........................PLATANUS, p. 243.
5. Terminal bud absent; sap milky; fruit a berry-like multiple
   of drupes..6
5. Terminal bud present; sap watery; fruit simple..............7
   6. Leaves velvety-hairy below; fruit globose, orange...........
     .........................BROUSSONETIA, p. 227.
   6. Leaves smooth to hairy below; fruit ovoid, purple, dark red,
     or white..............................MORUS, p. 227.
7. Twigs with sharp thorns; fruit a small, red pome............
   ....CRATAEGUS, p. 253.
7. Twigs unarmed (sometimes spinescent in Malus)............8
   8. Leaf scars with many bundle traces; fruit an acorn.........
     ....QUERCUS, p. 174.
   8. Leaf scars with 3 bundle traces........................9
9. Leaves toothed; fruit a pome; buds small......MALUS, p. 244.
9. Leaf lobes entire; fruit a capsule; buds large..POPULUS, p. 120

C. LEAVES ENTIRE

1. Leaves, twigs, and drupes silvery scurfy....................2
1. Plants not silvery scurfy...................................3
   2. Leaves elliptic to oblong...........SHEPHERDIA, p. 329.
   2. Leaves lanceolate..................ELAEAGNUS, p. 329.
3. Leaves heart-shaped; fruit a legume.........CERCIS, p. 273.

3. Leaves not heart-shaped; fruit not a legume..................4

    4. Sap milky; twigs with sharp axillary spines; fruit a globose multiple of drupes 4–5 inches across....MACLURA, p. 229.

    4. Sap watery; twigs and fruit not as above..................5

5. Leaves obovate-lanceolate, 10–12 inches long; stipules absent; buds minute; fruit a berry 3–5 inches long..ASIMINA, p. 237.

5. Leaves and fruit not as above...........................6

    6. Terminal bud present, conspicuous.....................7

    6. Terminal bud absent; lateral buds often minute.........13

7. Terminal bud large, with single caplike scale; leaves 4–30 inches long; fruit conelike aggregate............MAGNOLIA, p. 230.

7. Terminal bud scaly; leaves 1–7 inches long; fruit simple......8

    8. Stipules present; fruit an acorn.........QUERCUS, p. 174.

    8. Stipules absent; fruit not an acorn.....................9

9. Leaves with arcuate veins; petioles long and slender; flowers small in cymes; fruit a drupe..............CORNUS, p. 331.

9. Leaves with pinnate veins; petioles short..................10

    10. Twigs with conspicuous white lenticels, aromatic if crushed; leaves obtuse, oval to obovate, 4–6 inches long; fruit a dry drupe ¼ inch long.................COTINUS, p. 309.

    10. Twigs, leaves and fruit different.......................11

11. Leaves oblong to obovate, 2–7 inches long; pith diaphramed; fruit an oblong, fleshy drupe.................NYSSA, p. 327.

11. Leaves oblong, 2–4 inches long; pith solid; fruit a capsule; southeastern coastal plain.............................12

    12. Leaves 3–4 inches long, hairy below, early deciduous; twigs without lenticels; fruit a globose, 3–5 celled capsule ⅜ inch long............................ELLIOTTIA, p. 333.

    12. Leaves 2–3 inches long, smooth below, tardily deciduous; twigs with lenticels; fruit 2-celled, capsule-like indehiscent, ⅛ inch............................CYRILLA, p. 293.

13. Leaves unequal at base; pith chambered at nodes; fruit a dry drupe....................................CELTIS, p. 220.

13. Leaves equal at base; pith solid; fruit not a dry drupe.......14

    14. Stipules or their scars present........................15

    14. Stipules absent....................................18

15. Buds with single caplike scale; fruit a capsule...SALIX, p. 130.

15. Buds scaly or naked; fruit a drupe.......................16

    16. Twigs stout with thick pith; sap milky......RHUS, p. 289.

    16. Twigs slender, often spinescent; sap watery.............17

17. Leaves ½–¾ inch long; drupe ⅛ inch; southwest............
....CONDALIA, p. 317.

17. Leaves 1–7 inches long; drupe ¼–½ inch..RHAMNUS, p. 315.

    18. Leaves stellate-hairy below; buds naked, hairy; fruit a drupe ⅓ inch long enclosed in persistent calyx; southeastern

coastal plain.........................STYRAX, p. 343.

18. Leaves not stellate-hairy; buds scaly...................19

19. Twigs usually spinescent; leaves often fascicled on spur shoots; drupe black...........................BUMELIA, p. 339.

19. Twigs not spinescent; spur shoots absent..................20

20. Leaves glabrous; fruit a large berry subtended by woody persistent calyx; bark conspicuously blocky............... ....DIOSPYROS, p. 341.

20. Leaves woolly below; fruit a red drupe subtended by hairy calyx; bark thin, scaly................CORDIA, p. 359.

D. LEAVES TOOTHED

1. Buds naked, terminal present; leaves unequal at base, oval, crenately toothed; flowers yellow, appearing in fall; fruit a capsule...........................HAMAMELIS, p. 241.

1. Buds scaly (sometimes naked in Rhamnus); flowers in spring..2

2. Fruit a nut in bur or cup; leaves mostly penniveined.......3

2. Fruit not in bur or cup.................................5

3. Buds lance-shaped, ¾–1 inch long, terminal present; nut triangular in spiny bur; bark thin, smooth, blue-gray..FAGUS, p. 167.

3. Buds ovoid to globose ⅛–¼ inch long; fruit rounded.........4

4. Buds with 2–3 visible scales, terminal absent; leaves with sharp teeth; fruit in spiny bur.........CASTANEA, p. 169.

4. Buds many scaled, terminal present; leaves with rounded or short teeth; fruit in scaly cup...........QUERCUS, p. 174.

5. Fruit a nut or nutlet in strobile or leafy involucre; terminal bud absent..6

5. Fruit a samara, capsule, pome, or drupaceous..............10

6. Nutlet in persistent woody strobile; buds with 2 visible scales ....ALNUS, p. 156

6. Nut or nutlet with leafy involucre or strobile; buds many scaled...7

7. Nutlets winged in deciduous strobile; bark with horizontal lenticels, often papery....................BETULA, p. 146.

7. Nut or nutlets unwinged in involucres; bark not papery.......8

8. Nut large, edible, single; shrubby.......CORYLUS, p. 165.

8. Nutlet small in loose leafy strobile; small trees.............9

9. Nutlet enclosed in bladder-like sac; bark thin, gray, shreddy.... ....OSTRYA, p. 163.

9. Nutlet subtended by 3-lobed leafy involucre; bark smooth, blue-gray; stem fluted...................CARPINUS, p. 165.

10. Leaves unequal at base; fruit a samara or woody drupe; terminal bud absent..................................11

10. Leaves equal at base; fruit a capsule, pome, or drupaceous.14

11. Fruit a winged samara; leaves mostly doubly serrate........... ....ULMUS, p. 214.

11. Fruit a drupe; leaves singly serrate.......................12

12. Winter buds naked; fruit juicy; twigs often spinescent.... ....RHAMNUS, p. 315.

12. Winter buds scaly; fruit woody; twigs not spinescent.....13
13. Leaves 3-veined; buds ovoid; fruit globose.....CELTIS, p. 220.
13. Leaves many veined; buds minute, subglobose; fruit with conspicuous knob-like processes..............PLANERA, p. 221.
14. Fruit a capsule.....................................15
14. Fruit a pome or drupaceous.........................17
15. Buds small, partially embedded in bark, terminal absent; flowers and fruit in panicles................OXYDENDRON, p. 337.
15. Buds over ⅛ inch long, not embedded; flowers and fruit in aments...16
16. Buds scaly, terminal present..........POPULUS, p. 120.
16. Buds with single cap-like scale, terminal absent...........
....SALIX, p. 131.
17. Leaf base heart-shaped; fruit nut-like drupe attached to persistent, leafy bract...........................TILIA, p. 319.
17. Leaf base not heart-shaped; no persistent, leafy bract........18
18. Fruit fleshy; pith solid.............................19
18. Fruit dry; pith chambered.........................25
19. Fruit a berry-like multiple; sap milky; terminal bud absent.....
....MORUS, p. 227.
19. Fruit single; sap watery; terminal bud present.............20
20. Leaf scars with single bundle trace; leaves simply toothed...
.....................................ILEX, p. 291.
20. Leaf scars with 3 bundle traces; leaves mostly doubly toothed
....21
21. Fruit a drupe; leaves mostly lanceolate......PRUNUS, p. 256.
21. Fruit a pome; leaves mostly oblong to ovate................22
22. Twigs with sharp thorns..........CRATAEGUS, p. 253.
22. Twigs without thorns (often spinescent)...............23
23. Fruit pyriform...........................PYRUS, p. 346.
23. Fruit globose or nearly so...............................24
24. Pome over ½ inch; buds ovoid to globose..MALUS, p. 244.
24. Pome under ½ inch; buds acute to acuminate...........
.............................AMELANCHIER, p. 251.
25. Leaves leathery; fruit brown, ½ inch long; crowned with persistent calyx........................SYMPLOCOS, p. 343.
25. Leaves thin; fruit nutlike, 2-4 winged; about 2 inches long.....
....HALESIA, p. 341.

HANDBOOK OF
NORTH AMERICAN TREES

PINACEAE

THE PINES

Characteristics of the Genus *Pinus* L.

HABIT. Evergreen trees with straight, unbranched, cylindrical trunks, and whorled, spreading branches.

LEAVES. Needle-like; in fascicles or bundles of 1–5; enclosed in bud by 6–12 scales which form a persistent or soon-deciduous basal sheath; usually with several lines of stomata on each surface; juvenile leaves on young shoots differ in being spirally arranged, single, and scalelike.

FLOWERS. Monoecious; male, or pollen-producing, consisting of spirally arranged, sessile anthers, yellow, orange, or scarlet; female, or cone- and seed-producing, small, conelike bodies consisting of numerous spirally arranged, 2-ovuled scales, each subtended by a small bract.

FRUIT. A cone, usually pendent, composed of the hardened, woody scales of the flower; scales more or less thickened on the exposed terminal surface (the apophysis) with the ends of the growth of the previous year appearing as a terminal or dorsal, brown protuberance or scar (the umbo), which is often armed with a prickle; maturing in 2 (rarely 3) seasons. Seed: 2 borne at the base on inner face of each fertile scale; with thin, terminal, papery wing or wingless.

BUDS. Variable in size, shape, and color; covered by fringed or papery-margined overlapping scales; these component scales each protecting a tiny bud which, after the main bud unfolds, develops into a fascicle of leaves or occasionally into a female flower.

WOOD. Among our most important trees; properties extremely variable; numerous, large, easily visible resin ducts: resinous scent. Some species produce, in addition to lumber, naval stores and edible nuts.

GENERAL. The largest and most important genus of conifers, including about 80 species widely scattered over the Northern Hemisphere; 36 species are native to the United States and Canada; the North American species can be conveniently grouped into the soft or white pines, and hard, pitch, or yellow pines.

[2]

KEY TO THE SPECIES OF PINES

1. Needles in clusters of 5 (except Pinyons), the cluster sheath deciduous and absent on mature needles; one fibrovascular bundle in cross section of needle; cone scales without prickles (except Foxtails)..... ....Soft Pines.
   2. Needles in clusters of 1–4; cones globose, few-scaled; seed large and edible, without wing; western..............Pinyon Pines.
      3. Needles single; Idaho, Nevada, Utah, Arizona, California..... ....*P. monophylla*, Singleleaf Pinyon, p. 15.
      3. Needles predominantly in 2's; Colorado, Utah.............. ....*P. edulis*, Pinyon, p. 15.
      3. Needles in 3's; southern Arizona, New Mexico, Texas........ ....*P. cembroides*, Mexican Pinyon, p. 15.
      3. Needles predominantly in 4's; southern California........... ....*P. quadrifolia*, Parry Pinyon, p. 15.
   2. Needles in clusters of 5; cones many-scaled.
      4. Cone scales thin, without prickles; seeds long-winged; needles slender, 2–4" long, persistent 2–4 years.........White Pines.
         5. Cones 4–8" long, scales flexible; eastern Canada to Iowa, Illinois, and Georgia.*P. strobus*, Eastern White Pine, p. 9.
         5. Cones 5–11" (most about 8") long; scales flexible; western Canada to Montana and California...................... ....*P. monticola*, Western White Pine, p. 9.
         5. Cones 12–18" long; scales rigid; Oregon, California, Nevada ....*P. lambertiana*, Sugar Pine, p. 7.
      4. Cone scales thick; needles stout, 1–3" long, persistent 5–17 years; western.
         6. Cone scales without prickles; seed wing absent or short; needles 1½–3" long, persistent 5–8 years.....Stone Pines.
            7. Cones 1½–3" long, subglobose, remaining closed; alpine from southern Canada to California and Wyoming...... ....*P. albicaulis*, Whitebark Pine, p. 11.
            7. Cones 3–10" long, subcylindrical, opening at maturity; through west...........*P. flexilis*, Limber Pine, p. 11.
         6. Cone scales with prickles; seed with long wing; needles 1–1½" long, resin-dotted, persistent 10–17 years.......... ....Foxtail Pines.
            8. Cones with long, slender prickles, alpine from Colorado to California and south............................ ....*P. aristata*, Bristlecone Pine, p. 13.
            8. Cones with minute, incurved prickles; California alpine.. ....*P. balfouriana*, Foxtail Pine, p. 13.
1. Needles in clusters of 2 or 3 (5 in Torrey and Arizona Pine), the cluster sheath persistent (deciduous in Chihuahua Pine); 2 fibrovascular bundles in cross section of needle; cone scales usually armed with prickles.......................................Hard Pines.
   9. Eastern Hard Pines (Northeast and Central States).
      10. Needles in 3's or 2's and 3's, 3–5" long, twisted; cones 1½–3½" long, persistent on branch.
         11. Needles in 3's, rigid; cones ovoid with stout prickles; New Brunswick and Ontario to Georgia..................... ....*P. rigida*, Pitch Pine, p. 21.
         11. Needles in 2's and 3's, soft and flexible; cones oblong with weak prickles; New York to Missouri and south........ ....*P. echinata*, Shortleaf Pine, p. 23.
      10. Needles in 2's.
         12. Needles 4–6" long; cones symmetrical.
            13. Cones 2–3½" long, persistent several years, falling entire; scales yellow-brown with short spine; widely planted exotic.......*P. nigra*, Austrian Pine, p. 17.

[3]

13. Cones 1½–2½″ long, falling in one year and leaving basal scales on limb; scales red-brown and unarmed; southern Canada to Minnesota and West Virginia . . . .*P. resinosa*, **Red Pine**, p. 17.

12. Needles 1–3″ long.

 14. Bark distinctly orange-colored; cones 1½–2½″ long, unsymmetrical, opening at maturity and falling when ripe; scales often pyramidally thickened; widely planted and naturalized in Northeast . . . .*P. sylvestris*, **Scotch Pine**, p. 17.

 14. Bark not distinctly orange-colored; cones long persistent; scales not pyramidally thickened.

  15. Cones 2–3½″ long, heavy; scales with much thickened ends and armed with conspicuous sharp spurs; Appalachian Mountains, New Jersey to Georgia . . . .*P. pungens*, **Table Mountain Pine**, p. 29.

  15. Cones 1½–2″ long; thin-scaled, with slender or minute prickles.

   16. Cones strongly incurved, commonly remaining closed; scales irregularly developed; Canada to New York, Indiana, Wisconsin, and Minnesota . . . .*P. banksiana*, **Jack Pine**, p. 19.

   16. Cones symmetrical, opening at maturity; New York to Indiana, south to Georgia and Mississippi . . . .*P. virginiana*, **Virginia Pine**, p. 19.

9. Southern Yellow Pines (Gulf and South Atlantic States).

 17. Needles 6–18″ long, in 3's (2's and 3's in Slash Pine).

  18. Cones 2–2½″ long and broad, often remaining closed, long persistent; needles 6–8″ long; New Jersey to Florida . . . .*P. serotina*, **Pond Pine**, p. 21.

  18. Cones 2–10″ long, much longer than broad, opening at maturity and not persistent.

   19. Needles 8–18″ long; cone 6–10″ long; conspicuous thick twigs and large silvery-white buds; Virginia to Florida and Texas . . . .*P. palustris*, **Longleaf Pine**, p. 27.

   19. Needles 6–12″ long; cone 2–6″ long; twigs not conspicuously stout; buds red-brown.

    20. Needles in 3's, 6–9″ long; cone light brown with stout spine; New Jersey to Oklahoma and Texas . . . .*P. taeda*, **Loblolly Pine**, p. 25.

    20. Needles in 2's and 3's, 8–12″ long; cone chocolate-brown with small spine or prickle; South Carolina to Louisiana . . . .*P. elliottii*, **Slash Pine**, p. 29.

 17. Needles 1½–5″ long, in 2's (2's and 3's in Shortleaf Pine).

  21. Needles 3–5″ long, in 2's and 3's, widely distributed on dry soils; New York to Missouri and south . . . .*P. echinata*, **Shortleaf Pine**, p. 23.

  21. Needles 1½–3½″ long, in 2's.

   22. Cone 2–3½″ long, often remaining closed and persistent for years; dry sandy soils in Florida . . . .*P. clausa*, **Sand Pine**, p. 25.

   22. Cone ½–2″ long, opening at maturity and falling in few years; coastal bottomlands . . . .*P. glabra*, **Spruce Pine**, p. 23.

9. Western Yellow Pines (region west of Great Plains).

 23. Needles in 5's.

  24. Needles 5–7″ long; cones thin-scaled, 2–3½″ long; Arizona and New Mexico . . . .*P. ponderosa arizonica*, **Arizona Pine**, p. 31.

  24. Needles 8–13″ long; cones thick-scaled, 4–6″ long; southern California . . . .*P. torreyana*, **Torrey Pine**, p. 41.

[4]

23. Needles in 2's and 3's, or 3's.
  25. Cones massive, 6–14″ long, clawlike spines; needles in 3's.
    26. Cones yellow-brown, 10–14″ long; seeds shorter than wings; southern and lower California.............
        ....*P. coulteri*, Coulter Pine, p. 37.
    26. Cones red-brown, 6–10″ long; seeds longer than wings; dry California foothills.......................
        ....*P. sabiniana*, Digger Pine, p. 37.
  25. Cones not massive; without clawlike spines.
    27. Cones unsymmetrical with thickened scales, often remaining closed and persistent for years.
      28. Needles in 2's, 1–3″ long; cone under 2″ long.
        29. Cones with knoblike scales and long prickles.
          30. Needles 1–1½″ long; small contorted tree of coastal area......................
            ....*P. contorta*, Shore Pine, p. 35.
          30. Needles 1–3″ long; straight, slender, mountain tree throughout West.......*P. contorta latifolia*, Lodgepole Pine, p. 35.
        29. Cones with thin scales and minute prickle; Canada and Northeastern United States.....
          ....*P. banksiana*, Jack Pine, p. 19.
      28. Needles 3–7″ long; cones 2–6″ long; Oregon and California.
        31. Needles in 2's; cones 2–3½″ long, with stout, spurlike prickles.....................
          ....*P. muricata*, Bishop Pine, p. 41.
        31. Needles in 3's; cones 3–7″ long, without spurlike prickles.
          32. Thickened cone scales, flattened, pyramidal; California and Oregon dry foothills; ....*P. attenuata*, Knobcone Pine, p. 39.
          32. Thickened cone scales, rounded, domelike; California coast.................
            .....*P. radiata*, Monterey Pine, p. 39.
    27. Cones symmetrical, thin-scaled.
      33. Needles in 3's, 2–4″ long, cluster sheath deciduous; cone 1½–2″ long, maturing in 3 years, long-stalked, often remaining closed, long persistent, southern Arizona and southern New Mexico.....
        ....*P. leiophylla*, Chihuahua Pine, p. 35.
      33. Needles over 4″ long, sheath persistent; cone 2–15″ long, maturing in 2 years, short-stalked, opening, deciduous, the basal scales remaining on twig.
        34. Cones 2–3½″ long; needles 4–6″ long; rare and local in Washoe County, Nevada.......
        P. washoensis M. & S., Washoe Pine, p. 33.
        34. Cones 3–15″ long; needles 4–15″ long.
          35. Cones 5–15″ long; needles 4–9″ long, persistent 6–9 years; twigs purplish with lemon-like odor; buds not covered with resin droplets; California and Oregon....
            ....*P. jeffreyi*, Jeffrey Pine, p. 33.
          35. Cones 3–6″ long; needles persistent 2–3 years; twigs orange to red with turpentine odor; buds often covered with resin droplets.
            36. Needles 4–11″ (mostly 5–7″) long, in 2's and 3's, yellow-green; throughout west...................
            P. ponderosa, Ponderosa Pine, p. 31.
            36. Needles 8–15″ long, in 3's (rarely 2–5), dark green; Arizona and New Mexico *P. engelmannii*, Apache Pine, p. 33.

a. Seed, x ½.

b. Cone, x ¼.

c. Foliage, x ½.

PINACEAE

SUGAR PINE

Pinus lambertiana Dougl.

HABIT. The largest American pine, commonly 175–200 feet high and 3–5 feet in diameter (max. 246 by 10 feet); on good sites with a long, clear bole and a short crown of large, often contorted, horizontal branches.

LEAVES. In fascicles of 5; 2–4 inches long; stouter than in white pine; twisted; blue- to gray-green; persistent 2–3 years; sheath deciduous; margin with minute teeth; often silvery with conspicuous white lines of stomata.

FLOWERS. Male yellow; female bright pink with purple scale margins.

FRUIT. Cones long-stalked; 10–26 inches long and 4–5 inches in diameter; scales slightly thicker and more rigid than in white pine, unarmed and with terminal umbo. Seed: ½ inch long, dark brown to black, with wing 1–1½ inches long.

TWIGS. Slender to stout; at first rusty-pubescent, later smooth and orange-brown. Winter buds: ⅓ inch long, sharp-pointed, chestnut-brown.

BARK. On young stems thin, smooth, and gray-green; on mature boles 1½–4 inches thick, in thick platelike ridges covered with purplish to reddish scales.

WOOD. Very important; similar to white pine but more coarse in texture; sash, door, pattern work, etc.; a sweet, sugar-like substance, pinite, exudes from wounds and gives the tree its name.

SILVICAL CHARACTERS. Intolerant; maturity reached in 200–350 years (extreme age 623 years); reproduction generally sparse; tree windfirm with well developed tap and lateral root system; blister rust and bark beetles cause damage.

HABITAT. Transition zone; altitudinal range from 3,000–10,000 feet; best development on west slopes of Sierra range between 4,500–5,500 feet; in mixed stands with ponderosa and Jeffrey pines, Douglas-fir, and other conifers; on cooler and moister sites than associated pines.

[7]

WHITE PINE

WESTERN WHITE PINE

EASTERN WHITE PINE

a. Cone, x ½.
b. Seed, x 1.
c. Needles, x 1.

[8]

PINACEAE

WESTERN WHITE PINE
Pinus monticola Dougl.

HABIT. A tree 90–180 feet high and 2½–5 feet in diameter (max. 200 by 8 feet); on good sites a tall bole with narrow, symmetrical crown and slender, drooping branches.

LEAVES. In fascicles of 5; 2–4 inches long; slender; twisted; blue-green; persistent 3–4 years; sheath deciduous; margin with minute teeth; all sides marked by stomata.

FLOWERS. Male yellow; female red-purple in clusters.

FRUIT. Cones long-stalked; 5–15 (mostly 8–11) inches long; narrow; scales thin, unarmed, with terminal umbo. Seed: ¼ inch long with wing about 1 inch long; red-brown.

TWIGS. Slender; at first rusty-pubescent, later smooth and red-brown to purple-brown. Winter buds: ½ inch long; oblong ovoid.

BARK. On young stems thin, smooth, and light gray; on mature trees rarely over 1½ inches thick in square or rectangular, dark gray plates.

WOOD. Very important; soft, light in weight, and not strong; light brown heartwood; similar to eastern white pine; planing mill products, building, construction, patterns, etc.

SILVICAL CHARACTERS. Tolerant when young, becoming intolerant with age; maturity reached in 200–350 years (extreme age, 400–500 years); reproduction generally sparse; tree windfirm with well developed tap and lateral root system; fire, blister rust, and bark beetles cause damage.

HABITAT. Canadian zone; altitudinal range from 2,000–7,000 feet; best on rich, porous, moist soils; often forming extensive pure forests and elsewhere in mixtures with other conifers.

* * *

EASTERN WHITE PINE
Pinus strobus L.

Until about 1890 this species was the most important forest tree in North America. It is still an important species and very similar in appearance to western white pine, from which it can be distinguished by its distribution, its cone length which varies from 4–8 (mostly about 5) inches long, and its needle persistence of 2 (rarely 3) years.

[9]

LIMBER PINE

a. Foliage with mature closed cone, x ½.
b. Upper side of cone scale with seeds, x ⅔.

WHITEBARK PINE

a. Mature cone, x ⅔.
b. Seeds, x ⅔.
c. Leaf bundle, x ⅔.

PINACEAE

LIMBER PINE

Pinus flexilis James

HABIT. A tree 25–50 feet high (max. 85 by 6⅓ feet); crown broad, open, with large, plumelike, often drooping branches.

LEAVES. In fascicles of 5; 1½–3 inches long; stout; rigid; dark green; persistent 5–6 years; sheath deciduous; margins with minute teeth; marked on all sides by rows of stomata.

FLOWERS. Male red; female clustered, red-purple.

FRUIT. Cones short-stalked; 3–10 inches long; subcylindrical; open at maturity; scales greatly thickened and often slightly reflexed, with terminal unarmed umbo. Seed: ⅓–½ inch long; wingless; thick, light brown shell. The variety *reflexa* Engelm. (*P. strobiformis* Engelm.) of the Mexican border has strongly reflexed cone scales.

TWIGS. Stout and tough; smooth and silver-white or gray. Winter buds: ⅓–½ inch long; broad ovoid and pointed.

BARK. Characteristically thin, smooth, white-gray.

WOOD. Unimportant; moderately light and soft; close-grained; used locally for mine props, railroad ties, etc.

SILVICAL CHARACTERS. Very intolerant; growth slow; maturity reached in 200–300 years; tree very windfirm with taproot; fire, blister rust, and bark beetles cause damage.

HABITAT. Upper Sonoran to Hudsonian zones; altitudinal range from 4,000–11,500 feet; adapted to wide variety of sites, but typical of summits and rocky foothills.

* * *

WHITEBARK PINE

Pinus albicaulis Engelm.

A subalpine tree almost indistinguishable from limber pine except for its very characteristic cones.

FRUIT. Cones short-stalked; 1½–3 inches long; subglobose; closed at maturity and opening by disintegrating at the axis; purple-brown; scales thick with stout, pointed umbos.

BRISTLECONE (DOTS)
AND
FOXTAIL PINE (SOLID)

a. Foliage and cones, x ¾.

b. Seed, x ¾.

c. Leaf bundles, x ¾.

PINACEAE

BRISTLECONE PINE

Pinus aristata Engelm.

HABIT. A subalpine tree 30–40 feet high and 1–2 feet in diameter (max. 60 by 3 feet); bole short, stocky, and commonly malformed; crown dense, irregular, bushy in appearance, and frequently clothing the stem nearly to the ground.

LEAVES. In fascicles of 5; 1–1½ inches long; stout and curved; deep green; persistent for 10–17 years; in dense, often appressed, clusters; sheath deciduous; lustrous on back, marked on lower or ventral surfaces by numerous rows of stomata; usually showing conspicuous whitish exudations of resin.

FLOWERS. Male dark orange-red; female purple.

FRUIT. Cones short-stalked, 3–3½ inches long; ovoid-oblong; open at maturity; scales thick, with dark chocolate-brown apophysis; umbo dorsal, with long, bristle-like, fragile, incurved prickle. Seed: ¼ inch long; with long terminal wing.

TWIGS. Stout; orange-colored, becoming nearly black; long tufts of foliage at ends. Winter buds: ⅓ inch long, brown.

BARK. Thin, smooth, and gray-white on young stems; ½–¾ inch thick on mature trunks, red-brown and furrowed.

WOOD. Unimportant; moderately soft; heartwood pale red-brown; used locally for fuel and mine props.

SILVICAL CHARACTERS. Very intolerant; growth slow; maturity reached in 200–250 years, attains great age, some trees over 2,000 years old and possibly the oldest living organism; reproduction sparse and scattered; tree windfirm.

HABITAT. From typical Hudsonian to Transition zones; altitudinal range from 7,500–10,800 feet; typical of exposed sites; usually in mixture with limber pine, fir, and spruce.

* * *

FOXTAIL PINE

Pinus balfouriana Grev. & Balf.

This California subalpine species closely resembles *Pinus aristata* except for its cones which are dark purple, 3–5 inches long, and armed with a minute, incurved, deciduous prickle.

P. Cembroides

P. Monophylla

P. Edulis

P. Quadrifolia

a. Foliage, x 1.

b. Top view of cone, x 1.

c. Side view of cone, x 1.

PINACEAE

Mexican Pinyon. Nut Pine
Pinus cembroides Zucc.

HABIT. A tree 10–40 feet high and 1–2 feet in diameter (max. 50 by 3 feet); bole often divided with a spreading, rounded crown, giving the tree a bushy appearance.

LEAVES. In fascicles of 3, or 2 and 3 (rarely from 1 to 5); 1–2 inches long; moderately slender (less than 1 mm.); blue-green; incurved; sharp-pointed; persistent 3–4 years; margins with minute teeth; fascicle sheath only partially deciduous.

FLOWERS. Male yellow in crowded clusters; female red.

FRUIT. Cone 1–2½ inches long; ovoid to globose; scales few and unarmed. Seed: ½–¾ inch long, wingless, edible, hard-shelled.

TWIGS. Moderately stout; orange-colored to brown.

BARK. Rarely over ½ inch thick on mature trees; divided into ridges separated by shallow fissures; light red-brown.

WOOD. Unimportant; rather hard; fine-textured; light yellow heartwood; used locally for fuel, ties, and posts.

SILVICAL CHARACTERS. Very intolerant; growth slow; maturity reached in 250–350 years; reproduction generally sparse and scattered; tree very windfirm.

HABITAT. Upper Sonoran zone; arid, gravelly slopes; usually in mixture with junipers and scrub oaks.

* * *

The following species are very similar to *Pinus cembroides* but differ from it in distribution and the following characters:

Pinyon. Colorado Pinyon
Pinus edulis Engelm. (*Pinus cembroides* var. *edulis* Voss)

LEAVES. In fascicles of 2 (rarely 1 or 3); over 1 mm. thick; yellow-green; persistent 3–9 years; margins entire.

FRUIT. Seed thin-shelled, easily cracked with teeth.

Singleleaf Pinyon
Pinus monophylla T. & F. (*Pinus cembroides* var. *monophylla* Voss)

LEAVES. Single (rarely in 2's); over 1 mm. thick; pale green; persistent 4–12 years; margins entire.

Parry Pinyon
Pinus quadrifolia Parl. (*Pinus cembroides* var. *parryana* Voss)

LEAVES. In fascicles of 4 (rarely 3–5; over 1 mm. thick; blue-green; persistent 3 years; margins entire or toothed.

a. Cluster of leaves, x 1.

b. Opened cone, x 1.

c. Cone-scale with seeds, x 1.

SCOTCH PINE

Cone, x 1.

AUSTRIAN PINE

Cone, x ½.

PINACEAE

RED PINE

Pinus resinosa Ait.

HABIT. A tree 60–80 feet high and 2–3 feet in diameter (max. 120 by 5 feet); bole symmetrical, clear; crown broad, rounded, open.

LEAVES. In fascicles of 2; 4–6 inches long; slender; straight; brittle; dark yellow-green; persistent 4–5 years; margins with minute teeth; basal sheath persistent.

FLOWERS. Male purple; female scarlet.

FRUIT. Subsessile; 1½–2¼ inches long; ovoid-conic; chestnut-brown; umbo dorsal and unarmed. Seed: 3⁄16 inch long; wing ⅔ inch long.

TWIGS. Stout; rough; orange to red-brown. Winter buds: ½–¾ inch long; scales red-brown with white fringed margins.

BARK. 1–1½ inches thick; light red-brown; broken into scaly plates.

WOOD. Important; rather light and soft; heartwood light red-brown; used for construction, ties, etc.

SILVICAL CHARACTERS. Intermediate in tolerance; moderate rate of growth; extreme age about 350 years; roots wide-spreading with taproot; reproduction vigorous; hardy and resistant to enemies.

HABITAT. Light, sandy soils; in pure stands, or mixed with white pine on better sites and jack pine on poorer.

* * *

Two related European pines have been widely planted:

Scotch pine, *Pinus sylvestris* L., has become naturalized in the northeast. This species is easily identified by its twisted needles, 1½–3 inches long, in clusters of 2; by yellow-brown cones 1–2½ inches long with flat or pyramidally thickened scales; and by bark which is distinctly orange in color.

Austrian pine, *Pinus nigra* Arnold, resembles red pine in its needles, but can be distinguished from it by its dark brown bark; silvery-white buds; and yellow-brown cones 2–3 inches long, armed with a short spine, which fall intact from the twigs.

[17]

JACK PINE

a. Foliage, x ½.
b. Seed, x ⅔.
c. Mature cones, x ½.

VIRGINIA PINE

a. Cluster of leaves, x

b. Cone, x ⅓.

PINACEAE

JACK PINE
Pinus banksiana Lamb.

HABIT. A tree rarely 60–80 feet high (max. 90 by 2 feet); bole often crooked; crown open, irregular, scraggly.

LEAVES. In fascicles of 2; ¾–1½ inches long; divergent; stout; twisted; yellow-green; persistent 2–3 years; margins with minute teeth; basal sheath persistent.

FLOWERS. Male yellow; female dark purple; clustered.

FRUIT. Sessile; 1½–2 inches long; oblong-conic; unsymmetrical; often remaining closed and on tree for years; scales irregularly developed, unarmed or with minute, deciduous prickle. Seeds: 1/12 inch long, black; wing about ⅓ inch long.

TWIGS. Thin, tough, flexible; becoming rough and red-brown. Winter buds: ¼ inch long, ovoid, pale cinnamon-brown.

BARK. Thin; dark red-brown; shallowly ridged.

WOOD. Moderately important; light and soft; heartwood light-brown; used for pulp, fuel, posts, etc.

SILVICAL CHARACTERS. Very intolerant; short-lived; wide-spreading roots with a taproot; reproduction vigorous.

HABITAT. Essentially Canadian, extending farther north than other pines; dry, sterile soils; mostly in pure stands.

* * *

VIRGINIA PINE
Pinus virginiana Mill.

This species is similar to jack pine in habit, twigs, bark, wood, silvical characters, and site; it differs from jack pine in distribution and the following characters:

LEAVES. In fascicles of 2; 1½–3 inches long; divergent; stout; twisted; gray-green; persistent 3–4 years; margins with minute teeth; short-needled trees hardly distinguishable from jack pine.

FLOWERS. Male orange-brown; female pale green tinged with rose.

FRUIT. Subsessile; 1½–3 inches long; ovoid-conic; symmetrical; opening at maturity but persisting on twigs 3–4 years; scales thin, flat, with persistent prickle and deep purple inner lip. Seed: ¼ inch long, pale brown, with wing about 1 inch long.

PITCH PINE   POND PINE

a. Cluster of leaves, x 1.
b. Unopened cone, x 1.
c. Opened cone, x ½.
d. Cone-scale with seeds, x 1.

PINACEAE

Pitch Pine

Pinus rigida Mill.

HABIT. A tree 40–60 feet high and 1–2 feet in diameter (max. 100 by 3 feet); on good sites with a straight bole and open, irregular crown of large branches.

LEAVES. In fascicles of 3; 3–5 inches long; stout; stiff; usually twisted; standing out at nearly right angles to twig; yellow-green; often produced on trunk; persistent 2–3 years; margins with minute teeth; basal sheath persistent.

FLOWERS. Male yellow; female red-green.

FRUIT. Nearly sessile; 1½–3½ inches long; ovoid-conic; opening at maturity but persistent for many years; scales armed with short, rigid prickle. Seeds: ¼ inch long, dull black, winged.

TWIGS. Stout; rough; gray-brown. Winter buds: ½–¾ inch long, scales chestnut-brown and fringed.

BARK. Thick; dark red-brown; flat plates separated by furrows.

WOOD. Of little importance; light and soft; heartwood light brown; used for lumber, ties, props, fuel.

SILVICAL CHARACTERS. Very intolerant; short-lived; taproot in youth; reproduction vigorous; young trees produce sprouts.

HABITAT. Typically dry, sterile sites; pure or mixed stands, with scrub oak, red maple, gray birch, etc.

* * *

Pond Pine

Pinus serotina Michx.

(*Pinus rigida* var. *serotina* (Michx.) Loud.)

This closely related southern species which is found in swamps and low, wet flats differs from pitch pine in having flexible needles 6–8 inches long and nearly globose cones armed with weak, deciduous prickles which remain closed for several years. This species has remarkable ability to sprout following fire.

SHORTLEAF PINE

a. Clusters of leaves, x 2/3.
b. Open cone, x 2/3.
c. Closed cones, x 2/3.
d. Scales and seeds, x 2/3.

SPRUCE PINE

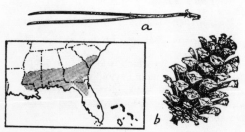

a. Cluster of leaves, x 2/3.
b. Cone, x 2/3.

PINACEAE

Shortleaf Pine

Pinus echinata Mill.

HABIT. A tree 80–100 feet high and 2–3 feet in diameter (max. 130 by 4 feet); long, clear bole; narrow, pyramidal crown.

LEAVES. In fascicles of 2 and 3; 3–5 inches long; slender; flexible; yellow-green; persistent 2–4 years; often produced on trunk; basal sheath persistent.

FLOWERS. Male pale purple; female pale rose color.

FRUIT. Nearly sessile; 1½–2½ inches long; oblong to conical; opening at maturity and persistent several years; red-brown; scales thin, armed with small sharp prickle. Seeds: ³⁄₁₆ inch long, brown with black markings, wing ½ inch long.

TWIGS. Slender; flexible; roughened; red-brown. Winter buds: ¼ inch long, red- to gray-brown.

BARK. Thin; nearly black and scaly on young trees; later becoming red-brown and scaly plated.

WOOD. Very important; intermediate between longleaf and western pines in strength and hardness; wide variety of uses.

SILVICAL CHARACTERS. Intolerant; growth very rapid on good sites; deep taproot system; reproduction aggressive; young trees capable of producing sprouts if stems killed by fire or cutting.

HABITAT. Typical of dry, light soils in pure or mixed stands.

* * *

Spruce Pine

Pinus glabra Walt.

Nowhere common, this unimportant medium-sized tree is found as a scattered tree among hardwoods on moist sandy loams. It is very tolerant and resembles shortleaf pine in appearance.

LEAVES. In fascicles of 2; 1½–3 inches long; slender; dark-green.

FRUIT. Similar to shortleaf, but more globose and smaller.

BARK. Thin; gray; furrowed; resembling black oak.

LOBLOLLY PINE

D. Olszewski del.

a. Cluster of leaves, x ⅓.
b. Closed cone, x ⅔.
c. Open cone, x ⅔.
d. Scale with seeds, x 1.
e. Scale, x 1.

LOBLOLLY PINE

SAND PINE

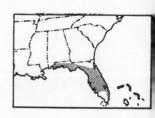

PINACEAE

LOBLOLLY PINE

Pinus taeda L.

HABIT. A tree 90–110 feet high and 2–3 feet in diameter (max. 150 by 5½ feet); long, clear bole; crown rounded, dense.

LEAVES. In fascicles of 3 (rarely 2); 6–9 inches long; slender; yellow-green; persistent 3 years; basal sheath persistent.

FLOWERS. Male yellow; female short-stalked, yellow.

FRUIT. Sessile; 2½–6 inches long; typically oblong-conic; opening at maturity and falling next year; dull, pale, red-brown; scales thin, armed with a stout, sharp spine. Seeds: ¼ inch long, brown with black markings, wing ¾ inch long.

TWIGS. Moderately slender; roughened; yellow- to red-brown. Winter buds: ½ inch long, red-brown, oblong, resinous.

BARK. Thin, becoming ¾–2 inches thick; scaly and nearly black on young trees, becoming bright red-brown and scaly plated.

WOOD. Important; intermediate between longleaf and western pines in strength and hardness; marketed as shortleaf pine.

SILVICAL CHARACTERS. Most tolerant of important southern pines; growth very rapid; windfirm; reproduction very aggressive; not resistant to fire; in pure or mixed stands.

HABITAT. Typical of wet bottom lands; aggressive on drier cut-over or abandoned areas when protected from fire; in pure stands or mixed with pines and hardwoods.

* * *

SAND PINE

Pinus clausa (Chapm.) Vasey

This unimportant small tree is common in Florida on very dry, sterile, sandy soils; it comes in aggressively after fires. It is easily identified by its needles and characteristic cones.

LEAVES. In fascicles of 2; 2–3½ inches long; slender, dark green.

FRUIT. Short-stalked; 2–3½ inches long; some cones remaining closed and persistent for years; yellow-brown; scales armed with short prickle.

a. Cluster of needles, x ½.

b. Cone, x ½.

c. Seed, x ½.

PINACEAE

Longleaf Pine

Pinus palustris Mill. (*Pinus australis* Michx.)

HABIT. A medium-sized tree 80–120 feet high and 2–3 feet in diameter (max. 150 by 4 feet); long ,clear bole; small, open crown with needles in dense tufts at ends of branches.

LEAVES. In fascicles of 3; 8–18 inches long; slender; flexible; bright green; persistent 2 years; basal sheath persistent. ⅓ to ½ inch long.

FLOWERS. Male dark rose-purple; female dark purple.

FRUIT. Nearly sessile; 6–10 inches long; narrowly ovoid-cylindric; opening at maturity; in falling, leaving basal scales attached to twig; red-brown; scales thin, with an incurved prickle. Seeds: ½ inch long, pale with dark blotches; wings 1½ inches long.

TWIGS. Very stout, the terminal leader up to 1 inch in diameter; roughened by leaf bases; orange-brown. Winter buds: ½–1 inch long, conspicuously white, covered by silvery, lustrous, fringed scales which make the bud remarkably resistant to fire.

BARK. Thin, becoming ¾ to 1½ inches thick on old stems; orange-brown; in rough, scaly plates.

WOOD. Very important; heavy, hard, and strong; used for construction timbers, lumber, flooring, boxes, ties, posts, poles, etc.; the chief source of naval stores.

SILVICAL CHARACTERS. Very intolerant; growth generally slow; maturity reached in about 150 years with extreme age of 300 years; practically no above ground growth for 3–6 years while taproot becoming established; windfirm with deep taproot system; reproduction vigorous and plentiful; very resistant to fire and disease.

HABITAT. On variety of sites but typical of dry, sterile, sandy sites; usually in pure stands or with scrub oak. The only tree that will produce timber over much of its range.

GENERAL. A hybrid between longleaf and loblolly pines has been named *Pinus sondereggeri* H. H. Chap. This has been reported as not uncommon in Louisiana, North Carolina, and Texas.

a. Cluster of leaves, x ⅔.
b. Cone, x ⅔.
c. Scale and seeds, x 1.

SLASH PINE

TABLE-MOUNTAIN PINE

PINACEAE

Slash Pine

Pinus elliottii Engelm. (*Pinus caribaea* Morelet)

HABIT. A tree 80–100 feet high and 2–3 feet in diameter; long, clear bole; crown rounded, dense.

LEAVES. In fascicles of 2 and 3; 8–12 inches long; stout; dark glossy green; persistent 2 years; basal sheath persistent.

FLOWERS. Male dark purple; female pink.

FRUIT. Stalked; 2½–6 inches long; ovoid-conic; opening at maturity and falling following year; chocolate-brown; (shining as if varnished); scales thin, armed with small sharp spine. Seeds: ¼ inch long, black, wing about 1 inch long.

TWIGS. Stout; roughened by leaf bases; orange-brown. Winter buds: ½–¾ inch long, scales silvery brown.

BARK. Thin, becoming ¾–1½ inches thick; orange to purple-brown plated; peeling off in thin, papery, characteristic layers.

WOOD. Important; heavy, hard, and strong; marketed as longleaf pine and used for same purposes; important source of naval stores.

SILVICAL CHARACTERS. Intolerant, but less so than longleaf; growth very rapid; windfirm on deep soils; reproduction aggressive; not resistant to fire.

HABITAT. Old stands in low, wet sites because of fire damage; aggressive on cutover areas if protected; pure or mixed stands. The south Florida variety with very dense wood and grass like seedlings is designated *P. elliottii* var. *densa* L. & D. This species was incorrectly listed as *Pinus caribaea* Morelet, a species of the Bahama Islands.

* * *

Table-Mountain Pine

Pinus pungens Lamb.

This unimportant species, characteristic of the table lands of the Appalachians, is a small, intolerant tree. It is easily identified by its needles and characteristic cones.

LEAVES. In fascicles of 2; 1½–3½ inches long; yellow-green.

FRUIT. Sessile; 2½–3½ inches long; ovoid; opening at maturity, but persistent for years; heavy, the thick scales armed with conspicuous, sharp, hooked spines or claws.

a. Leaf bundles, x ½.

b. Mature cone, x 1.

c. Seed, x 1.

PINACEAE

PONDEROSA PINE. WESTERN YELLOW PINE

Pinus ponderosa Laws.

HABIT. A tree 150–180 feet high and 3–4 feet in diameter (max. 232 by 8 feet on Pacific Coast); bole symmetrical, clear; crown short, conical or flat-topped.

LEAVES. In fascicles of 3, or 2 and 3 (rarely from 1–5); 3–11 inches long (mostly 4–7 inches); stout; dark to yellow-green; persistent 2–7 years (usually 4–6 years); cross section shows 2–5 resin ducts; basal sheath ¼–¾ inch long, persistent.

FLOWERS. Male yellow; female red, clustered or paired.

FRUIT. Subsessile; 2½–6 inches long; ovoid; open at maturity; basal scales remaining attached to twig when cones shed; scales thin, armed with short prickles. Seed: ¼ inch long; brown-purple, often mottled; wing 1 inch long.

TWIGS. Stout; orange-colored; turpentine odor when bruised. Winter buds: about ½ inch long; often resinous.

BARK. Black and furrowed on young trees; on old trunks 2–4 inches thick; yellow-brown to cinnamon-red; in large, flat plates.

WOOD. Very important; rather light and soft; sapwood very thick with properties of white pine; heartwood light brown; uses include construction, planing mill products, ties, etc.

SILVICAL CHARACTERS. Intolerant; growth slow; maturity in 350–500 years (extreme age 660 years); reproduction vigorous; long taproot; fire and bark beetles cause damage.

HABITAT. Transition zone; large altitudinal range, from 2,000–8,000 feet; exceedingly drouth resistant; in open pure stands or more commonly the most abundant tree in mixed coniferous stands.

GENERAL. The Rocky Mountain variety is designated *P. ponderosa* var. *scopulorum* Engelm. Arizona pine, *P. ponderosa* var. *arizonica* (Engelm.) Shaw, of southern New Mexico, Arizona, and northern Mexico, differs in having needles in fascicles of 5 and cones less than 3½ inches long.

JEFFREY PINE

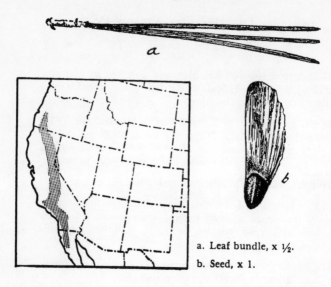

a. Leaf bundle, x ½.
b. Seed, x 1.

APACHE PINE

a. Leaf bundle, x ½.

PINACEAE

JEFFREY PINE

Pinus jeffreyi Grev. & Balf. (*Pinus ponderosa*
var. *jeffreyi* Vasey)

A tree similar in most of its characteristics to *Pinus ponderosa* and differing from it in the following ways:

HABIT. A tree 100–80 feet high and 4–6 feet in diameter; not quite reaching the proportions of ponderosa pine; lumber is sold as ponderosa.

LEAVES. In fascicles of 3, or 2 and 3; 4–9 inches long; blue-green; persistent 6–9 years.

FRUIT. 5–15 inches long; scales thin, armed with a stout, long, incurved prickle.

TWIGS. Stout; purple; with pineapple-like odor when bruised. Winter buds: not resinous.

HABITAT. Endures greater extremes of climate than ponderosa; mixed with ponderosa pine and other conifers.

* * *

APACHE PINE

Pinus engelmannii Carr. (*Pinus apacheca* Lemm.)

A tree similar in most of its characteristics to *Pinus ponderosa*, and differing from it in the following ways:

HABIT. A tree 50–60 feet high and 1–2 feet in diameter (max. 75 by 3 feet).

LEAVES. In fascicles of 3 (occasionally 2–5); 8–15 inches long, (mostly about 10 inches; dark green; with conspicuously fringed margins; persistent 2 years; cross section shows 11–14 resin ducts; basal sheath ¾–1 inch long.

HABITAT. Transition zone; altitudinal range 5,500–8,200 feet; otherwise similar to ponderosa pine.

GENERAL. Some authors consider this tree a synonym of *Pinus ponderosa;* it is characterized during its first few years by development of a very deep taproot and little height growth.

* * *

WASHOE PINE

Pinus washoensis Mason & Stock.

This rare and local species was described from Washoe County, Nevada in 1945. It is related to *P. jefferyi*.

[33]

(a) Foliage, x ⅔; (b) Mature cone, x ⅔; (c) Seed, x ⅔.

CHIHUAHUA PINE

(a) Mature cone, x ⅔; (b) Seed, x ⅔; (c) Leaf bundle, x ⅔.

[34]

PINACEAE

LODGEPOLE PINE
Pinus contorta Dougl.

HABIT. A tree 70–80 feet high and 1¼–2½ feet in diameter (max. 150 by 3 feet); long, slender bole; short crown.

LEAVES. In fascicles of 2; 1–3 inches long; stout; often twisted; bright yellow-green; persistent 4–6 years; margins with minute teeth; basal sheath persistent.

FLOWERS. Orange-red; male in spikes; female clustered.

FRUIT. Subsessile; ¾–2 inches long; ovoid; frequently remaining closed and on the tree for many years; scales at base knoblike, armed with long prickle. Seed: ⅙ inch long; thin, dark red-brown shell; wings ½ inch long.

TWIGS. Stout; light orange-brown, becoming black. Winter buds: ¼ inch long, ovoid, dark chestnut-brown, resinous.

BARK. Very thin, rarely over ⅖ inch thick; orange-brown to gray; covered by thin, loosely appressed scales.

WOOD. Moderately important; soft; fine-textured; sapwood thick; heartwood pale brown; tangential surface with many indentations; used for lumber, ties, poles, and mine timbers.

SILVICAL CHARACTERS. Intolerant; growth slow; maturity reached in about 200 years; shallow root system; reproduction vigorous, typically forming dense stands following fires; fire, bark beetles, and mistletoe cause damage.

HABITAT. Canadian zone; altitudinal range from 6,000–11,000 feet; adapted to variety of soil types; in pure, dense, even-aged stands, or in mixture with various conifers.

GENERAL. Some authors distinguish two varieties: Shore Pine, *P. contorta* var. *contorta*, a stunted, short-leaved, twisted cone tree of the Pacific Coast; and Lodgepole Pine, *P. contorta* var. *latifolia* Engelm., the taller inland tree described above.

* * *

CHIHUAHUA PINE
Pinus leiophylla var. *chihuahuana* (Engelm.) Shaw

This small essentially Mexican tree is unique in that it matures its cones in 3 years and is a hard pine with a deciduous basal sheath. The needles are in clusters of 3, 2–4 inches long, and persistent 4 years. The cones are 1½–2 inches long, long-stalked, ovoid, and often remaining closed. It is characteristic of poor, dry sites.

[35]

COULTER PINE

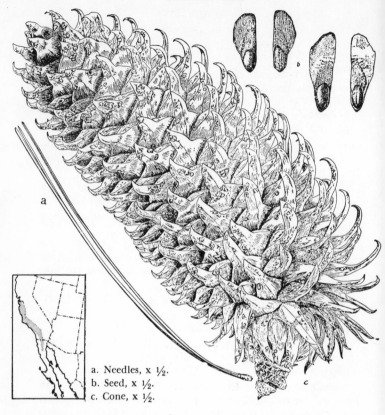

a. Needles, x ½.
b. Seed, x ½.
c. Cone, x ½.

DIGGER PINE

a. Seed, x ½.
b. Needles, x ½.

PINACEAE

Coulter Pine

Pinus coulteri D. Don

HABIT. A small tree 40–50 feet high and 1–2½ feet in diameter (max. 80 by 3½ feet); large, open, unsymmetrical crown.

LEAVES. In fascicles of 3; 6–12 inches long; dark blue-green; rigid; persistent 3–4 years; basal sheath persistent.

FLOWERS. Male yellow; female dark red-brown.

FRUIT. Short-staked; 10–14 inches long; oblong-ovoid; opening at maturity and persistent several years; light yellow-brown; thick scales terminating in large claw; the largest American pine cone, weighing up to 5 pounds. Seed: ½ inch long, thick-shelled, wing longer than seed (about 1 inch long).

TWIGS. Very stout; rough; orange-brown. Winter buds: ½ inch, brown.

BARK. Nearly black; 1½–2 inches thick; broad, scaly ridges.

WOOD. Unimportant; soft and weak; used for fuel.

SILVICAL CHARACTERS. Intolerant; maturity reached in about 150 years; growth slow; wide, deep roots; reproduction scanty.

HABITAT. Dry, rocky slopes from 3,000–7,000 feet; pure or mixed stands.

* * *

Digger Pine

Pinus sabiniana Dougl.

HABIT. A small tree 40–50 feet high and 1–2 feet in diameter; bole often forked; open, sparsely foliaged crown.

LEAVES. In fascicles of 3; 7–12 inches long; pale blue-green; flexible; pendant; persistent 3–4 years; basal sheath persistent.

FLOWERS. Male yellow; female dark purple.

FRUIT. Similar to Coulter pine, but smaller (6–10 inches long) and chocolate-brown. Seed: ¾ inch long, thick-shelled, edible, wing about ½ as long as seed.

TWIGS, BARK, WOOD, and SILVICAL CHARACTERS. Similar to Coulter pine.

HABITAT. Dry foothills from 100–5,000 feet; able to survive on exceedingly dry sites; in pure stands or mixed with oaks.

KNOBCONE PINE

a. Cone, x ⅔.
b. Needles, x ⅔.

MONTEREY PINE

a. Seed, x ⅔.
b. Cone, x ⅔.
c. Needles, x ⅔.

PINACEAE

KNOBCONE PINE
Pinus attenuata Lemm.

HABIT. A small tree 20–60 feet high and 1–2 feet in diameter (max. 100 by 3 feet); open, sparse crown.

LEAVES. In fascicles of 3; 3–7 inches long; yellow-green; slender; persistent 4–5 years; basal sheath persistent.

FLOWERS. Male orange-brown; female fascicled, purple.

FRUIT. Short-stalked; 3–6 inches long; ovoid-conic; light yellow-brown; unsymmetrical with outer basal scales pyramidally knoblike; remaining closed and persistent many years with clusters characteristically encircling stems of even small trees. Seed: ¼ inch long with wing 1¼ inches long.

TWIGS. Slender; smooth; orange-brown. Winter buds: ½ inch, brown.

BARK. Thin; gray-brown; low, scaly ridges.

WOOD. Unimportant; soft and weak; used locally for fuel.

SILVICAL CHARACTERS. Intolerant; short-lived; rapid growth; wide, deep roots; reproduction aggressive, especially following fire.

HABITAT. Very dry mountain slopes to 5000 feet; pure or mixed stands.

* * *

MONTEREY PINE
Pinus radiata D. Don (*Pinus insignis* Dougl.)

HABIT. A handsome tree 40–100 feet high and 2–5 feet in diameter; rounded, open crown; common ornamental.

LEAVES. In fascicles of 3; 4–6 inches long; bright green; slender; flexible; persistent 3 years; basal sheath persistent.

FLOWERS. Male yellow in spikes; female, dark purple.

FRUIT. Short-stalked; 3–7 inches long; ovoid; yellow-brown; unsymmetrical with outer basal scales round, thickened and domelike; remaining closed and persistent. Seed: ¼ inch, wings ¾ inch.

TWIGS. Slender; dark orange. Winter buds: ½ inch, brown.

BARK. Thick; red-brown to nearly black; furrowed.

WOOD. Unimportant in the United States; soft and weak.

SILVICAL CHARACTERS. Moderately tolerant; short-lived; rapid growth; prolific seed production. An important forest tree in Australia, New Zealand, and South Africa.

HABITAT. Dry soil (17 inches rain annually) but humid air; in pure stands or mixed with Bishop pine and cypress.

BISHOP PINE

a. Seed, x 1/2.
b. Needles, x 1/2
c. Cones, x 1/2.

TORREY PINE

a. Cone and needles, x 1/2.

PINACEAE
BISHOP PINE
Pinus muricata D. Don

HABIT. A tree 30–80 feet high and 1–3 feet in diameter; handome, rounded crown of dense tufted foliage.

LEAVES. In fascicles of 2; 4–6 inches long; dark yellow-green; thick; rigid; persistent 2–3 years; basal sheath persistent.

FLOWERS. Male in orange-colored spikes; female in whorls.

FRUIT. Sessile; in clusters of 3–7; 2–4 inches long; ovoid; yellow-brown; unsymmetrical with outer basal scales knoblike and extended into spurlike spines; often remaining closed and persistent for years. Seed: ¼ inch long, black.

TWIGS. Stout; rough; orange-brown. Winter buds: ½ inch long, brown.

BARK. Thick; purple-brown; rough; furrowed.

WOOD. Unimportant; moderately light and strong; lumber and fuel.

SILVICAL CHARACTERS. Moderately tolerant; short-lived; rapid growth; reproduction aggressive, especially following fire.

HABITAT. Variety of sites from wet clays and peat bogs to dry sandy ridges; pure stands or mixed with lodgepole, madrone, and oaks; commonly planted ornamental.

* * *

TORREY PINE
Pinus torreyana Parry

HABIT. A rare, local tree 25–60 feet high and 8–14 inches in diameter; few, stout, spreading branches; rounded crown.

LEAVES. In fascicles of 5; 7–13 inches long; dark yellow-green; rigid; persistent 3–4 years; basal sheath persistent.

FLOWERS. Male yellow in heads; female on long stalks.

FRUIT. Long-stalked; 4–6 inches long; broad-ovoid; chocolate-brown; thick-scaled; persistent 3–4 years. Seed: ¾ inch, wing ½ inch, edible.

TWIGS. Very stout; smooth; green first year becoming black.

BARK. About 1 inch thick; red-brown; rough; furrowed.

WOOD. Unimportant; too rare to be of any use.

SILVICAL CHARACTERS. Intolerant; short-lived; reproduction abundant.

HABITAT. Dry soil (15 inches rain annually) but very humid air; in pure, open groves; smallest range of any American pine, on Santa Rosa Island and north of San Diego.

PINACEAE

The Larches

Characteristics of the Genus *Larix* Mill.

HABIT. Tall, pyramidal trees; open crowns, with slender, irregularly disposed, horizontal or pendulous branches; dwarfed, short, spurlike lateral branchlets.

LEAVES. Deciduous, needle-shaped or linear; produced in dense false whorls or clusters on spurlike lateral branches; solitary and spirally arranged on new shoots; numerous lines of stomata on all surfaces; 2 resin canals in cross section.

FLOWERS. Monoecious, terminal, single, appearing with leaves; male naked, globose to oblong, consisting of several yellow, spirally arranged scales, each bearing two pollen sac; female erect, consisting of few or many rounded, red-purple scales in the axes of much longer scarlet bracts, each scale bearing 2 small inverted ovules.

FRUIT. Woody, erect, short-stalked cones; maturing in one season; cone scales thin, persistent, concave, longer or shorter than their long-pointed bracts. Seed: 2 under each scale; triangular and light brown; large terminal wing.

TWIGS. Smooth and glaucous, or hairy. Winter buds: subglobose, small, nonresinous, with accrescent inner scales which mark lateral spur branches with prominent ringlike scars.

WOOD. Rather strong and durable; small, scattered resin ducts; thin, white sapwood and sharply defined, red to russet-brown heartwood.

SILVICAL CHARACTERS. Intolerant, slow-growing, and found on a variety of habitats; extensive forests occasionally destroyed by larch sawfly (*Nematus erichsonii*).

GENERAL. This genus contains about 10 species scattered through the Northern Hemisphere. In North America 3 species are native. The European larch (*Larix decidua* Mill.), an important tree, has been planted in the United States for ornamental purposes. It can be identified by its puberulous cones, ¾–1½ inches long, with inserted bracts and 40–50 suborbicular scales.

KEY TO THE SPECIES OF LARCHES

1. Cones with bracts shorter than scales and usually concealed; twigs slender, yellowish, glabrous.
   2. Cones ½–¾ " long, composed of 12–15 glabrous scales; twigs glabrous, covered at first with glaucous bloom; eastern and far northern.....................*L. laricina*, **Tamarack,** p. 45.
   2. Cones ¾–1½ " long, composed of 40–50 hairy scales; twigs without bloom; ornamental exotic............................
   ....*L. decidua*, **European Larch,** p. 42.
1. Cones with bracts conspicuous and exserted beyond the 40 or more scales; twigs stout, brownish, hairy; western.
   3. Twigs with pale hairs, brittle; bark thick, red-brown plated and deeply furrowed; cones 1–1¾ "long; needles flatly 3-angled; western...............*L. occidentalis*, **Western Larch,** p. 47.
   3. Twigs densely woolly, tough; bark thin, gray, scaly; cones 1½–2 " long; needles 4-angled; western alpine.............
   ....*L. lyallii*, **Subalpine Larch,** p. 47

a. Foliage, x 1.

b. Seed, x 1.

c. Branchlet with cones, x 1.

PINACEAE

Tamarack. Eastern Larch

Larix laricina (Du Roi) K. Koch (*Laria alaskensis* Wight)

HABIT. A small to medium-sized tree seldom over 60 feet high and 1–2 feet in diameter (max. 100 by 2½ feet); long, clear, cylindrical bole; and an open, pyramidal, irregular crown with slender horizontal branches.

LEAVES. Linear; triangular in cross section; ¾–1¼ inches long; bright blue-green; falling in September or October; in clusters of 12–20.

FLOWERS. Male subglobose and sessile; female oblong and short-stalked.

FRUIT. ½–¾ inch long; short-stalked, oblong to subglobose, chestnut-brown, and falling during second year; cone scale less than 20, slightly longer than broad, erose at margin, glabrous and lustrous and twice as long as their bracts except at base of cone. Seed: ⅛ inch long with light chestnut-brown wings about ¼ inch long.

TWIGS. Slender, smooth, glaucous at first, becoming orange-brown during first year. Winter buds: conspicuous, globose, small, lustrous, and dark red.

BARK. Thin and smooth on young stems; ½–¾ inch thick, red-brown and scaly on mature trunks.

WOOD. Heartwood yellow-brown, medium texture, strong, hard, heavy, and durable; not widely used, chief uses being poles, railroad ties, and rough lumber.

SILVICAL CHARACTERS. Intolerant; growth moderate, maturity being reached in 100–200 years; reproduction vigorous on favorable sites; shallow root system; larch sawfly and fire cause serious damage.

HABITAT. Hudsonian and Canadian zones; restricted to sphagnum bogs or swamps in southern part of range and making best growth on moist beaches and well-drained uplands further north; chiefly with black spruce, also balsam fir, aspen, birch, and jack pine; extending northward to limits of tree growth.

a. Seed, x 1.

b. Branchlet with cones, x 1.

PINACEAE

Western Larch

Larix occidentalis Nutt.

HABIT. A tree 140–180 feet in height and 3–4 feet in diameter; long, clear, cylindrical bole, often with a swollen butt; short, open crown of small, horizontal branches.

LEAVES. Linear, flatly triangular in cross section, 1–1¾ inches long, light pale green becoming yellow, and falling in early autumn, in clusters of 14–30.

FLOWERS. Male short, oblong; female oblong, subsessile.

FRUIT. 1–1½ inches long, short-stalked, oblong, purple-red to red-brown, falling first year; cone scales 40 or more, broader than long, sometimes toothed at reflexed apex, usually white woolly on the outside, and shorter than exserted long-tipped bracts. Seed: ¼ inch long, with wings ½ inch long.

TWIGS. Stout, brittle, at first with a pale pubescence, soon becoming glabrous and orange-brown. Winter buds: ⅛ inch in diameter, subglobose, chestnut-brown.

BARK. Scaly on young stems; 4–6 inches thick, plated, and deeply furrowed on old trunks; red-brown to cinnamon-red.

WOOD. Heartwood red-brown, heavy, strong, and durable; similar to and sold as Douglas-fir, for lumber, poles, ties, etc.

SILVICAL CHARACTERS. Intolerant; growth rather slow, maturity being reached in 300–400 years (trees over 700 years reported; reproduction vigorous, competing with lodgepole pine on burned areas; windfirm with deep, widespreading root system; fungi and mistletoe often cause damage.

HABITAT. Transition zone; altitudinal range 2,000–7,000 feet; best development on deep, moist soils but does well on dry, gravelly slopes; in nearly pure stands or with Douglas-fir, western white, ponderosa and lodgepole pines, western hemlock, Engelmann spruce, and alpine and grand fir.

* * *

Subalpine larch, *Larix lyallii* Parl., is a small timber-line tree in regions of heavy snows that fall early and remain late. Its range lies within that shown for western larch. It is characterized by densely woolly twigs and cone scales, cones 1½–2 inches long with exserted bracts, 4-angle needles, and thin, furrowed, scaly bark.

PINACEAE

THE SPRUCES

Characteristics of the Genus *Picea* Dietr.

HABIT. Evergreen trees with sharp-pointed, pyramidal crowns, and straight, tapering trunks; branches in regular whorls.

LEAVES. Spirally arranged, linear, sessile, stiff, and single; extending from all sides of twigs; persistent 7–10 years, but deciduous when dried; 4–angled or flattened; when falling, leaving basal peglike projections (sterigmata) on the twig.

FLOWERS. Monoecious, catkin-like, solitary; male, or pollen-bearing, auxillary, yellow to red or purple, ¾–1 inch long, consisting of numerous spirally arranged scales, each bearing two pollen sacs; female, or cone- and seed-producing, terminal, erect, yellow-green or red, ¾–1¼ inches long, consisting of numerous 2-ovuled, bracted scales.

FRUIT. Woody, pendent cone; matures in one season; borne mostly near top of crown; scales numerous, thin, unarmed, persistent, much longer than bracts. Seed: 2 under each fertile scale, small, compressed; highly buoyant with thin wing.

TWIGS. Roughened by sterigmata. Winter buds: ovoid or conical, of overlapping scales, and usually not resinous.

BARK. Thin and scaly (furrowed on old trunks in blue spruce).

WOOD. Light, soft, resilient, fine-textured, long-fibered and straight-grained; small, scattered resin ducts; not resinous; high satiny luster; strong for weight; highly important for paper pulp, lumber, boxes, etc.

SILVICAL CHARACTERS. Tolerant; no taproot and generally shallow-rooted. Natural enemies: fire, leaf aphis (*Adelges abietis*) which causes conelike gall, spruce budworm (*Harmologa fumiferana*), which often destroys young stands, and white pine weevil (*Pissodes strobi*).

HABITAT. Cool, moist sites; typically in swampy areas or along the margins of streams and lakes.

GENERAL. This genus contains about 40 species, largely restricted to cooler regions in the Northern Hemisphere. In North America there are 7 indigenous species. The Norway spruce, *Picea abies* (L.) Karst., characterized by cones 4–7 inches long, is commonly planted throughout the United States and has become naturalized in the east.

[48]

KEY TO THE SPECIES OF SPRUCES

1. Cone scales rounded at tip, smooth or wavy (erose) on margin.
   2. Cones under 2 inches long; needles 4-sided; eastern or north-western.
      3. Cones ½–1½ inches long, ovoid, purple, persistent many years; scales stiff, rigid, brittle, with wavy margins; twigs hairy; needles blunt-pointed; transcontinental and northern ....*P. mariana*, **Black Spruce**, p. 53.
      3. Cones 1¼–2 inches long, oblong, brown, falling in 1 year; scales smooth on margin or nearly so; needles pointed.
         4. Cone scales stiff and rigid at maturity; twigs more or less hairy; eastern United States and Canada.............. ....*P. rubens*, **Red Spruce**, p. 55.
         4. Cone scales soft and flexible at maturity; twigs not hairy; transcontinental and northern....................... ....*P. glauca*, **White Spruce**, p. 51.
   2. Cones 2–4 inches long; scales with entire margins; needles flattened; alpine in California and Oregon................ ....*P. breweriana*, **Brewer Spruce**, p. 59.
1. Cone scales wedge-shaped at tip, margin wavy (erose).
   5. Cones 4–7 inches long; drooping foliage; needles 4-sided, not prickly; common European ornamental.................... ....*P. abies*, **Norway Spruce**, p. 48.
   5. Cones rarely 4 inches long; native and western.
      6. Needles flattened, not prickly, yellow-green; cone 2½–4 inches long; Pacific Coast area......................... ....*P. sitchensis*, **Sitka Spruce**, p. 59.
      6. Needles 4-sided, blue-green; western mountain region.
         7. Cone 1–2½ inches long, persistent 1 year; needles flexible, acute but not prickly to touch; twigs minutely hairy; buds ⅛–¼ inch long with scales usually appressed; bark on mature trees thin and scaly.......... ....*P. engelmanii*, **Engelmann Spruce**, p. 57.
         7. Cone 2¼–4½ inches (mostly about 3½ inches) long, persistent 2 years; needles stiff, bristle-pointed; twigs glabrous; buds ¼–½ inch long with scales usually reflexed, bark on mature trees thick and furrowed; central Rocky Mountains.......*P. pungens*, **Blue Spruce**, p. 61.

a. Branchlet with cone, x 1.
b. Seed, x 1.

PINACEAE

WHITE SPRUCE

Pieca glauca (Moench) Voss (*Picea canadensis* B.S. & P.)

HABIT. A tree 60–70 feet high and 1½–2 feet in diameter (max. 120 by 4 feet); slender symmetrical bole; crown narrowly to broadly pyramidal with long, thick branches.

LEAVES. Tending to be crowded on upper side of branch by twisting of those on lower side; ⅓–¾ inch long; 4–angled; blue-green, occasionally with whitish tinge; rigid acute tips; odor pungent when crushed; 2 resin ducts in cross section.

FLOWERS. Male pale red to yellow; female with red or yellow-green scales.

FRUIT. 1–2½ inches long; oblong-cylindrical; nearly sessile; cone scales flexible, rounded and smooth at apex; light green or reddish before shedding seed, and becoming light brown and falling soon after. Seed: ⅛ inch long, pale brown, oblique wing ¼–⅜ inch long.

TWIGS. Glabrous, or in far Northwest downy; rather slender; orange-brown; skunklike odor when bruised. Winter buds: ⅛–¼ inch long; ovoid, obtuse, and chestnut-brown.

BARK. Thin, ¼–½ inch thick; ash-brown with silvery inner bark, separated into irregular thin plates or scales.

WOOD. Important in Northeast; used for pulp, construction lumber, boxes and crates, sounding boards, etc.

SILVICAL CHARACTERS. Tolerant of considerable shade, recovers from suppression well; growth slow, but faster than black spruce; tree attains age of 250–300 years; reproduction abundant on moist sites; shallow, spreading root system.

HABITAT. Hudsonian and Canadian zones; typical of low, damp woods, and banks of streams and lakes; altitudinal range from sea level to 5,000 feet; frequently gives way to black spruce or tamarack on wet sites, and to lodgepole pine on dry sites; often forms pure, dense forests, but also in mixture with black spruce, fir, birch, poplars, and willows.

GENERAL. The western white spruce, *Picea glauca* var. *albertiana* (S. Brown) Sarg., is the form found in the Rocky Mountain region and Black Hills. It is characterized by somewhat shorter and broader cones and a narrow crown.

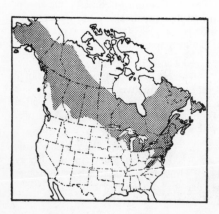

a. Branchlets with cones, x 1.
b. Seed, x 1.

PINACEAE

Black Spruce

Picea mariana (Mill.) B.S.P.

HABIT. A tree sometimes 40–80 feet high and ⅔–3 feet in diameter, but commonly much smaller; short slender bole, usually pruning poorly; crown open, conical, more or less irregular.

LEAVES. Spreading in all directions; ¼–¾ inch long; 4–angled; pale blue-green and glaucous; blunt at apex; more or less incurved; hoary on upper surface from broad bands of stomata; lustrous and slightly stomatiferous below; 2 resin ducts in cross section.

FLOWERS. About ½ inch long; male red; female purple.

FRUIT. ½–1½ inches long; ovoid; on strongly incurved, short stalks; cone scales stiff, brittle, rigid, rounded, smooth or erose at apex, puberulous, and dull gray-brown; persistent many years. Seed: ⅛ inch long, dark brown, with pale brown oblique wing ¼–⅜ inch long.

TWIGS. Rusty-pubescent and rather slender; at first green, becoming dull red-brown. Winter buds: ⅛ inch long, ovoid, acute, light red-brown, puberulous.

BARK. Thin, ¼–½ inch thick; gray-brown; separated into thin, closely appressed scales or flakes; inner bark often olive-green.

WOOD. Not important except for pulp; used interchangeably with white spruce.

SILVICAL CHARACTERS. Very tolerant, recovering from suppression at an advanced age; growth slow; tree rather short-lived, attaining an age of 200 years; shallow, spreading root system; reproduction good on moist sites; lower branches often take root, forming clusters of small trees.

HABITAT. Hudsonian and Canadian zones; typical of cold sphagnum bogs and swamps, but also found on dry slopes in Northwest; altitudinal range from 100–3,500 feet; with white spruce and tamarack, reaches northern limit of tree growth; in dense, pure stands, or in mixture with tamarack, balsam fir, white spruce, white birch, aspen, etc.

a. Twig, x 1.

b. Needles, x 1½.

c. Cone, x 1.

d. Scale with seed, x 1.

PINACEAE

Red Spruce

Picea rubens Sarg. (*Picea rubra* Link)

HABIT. A tree 70–80 feet high and 1½–2 feet in diameter (max. 120 by 3½ feet); slender, symmetrical bole; grown narrow and conical with long branches.

LEAVES. Extending at nearly right angles from all sides of twig; ½–⅝ inch long; 4-angled; dark yellow-green; blunt or pointed at apex.

FLOWERS. Male bright red at maturity; female on different branches, red-green.

FRUIT. 1¼–2 inches long; ovoid-oblong; nearly sessile; cone scales rigid, rounded, and smooth at apex; light green or purplish before shedding seed, becoming red-brown and falling the first winter or following spring. Seed: ⅛ inch long, dark brown, wing ¼ inch long.

TWIGS. More or less pubescent at first, becoming smooth second year; orange-brown. Winter buds: ¼–⅓ inch long, ovoid, acute, red-brown.

BARK. Thin, ¼–½ inch thick; gray-brown to red-brown, with red-brown inner bark; separating into irregular, close scales.

WOOD. Important; light; soft; even-grained; lustrous; used for lumber, pulp, musical instruments, containers, etc.

SILVICAL CHARACTERS. Very tolerant, though growing slowly under heavy shade; long-lived, attaining age of 400 years; good reproduction; spreading root system; susceptible to damage by fire and wind throw.

HABITAT. Varied, ranging from swamps and bogs where growth is slow to mountain tops; best growth on well-drained uplands and mountain slopes; in pure stands or mixed with yellow birch, beech, maple, white pine and hemlock on better sites and with black spruce, balsam fir, tamarack, and red maple on swampy sites. The common spruce in the mountains of New York and New England and with white pine the most important timber species in this region.

[55]

a. Branchlet with cones, x 1.

b. Seed, x 1.

c. Enlarged needles, x 2.

PINACEAE

ENGELMANN SPRUCE

Picea engelmannii Parry

HABIT. A tree 60–120 feet high and 1½–3 feet in diameter (max. 165 by 5 feet); bole long but limby, cylindrical; crown compact, somewhat scraggly, narrowly pyramidal, with short, whorled branches. A prostrate shrub at high elevations.

LEAVES. Tending to be crowded on the upper side of the branch by the curving of those on the lower side; 1–1⅛ inches long; 4–angled; blue-green, occasionally with whitish, glaucous bloom; blunt or acute tips (not very sharp to touch); flexible; no resin ducts in cross section.

FLOWERS. Male dark purple; female bright scarlet.

FRUIT. 1–2½ inches long; oblong-cylindrical; sessile or short-stalked; cone scales flexible, variable in outline and erose-dentate at apex; light chestnut-brown; falling during autumn or winter of first season. Seed: ⅛ inch long, nearly black; broad, oblique wing ½ inch long.

TWIGS. Minutely pubescent (visible with hand lens); rather stout; orange-brown to gray-brown. Winter buds: ⅛–¼ inch long; broadly ovoid to conic; pale chestnut-brown; but scales usually appressed.

BARK. Thin, ¼–½ inch thick; cinnamon-red to purple-brown; broken into large, thin, loosely attached scales.

WOOD. Properties similar to white spruce; this is the longest-fibered and lightest weight spruce, but at present not widely used because inaccessible; lumber, telephone poles, railroad ties, mine timbers, and fuel.

SILVICAL CHARACTERS. Tolerant and recovering well from prolonged suppression; growth generally rather slow because of short summer season; a long-lived tree, reaching ages of 350–500 or more years; reproduction abundant and vigorous; shallow, spreading root system.

HABITAT. Hudsonian and Canadian zones; varying from 1,500–5,000 feet in the northern Rockies to 10,000–12,000 feet in the southern Rockies; rich, loamy soils with abundance of moisture; in pure stands or in mixture with alpine fir, lodge-pole pine, and other conifers growing at high elevations.

SITKA SPRUCE

(a) Seeds, x ⅔; (b) Branch with cones, x ⅔.

BREWER SPRUCE

Twig with cone, x ⅔.

PINACEAE

Sitka Spruce

Picea sitchensis (Bong.) Carr.

HABIT. A large tree 180–200 feet high and 3–4½ feet in diameter (max. 300 by 16 feet); bole often clear for 100 feet, cylindrical; crown pyramidal, short, open.

LEAVES. Extending at nearly right angles from all sides of twig; ½–1⅛ inches long; flattened; bright yellow-green above, bluish-white, glaucous below; very sharp-pointed.

FLOWERS. Male dark red; female covered by elongated bracts.

FRUIT. 2–4 inches long; oblong-cylindrical; short-stalked; cone scales thin, rough, papery, stiff, wedge-shaped at apex and erose-dentate at margin; chestnut-brown; falling first season. Seed: ⅛ inch long, red-brown, wings ⅜ inch long.

TWIGS. Glabrous; slender; orange-brown to gray-brown. Winter buds: ¼–½ inch long, ovoid, red-brown.

BARK. Thin, ½–1 inch thick; red-brown to purple; broken into thin, loose, concave scales.

WOOD. Very important and much in demand for specialized uses such as wood aircraft; during World War II aircraft quality lumber reported to have sold for $600 per mbf.; soft, light, uniform grain.

SILVICAL CHARACTERS. Tolerant; growth fairly rapid; long-lived, ages of 700–800 years; reproduction vigorous; shallow roots.

HABITAT. A tidewater species; best development on deep, moist loams; in pure stands or mixed with hemlock, Douglas-fir, western redcedar, alder and maple.

* * *

Brewer spruce, *Picea breweriana* S. Wats., is an uncommon timber-line species restricted to the Siskiyou Mountains of southern Oregon and northern California. It is characterized by long pendulous weeping branches; flattened, blunt, dark green needles; rounded, entire-margined purplish cone scales; and cones 2–4 inches long.

a. Branchlet with cone, x ¾.

b. Seed, x 1.

c. Needles, x 1½.

PINACEAE

Blue Spruce. Colorado Blue Spruce

Picea pungens Englem. (*Picea parryana* Sarg.)

HABIT. A tree 80–100 feet high and 1–2 feet in diameter (max. 150 by 4 feet); bole symmetrical, tapering, knotty; crown typically dense and conical when young, becoming thin, ragged and pyramidal in age, and extending to the ground on open grown species. The State Tree of Colorado.

LEAVES. Extending at nearly right angles from all sides of twig; 1–1¼ inches long; 4–angled; blue-green, frequently with a silvery, glaucous bloom which persists for 3–4 years on young trees; rigid, tipped with long, bristle-sharp point; 1 resin duct in an angle of leaf in cross section.

FLOWERS. Male yellow, tinged with red; female pale green.

FRUIT. 2¼–4½ (mostly 3½) inches long, oblong-cylindrical; sessile or short-stalked; cone scales tough, stiff, spreading, with erose margins; shiny, light chestnut-brown; not falling until fall of second season. Seed: ⅛ inch long, dark chestnut-brown; broad oblique wing about ½ inch long.

TWIGS. Glabrous; stout and rigid; orange-brown to gray-brown. Winter buds: ¼–½ inch long; broadly ovoid and obtuse; light chocolate-brown; bud scales usually reflexed.

BARK. Pale to dark gray; thin and scaly on young trucks, becoming ¾–1½ inches thick and deeply furrowed with rounded ridges on old trunks.

WOOD. Rather similar to white spruce but brittle, knotty and of little value. The chief use of this tree is for ornamental planting.

SILVICAL CHARACTERS. Moderately tolerant, but least so of spruces; slow-growing; long-lived; reproduction generally scanty because of dense ground cover; widespread, moderately deep root system and decidedly windfirm.

HABITAT. Transition and Canadian zones, but mostly below the Engelmann spruce belt; varying from 6,000–9,000 feet in the north to 8,000–11,000 feet in the south; rich, moist soils, typically on stream banks; never abundant; in scattered pure groves or singly in mixture with ponderosa pine, Douglas-fir, alpine fir, Engelmann spruce, and hardwoods.

a. Branchlet with cones, x 1.

b. Seed, x 1.

c. Bud enlarged.

PINACEAE

DOUGLAS-FIR

Pseudotsuga taxifolia (Poir.) Britt. (*Pseudotsugo menziesii* Franco)

HABIT. A large evergreen tree attaining a height of over 300 feet on the west coast and 130 feet in the Rocky Mountains; compact, pyramidal crown, with irregularly disposed branches.

LEAVES. Linear, single, more or less flattened, blunt to pointed, spirally arranged, and petiolate; ¾–1¼ inches long; grooved above and stomatiferous below; persistent 5–8 years or longer.

FLOWERS. Monoecious; male orange-red; female red-green.

FRUIT. Pendent, woody cones; 2–4½ inches long, oblong-ovoid, maturing in one season; scales thin, rigid, rounded, much shorter than their long, exserted, 3-lobed bracts. Seed: ¼ inch long, with large, rounded, terminal wing.

TWIGS. Slender, pubescent, orange-brown, becoming gray-brown. Winter buds: ¼ inch long, characteristically long, conical, sharp-pointed, lustrous, brown.

BARK. Smooth, gray-brown and with resin blisters on young trees; becoming very thick (6–24 inches), rough, with red-brown ridges separated by deep furrows.

WOOD. Highly variable from yellowish, narrow-ringed, moderately light and soft, to red-brown, wide-ringed, with weak spring wood and very dense summer wood. This tree produces more timber than any other species.

SILVICAL CHARACTERS. Intermediate in tolerance; reproduction abundant and vigorous; well developed, wide-spreading lateral root system; attaining great age.

HABITAT. Sea level to 11,000 feet; adapted to variety of soils but best on moist, deep, porous soils of northern exposure; will endure considerable drought; in pure stands or mixed with Rocky Mountain conifers.

GENERAL. The check list assigns Douglas-fir the name *P. menziesii;* this author believes this was unwise and maintains the name *P. taxifolia.* European taxonomists have separated this species into 11 species; however this view is not commonly accepted in North America. The Rocky Mountain form is recognized as the separate geographical variety *glauca* (Mayr) Sudw.

* * *

The bigcone Douglas-fir *Pseudotsuga macrocarpa* (Vasey) Mayr, of Southern California is distinguished by its larger fruit (4–6½ inches long) with bracts only slightly longer than the thick, stiff cone scales.

[63]

PINACEAE

The Hemlocks

Characteristics of the Genus *Tsuga* (Endl.) Carr.

HABIT. Tall, broadly pyramidal, evergreen trees; long, slightly tapering trunks; pyramidal or conical crown with scattered, slender, horizontal, and often pendulous branches; leading shoots characteristically drooping.

LEAVES. Spirally arranged, often appearing 2-ranked by a twist of the petioles; linear; single; abruptly petiolate; flattened or rounded; persistent 3–6 years and leaving conspicuous, woody, persistent bases (sterigmata) when they fall; deciduous in drying; usually grooved above, with 2 conspicuous bands of stomata below; 1 centrally located resin duct in cross section.

FLOWERS. Monoecious, single, on twigs of previous season; male, or pollen-bearing, axillary, globose, of numerous short stamens; female, or cone- and seed-bearing, terminal, erect, of numerous, circular scales of nearly the same length as their membranous bracts.

FRUIT. Woody, pendent cones; maturing in one season; scales thin, rounded, entire-margined, several times longer than bracts. Seed: 2 under each scale; small, light, and widely disseminated; long, terminal, obovate wing; dotted with small, resin vesicles.

TWIGS. Slender; round; roughened by persistent leaf bases. Winter buds; small, nonresinous, ovoid to globose.

BARK. Rough, hard, ridged, deeply furrowed; clear chocolate-red color when broken; containing tannin.

WOOD. Moderately soft; moderately strong; resin ducts normally absent; light to red-brown; considered inferior to pine and Douglas-fir.

SILVICAL CHARACTERS. Tolerant trees; requiring abundant moisture; seldom attaining ages of more than 500 years; shallow, wide-spreading root system.

GENERAL. This genus contains 10 or more species widely scattered through North America and Asia. In North America there are 4 native species, 2 western and 2 eastern.

KEY TO THE SPECIES OF HEMLOCKS

1. Needles flat, obtuse, grooved above, with 2 whitish bands below; cones light brown, small (½–1½ inches long), ovoid.
   2. Needle margin finely toothed; needles mostly 2-ranked; cones ½–1 inch long.
      3. Needles tapering from base to apex, with well defined, narrow white bands below; cones stalked, ½–¾ inch long, oblong-ovoid, with scale margins smooth; buds ovoid, pointed; eastern. . . . *T. canadensis*, **Eastern Hemlock,** p. 67.
      3. Needles of uniform width from base to apex, with poorly defined bands below; cones sessile; ¾–1 inch long, ovoid, with scale margins undulate; buds globose; western . . . . *T. heterophylla*, **Western Hemlock,** p. 69.
   2. Needle margin entire; needles spreading in all directions; cones 1–1½ inches long; Appalachian Mountains. . . . . *T. caroliniana*, **Carolina Hemlock,** p. 67.
1. Needles rounded or keeled above, stomatiferous on all surfaces, spreading in all directions; bluntly pointed; cones yellow-green to purple, ¾–3½ inches long (mostly about 2 inches long), oblong-cylindric. . . . . . . *T. mertensiana*, **Mountain Hemlock,** p. 71.

a. Fruiting branch viewed from beneath, x ½.

b. Leaf, x 3.

c. Cross-section of leaf, enlarged.

d. Branchlet with partly opened cone, x 1.

e. Cone-scale with seeds, x 3.

EASTERN HEMLOCK   CAROLINA HEMLOCK

[66]

PINACEAE

EASTERN HEMLOCK
Tsuga canadensis (L.) Carr.

HABIT. A tree usually 60–70 feet high and 2–3 feet in diameter (max. 160 by 6 feet); dense, pyramidal crown with horizontal branches which extend nearly to the ground in open grown trees; typically flexible, drooping terminal leader.

LEAVES. Flattened; ⅓–⅔ inch long; tapering from base to apex; dark yellow-green and grooved above, 2 narrow, well defined bands of stomata below; abrupt slender petiole; appearing 2–ranked; rounded or notched at apex.

FLOWERS. Male yellow; female pale green, bracts shorter than scales.

FRUIT. ½–¾ inch long; oblong-ovoid; light brown; scales suborbicular, smooth-margined. Seed: 1/16 inch long with wing about ⅓ inch long; light brown.

TWIGS. Slender; light brown and pubescent during first year, becoming gray-brown and glabrous. Winter buds: ovoid, 1/16 inch long.

BARK. Scaly on young trees, becoming deeply furrowed and ridged; red to gray in color with purple streaks on freshly cut surfaces; important source of tannin.

WOOD. Light, brash, coarse-grained, splintery; used for poorer grades of lumber and pulp; knotty as a result of persistent branches.

SILVICAL CHARACTERS. Tolerant; growth rapid; maximum age about 600 years; reproduction abundant and vigorous; shallow, wide-spreading root system.

HABITAT. Cool, moist sites; in small pure groves, or more commonly in mixed stands with white pine, red spruce, or hardwoods.

* * *

Carolina hemlock, *Tsuga caroliniana* Engelm., is a handsome and somewhat rare tree found in the upper slopes of the Appalachian Mountains from Virginia to northern Georgia. This tree, which is commonly planted as an ornamental, differs from eastern hemlock in having the needles extending from all sides of the twigs and in having larger cones which are 1–1½ inches long.

[67]

a. Branchlet with cones, x 1.

b. Seed, x 1.

PINACEAE

Western Hemlock

Tsuga heterophylla (Rafn.) Sarg.

HABIT. A tree 125–175 feet high and 2–4 feet in diameter (max. 259 by 9 feet); tall, clear truck; short, open, pyramidal crown with typically flexible drooping terminal leader.

LEAVES. Flattened; ¼-¾ inch long; dark, shiny green and grooved above, 2 broad bands of stomata below; abrupt, slender petiole; mostly 2–ranked; rounded or blunt at apex.

FLOWERS. Male yellow; female red or purple with rounded bracts shorter than scales.

FRUIT. ¾–1 inch long, ovoid, light brown, scales suborbicular, wavy-margined. Seed: ¹⁄₁₆ inch long; ovoid; ⅓ as long as narrow, straw-colored wing.

TWIGS. Slender; pubescent for 5–6 years; pale yellow-brown becoming dark red-brown; drooping. Winter buds: ovoid, ¹⁄₁₆ inch long, blunt, bright chestnut-brown.

BARK. Thin (1–1½ inches) even on largest trees; young bark scaly, russet-brown; on old trunks hard, dark russet-brown with furrows separating wide flat ridges; inner bark dark red streaked with purple; used for its tannin content.

WOOD. Superior in quality to eastern hemlock; one of 4 major timber-producing species of Pacific Northwest; uniform texture and not very harsh or splintery; suitable for all uses but heavy construction, and most important pulpwood species of region.

SILVICAL CHARACTERS. Tolerant throughout life; growth rapid, comparing favorably with Douglas-fir, seldom attaining age of over 500 years; reproduction very abundant and vigorous; shallow, wide-spreading root system; susceptible to fire injury, and butt rot common in old trees.

HABITAT. Transition and Canadian zones; altitudinal range from sea level to 7,000 feet; prefers deep, moist, porous soils, but hardy in drier situations; in pure, dense stands or mixed at lower levels with Douglas-fir, silver and grand firs, giant arborvitae, redwood, and hardwoods; and at higher levels with noble fir, Alaska cedar, mountain hemlock, western white and lodgepole pines.

a. Branchlet with cones, x 1.

b. Opened cone, x 1.

c. Seed, x 1.

PINACEAE

Mountain Hemlock. Black Hemlock
Tsuga mertensiana (Bong.) Carr.

HABIT. An alpine tree 75–100 feet high and 2½–3½ feet in diameter; trunk tapering and long clear, or knotty and malformed; crown open, pyramidal, with slender, drooping branches and drooping terminal leader; a sprawling shrub at timber line.

LEAVES. Semicircular in cross section; ½–1 inch long; pale bluish-green and stomatiferous on all surfaces; upper surface often keeled or grooved; abruptly narrowed into straight or twisted petiole; extending from all sides of twig or crowded toward upper side; bluntly pointed.

FLOWERS. Male purple on slender drooping stems; female purple or green, slender-tipped bracts longer than scales.

FRUIT. ½–3½ inches long, (mostly 2 inches); oblong-cylindric; yellow-green to purple; scales oblong-obovate and spreading at right angles or reflexed when mature. Seed: ⅛ inch long; ¼ as long as wing.

TWIGS. Thin or stout; dense, short, pale, pubescence for 2–3 years; light red-brown, becoming gray-brown and scaly. Winter buds: conical, ⅛ inch long, acute, red-brown, outer scales with awl-like tip.

BARK. Rather thin on large trees (1–1½ inches), early broken and rough on young trees; on old trunks hard, purplish to red-brown, with deep, narrow furrows separating narrow, rounded ridges; contains large quantities of tannin.

WOOD. Little used and inferior in quality to western hemlock; light, soft, not strong, and close-grained.

SILVICAL CHARACTERS. Tolerant; growth slow; trees over 500 years of age seldom found; reproduction generally abundant; shallow, wide-spreading root system.

HABITAT. Hudsonian and Canadian zones; altitudinal range from sea level (Alaska) to 11,000 feet, but mostly near timber line; at its best on cool, moist, deep soils of northern exposure, moisture being essential; in pure stands or in mixture with alpine fir, alpine larch, Engelmann spruce, whitebark, lodgepole, and western white pines.

PINACEAE

The Firs

Characteristics of the Genus *Abies* Mill.

HABIT. Tall, pyramidal, evergreen trees; dense, spirelike crowns; slender, horizontal, whorled branches; and straight, gradually tapering trunks.

LEAVES. Spirally arranged, linear, sessile, and single; usually flat and blunt; extending from all sides of twig but mostly appearing 2-ranked by a twist near their base; persistent for 7-10 years; usually grooved above and with stomatiferous lines below; 2 resin canals in cross section; when falling, leaving a conspicuous, smooth, circular scar on twig.

FLOWERS. Monoecious, axillary, single; male, or pollen-bearing, numerous on lower sides of lower crown branches, oval or cylindrical, with yellow to scarlet anthers; female, or cone-and seed-bearing, on upper side of topmost branches, erect, globose to oblong, consisting of numerous, imbricated, 2-ovuled scales much shorter than their bracts.

FRUIT. Woody, erect cones; maturing in one season; scales thin, fan-shaped, and falling at maturity from the central, spikelike axis which persists many years. Seed: 2 under each scale; large, thin wing; peculiar, conspicuous resin-vesicles.

TWIGS. Smooth, glabrous, or pubescent. Winter buds: small, mostly subglobose or ovoid, with thin, loosely imbricated scales and usually thickly covered with resin.

BARK. Young bark thin, smooth, with numerous blister-like resin pockets; old bark smooth or furrowed; Canada balsam obtained from the resin blisters of balsam fir.

WOOD. Light, soft, and weak; color whitish to light brown, the summer wood frequently with a purplish tinge; resin ducts absent; used for pulp, containers, and general construction.

SILVICAL CHARACTERS. Tolerant, moisture-loving trees of cool sites; slow to fast growing; moderately long-lived.

GENERAL. This genus contains about 35 species widely scattered through North and Central America, Europe, Asia and northern Africa. There are 9 species native to North America.

KEY TO THE SPECIES OF FIRS

1. Winter buds subglobose, ⅛–⅓ inch long; needles not bristle-tipped; cones without spiny-tipped bracts.
    2. Needles crowded toward the upper side of the twigs; cones large and broad (3½–9 inches long); Pacific Coast region.
        3. Needles 4-sided, stomatiferous (covered with minute white dots) on all sides and usually glaucous; bark furrowed or scaly on mature trunks.
            4. Cones 4–6 inches long; bracts much longer than, and covering cone scales; needles with sharply defined groove on upper surface; Washington, Oregon, and northern California.................*A. procera*, **Noble Fir**, p. 87.
            4. Cones 6–9 inches long; bracts never covering scales; needles ribbed above and below.
                5. Cones with bracts inserted........................
                ....*A. magnifica*, **California Red Fir**, p. 85.
                5. Cones with bracts exserted.......................
                ....*A. magnifica shastensis*, **Shasta Red Fir**, p. 85.
        3. Needles flattened, dark green and lustrous above, with 2 distinct white bands (stomata) on lower surface; bark smooth and ashy gray on mature trunks; cones 3½–6 inches long with inserted bracts; British Columbia and Alaska to Washington and Oregon....*A. amabilis*, **Pacific Silver Fir**, p. 83.
    2. Needles flattened, on sterile branches spreading and not crowded, often 2-ranked; cones narrow, 2–5 inches long.
        5. Cones with bracts inserted.
            6. Needles on lower branches ¾–1¾ inches long; cones dark purple, scales slightly longer than broad.
                7. Needles dark green and lustrous above with 2 distinct white bands (stomata) below, 2-ranked on lower branches; northeastern United States to northwestern Canada..............*A. balsamea*, **Balsam Fir**, p. 75.
                7. Needles stomatiferous on both surfaces, nearly erect on lower branches; western.
                    8. Mature bark hard, smooth, gray; high western mountains......*A. lasiocarpa*, **Subalpine Fir**, p. 77.
                    8. Mature bark distinctly soft and corky, yellow-white; Colorado, Arizona, and New Mexico...........
                    ....*A. lasiocarpa arizonica*, **Corkbark Fir**, p. 77.
            6. Needles 1½–3 inches long; cones yellow to green-purple, scales slightly broader than long; western.
                9. Needles distinctly 2-ranked, 1½–2 inches long, dark green above with 2 white bands of stomata below; Montana to British Columbia and California........
                ....*A. grandis*, **Grand Fir**, p. 81.
                9. Needles spreading or obscurely 2-ranked, 2–3 inches long, stomatiferous and pale green on both surfaces; western United States..*A. concolor*, **White Fir**, p. 79.
        5. Cones with bracts exserted; needles ½–1 inch long; Appalachian Mountains............*A. fraseri*, **Fraser Fir**, p. 75.
1. Winter buds ovoid, pointed, ¾–1 inch long; needles 1½–2¼ inches long, flat, rigid, bristle-tipped; cones 3–4 inches long with spiny bracts exserted ¾–1¾ inches; California (Monterey County)
......................*A. bracteata*, **Bristlecone Fir**, p. 87.

a. Lower crown branchlet.

b. Branchlet with cone, x 1.

c. Upper and lower sides of cone scale, x 1.

d. Seed, x 1.

PINACEAE

BALSAM FIR

Abies balsamea (L). Mill.

HABIT. A medium-sized tree 40–60 feet high and 1–1½ feet in diameter (max. 85 by 2 feet); a dense, dark green, narrowly pyramidal crown with a slender spirelike tip.

LEAVES. On lower branches 2-ranked, ¾–1½ inches long, scattered, flattened, blunt, or notched; on upper branches shorter, spreading, and crowded; dark green above, with two silvery bands of stomata below.

FLOWERS. Male of yellow anthers; female, scales.

FRUIT. 2–4 inches long, oblong-cylindric, dark purple; scales longer than broad, and twice as long as short, pointed bracts. Seed: ¼ inch long, with broad purple-brown wings.

TWIGS. Slender; finely pubescent and yellow-green; becoming smooth and gray to purple. Winter buds: subglobose, resin-covered, ⅛–¼ inch long, with orange-green scales.

BARK. Thin, ash-gray, smooth except for numerous resin blisters on young trees; becoming ½ inch thick, red-brown, and broken into thin scales.

WOOD. Soft and brittle; used for pulp, boxes, etc.; resin in bark blisters is source of Canada balsam.

SILVICAL CHARACTERS. Tolerant (less so than spruce), recovering well from suppression; a short-lived tree reaching an age of 150 years, but generally defective before 90 years; reproduction plentiful and aggressive; shallow root system; lower branches sometimes take root, producing new trees.

HABITAT. Canadian and Hudsonian zones; demands abundant soil moisture and humid atmosphere; forms pure stands in swamps; on higher sites in mixture with spruce, hemlock, and broad-leafed species. The variety *phanerolephis* Fern. ranging north from northern Virginia has slightly exposed fruit bracts.

* * *

Fraser fir, *Abies fraseri* (Pursh) Poir., is a tree of the high mountains of Tennessee, North Carolina, and southwestern Virginia. It is very similar to balsam fir except for the long fruit bracts which extend beyond the scales and are strongly reflexed.

[75]

a. Branchlet with cone, x 1.
b. Different shaped scales, x 1.
c. Seed, x 1.

PINACEAE

Subalpine Fir

Abies lasiocarpa (Hook.) Nutt.

HABIT. A tree 60–100 feet high and 1½–2 feet in diameter (max. 160 by 3 feet); a dense, narrowly pyramidal, spirelike crown often extending to the ground, with short, thick branches; a prostrate shrub at timber line.

LEAVES. On lower branches, 1–1¾ inches long (mostly about 1 inch), flattened, blunt or notched; on upper branches ½ inch long and pointed; deep blue-green; crowded and nearly erect by a twist at their base; stomatiferous on both surfaces (less conspicuous above).

FLOWERS. Male dark indigo-blue; female dark purple.

FRUIT. 2–4 inches long, oblong-cylindric, dark purple; scales mostly longer than broad and 3 times longer than long-tipped bracts. Seed: ¼ inch long, with dark lustrous wings.

TWIGS. Stout, pubescent, and pale orange-brown; becoming smooth and gray or silver-white. Winter buds: subglobose, resinous, ⅛–¼ inch long, with light orange-brown scales.

BARK. Thin, gray, smooth except for numerous resin blisters on young trees; becoming shallowly fissured.

WOOD. Similar to balsam fir but little used except for fuel.

SILVICAL CHARACTERS. Tolerant (of its associates, only Engelmann spruce and mountain hemlock are more so); growth not rapid; reproduction abundant and vigorous; shallow root system; lower branches sometimes taking root.

HABITAT. Canadian and Hudsonian zones; growing from 3,500 feet to timber line in the north and from 10,500 feet to timber line in the south; in cool, moist sites; commonly with Engelmann spruce, lodgepole, whitebark, limber, or bristlecone pines, alpine larch, cork fir, and sapen.

GENERAL. Corkbark fir *A. lasiocarpa* var. *arizonica* (Merr.) Lemm. of New Mexico, Arizona, and southern Colorado, differs from alpine fir in having soft, corky, yellow-white to ash-gray trunk bark.

a. Cone scale and seed, x 1.

b. Mature cone, x 1.

c. Lower crown needles, x ¾.

PINACEAE

WHITE FIR

Abies concolor (Gord. & Glend.) Lindl.

HABIT. A tree 120–150 feet high and 3–4 feet in diameter (max. 200 by 6 feet); a dense conelike crown with heavily foliaged, long-persisting, short branches.

LEAVES. On lower branches 2–3 inches long, flat, straight, and acute at apex; on fertile branches, or on old trees, ¾–1½ inches long, thick, keeled above, usually curved, acute or rarely noticed at apex; silver-blue to silver-green; crowded; more or less obscurely 2-ranked or extending from all sides of twig; stomatiferous above and below.

FLOWERS. Male rose to dark red; female greenish.

FRUIT. 3–5 inches long, oblong, bright yellow to olive-green or purple; scales much broader than long, and twice as long as short-tipped bracts. Seed: ⅓–½ inch long, yellow-brown with rose-tinted broad wing.

TWIGS. Moderately stout, smooth, yellow-green to brown-green and ultimately gray-brown. Winter buds: subglobose, resin-covered, ⅛–¼ inch long, yellow-brown.

BARK. Thin, gray, smooth except for numerous resin blisters on young trees; becoming 4–7 inches thick, ash-gray, hard and horny, with deep furrows and wide ridges.

WOOD. Similar to balsam fir; used for lumber, pulp, boxes and novelties.

SILVICAL CHARACTERS. Tolerant, although less so than alpine fir; growth moderately rapid, maturity being reached in about 300 years; reproduction generally abundant and aggressive; root system normally shallow.

HABITAT. Transition and Canadian zones; altitudinal range from 6,000–11,000 feet; requires less moisture than other western firs, existing surprisingly well on poor, dry sites; seldom in pure stands, usually with ponderosa and limber pine, Douglas-fir, alpine fir, Engelmann spruce, and aspen.

GENERAL. The Pacific white fir, considered a variety by some authors, [*A. concolor* var. *lowiana* (Gord.) Lemm.] of Oregon and California differs from the species in having smaller buds and somewhat longer needles which are more pectinately arranged.

a. Branchlet with cone, x ½.

b. Seed, x 1.

c. Cone scales and seed, x 1.

PINACEAE

GRAND FIR. LOWLAND WHITE FIR

Abies grandis (Dougl.) Lindl.

HABIT. A tree 140–160 feet in height and 2–4 feet in diameter (max. 250 by 6 feet); rather open domelike crown, on old trees appearing wider in the middle because of the drooping of the lower branches.

LEAVES. On lower branches 1½–2 inches long, scattered, distinctly 2-ranked; on fertile branches 1–1½ inches long, more crowded, obscurely 2-ranked or nearly erect; blunt, flat, lustrous dark yellow-green and grooved above, white with 2 bands of stomata below.

FLOWERS. Male pale yellow; female light yellow-green.

FRUIT. 2–4½ inches long, cylindrical, yellow-green to green-purple; scales ⅓ broader than long, and 3–4 times longer than short-tipped bracts. Seed: ⅜ inch long, light brown, with straw-colored wing about ¾ inch long.

TWIG. Slender, yellow-green to orange-brown, puberulous becoming glabrous in second year. Winter buds: subglobose, ⅛–¼ inch long.

BARK. Thin, gray-brown, smooth except for resin blisters and chalky white blotches on young trees; becoming 2–3 inches thick, red-brown, plated or divided into flat ridges separated by deep furrows.

WOOD. Similar to balsam fir, but with disagreeable odor, and so known as "stinking fir"; lumber, pulp, and boxes.

SILVICAL CHARACTERS. Moderately tolerant, but less so than associated firs; growth moderate, maturity being reached in about 200 years; reproduction abundant if sufficient moisture and protection against frost present; windfirm with deep, spreading root system; subject to attach by spruce budworm and stringy brown-rot fungus.

HABITAT. Transition and Canadian zones; altitudinal range from sea level to 5,000 feet; on deep, moist, alluvial soils along streams or on mountain slopes; in limited pure stands, or more frequently in mixed hardwood and coniferous forests with ponderosa, western white, and lodgepole pines, Douglas-fir, western larch, alpine fir, Engelmann spruce, etc.

a. Seed, x 2/3.
b. Lower crown leaves, x 2/3.
c. Upper crown leaves and cone, x 2/3.

PINACEAE

Pacific Silver Fir

Abies amabilis (Dougl.) Forb.

HABIT. A tree 140–160 feet in height and 2–4 feet in diameter (max. 200 by 6 feet); crown spirelike or pyramidal; bole clear in dense forest, but clothed to the ground with rather short branches in open.

LEAVES. On lower branches ¾–1¼ inches long, crowded toward the upper side of the twig, flat, lustrous dark green and grooved above, silvery white with stomata below, notched or pointed at apex; on fertile branches often somewhat thickened and stomatiferous above at apex.

FLOWERS. Male red; female with broad scales and lustrous purple bracts.

FRUIT. 3½–6 inches long, cylindrical to barrel-shaped, deep purple; scales slightly broader than long, and longer than the spiny-tipped, inserted bracts. See: ½ inch long, light yellow-brown, with pale brown wings ¾ inch long.

TWIG. Stout, orange-brown and puberulous the first year becoming red-brown. Winter buds: subglobose, ¼ inch long, dark purple, resin-covered.

BARK. Thin, silver-white to ash-gray with chalk-colored blotches and resin blisters on trees at maturity; on overmature trunks becoming scaly at the base.

WOOD. Similar to balsam fir; used in limited quantites for lumber and pulp.

SILVICAL CHARACTERS. Moderately tolerant; growth moderate, maturity being reached in about 250 years; reproduction abundant; often planted as ornamental because of handsome crown shape and dense foliage; the most abundant fir of the northwest.

HABITAT. Transition and Canadian zones; altitudinal range from sea level to 6,000 feet; best on deep, moist soils with southern or western exposure; in pure stands or mixed with Sitka spruce, Douglas-fir, grand fir, western hemlock, and western redcedar.

a. Lower crown leaves, x ⅔.
b. Cone of variety shastensis, x ⅔.
c. Seed, x ⅔.

PINACEAE

CALIFORNIA RED FIR

Abies magnifica A. Murr.

HABIT. The largest of the firs, varying from 150–180 feet in height and 4–5 feet in diameter (max. 230 by 10 feet); crown narrow but round-topped; bole clear for much of its height, then with short, small branches.

LEAVES. On lower branches ¾–1½ inches long, somewhat flattened, rounded apex, and somewhat two-ranked; on upper, fertile branches almost equally 4-sided, erect, crowded, and with short callous tips; glaucous during first year, becoming blue-green; stomatiferous on all sides.

FLOWERS. Male red-purple; female with green bracts much longer than rounded scales.

FRUIT. 6–9 inches long; cylindrical to barrel-shaped; dark purplish brown; scales longer than broad and longer than the spiny-tipped, inserted bracts. Seed: ½–¾ inch long, dark brown, with large, broad, rose-colored wings.

TWIG. Stout; yellow-green and slightly rusty-pubescent the first year, becoming smooth and light red-brown. Winter buds: ovoid, ¼ inch long, slightly resinous at the tip, dark brown.

BARK. Distinctly reddish colored, thick (4–6 inches), and furrowed on old trunks; smooth and chalky gray on young trunks.

WOOD. Similar to and substituted for Noble fir; light and soft; used for lumber.

SILVICAL CHARACTERS. Moderately intolerant at maturity; growth rather slow, with maturity being reached in about 300 years; reproduction abundant on moist mineral soil; deep, spreading roots.

HABITAT. Transition zone to timber line in some places; altitudinal range from 5,000–10,000 feet; in pure stands or mixed with Douglas-fir, sugar and ponderosa pine, and numerous other species.

GENERAL. A distinctive variety, the Shasta red fir, *Abies magnifica* var. *shastensis* Lemm., is occasionally found throughout the range of the species. It is characterized by cone bracts which are exserted and strongly reflexed and by winter buds almost free of resin.

[85]

Noble Fir

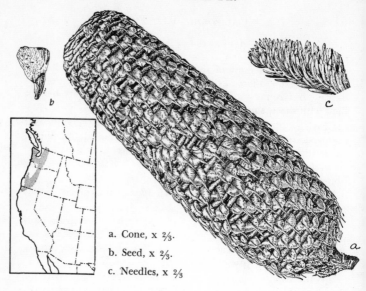

a. Cone, x ⅔.
b. Seed, x ⅔.
c. Needles, x ⅔

Bristlecone Fir

a. Cone, x ⅔.
b. Scale, x ⅔.
c. Seed, x ⅔.
d. Needle, x 1½.

PINACEAE

Noble Fir

Abies procera Rehd. [*Abies nobilis* (Dougl.) Lindl.]

HABIT. A large tree 150–200 feet high and 4–6 feet in diameter (max. 250 by 8 feet); crown broad and rounded; bole clear for much of its length.

LEAVES. On lower branches 1–1½ inches long, flattened, rounded and often notched at the apex; on upper fertile branches almost equally 4-sided, with long, rigid, callous tips; marked on upper surface by sharply defined groove; glaucous during first year, becoming blue-green; stomatiferous on all sides.

FLOWERS. Male red-purple; female with orbicular bracts much longer than rounded scales.

FRUIT. Very distinctive; 4–6 inches long; cylindrical; purple or olive-brown; scales wider than long, nearly or entirely covered by strongly reflexed, greenish bracts. Seed: ½ inch long, red-brown, with short, lustrous, light brown wings.

TWIG. Slender, red-brown, rusty-pubescent. Winter buds: oblong-conic, ⅛ inch long, slightly resinous at tip, red-brown, blunt.

BARK. 1–2 inches thick, red-brown, and fissured on old trunks; smooth and gray for many years on younger trunks, with prominent resin blisters.

WOOD. Best quality of native true firs, used in aircraft; light, straight-grained, not durable.

SILVICAL CHARACTERS. Seedlings and trees both intolerant; growth rather rapid; maturity reached in about 350 years; reproduction sparse; deep, spreading roots.

HABITAT. Transition zone; in stands of mixed conifers; altitudinal range from 2,000–5,000 feet; on cool, deep, moist sites.

* * *

Bristlecone Fir

Abies bracteata D. Don. [*Abies venusta* (Dougl.) K. Koch]

This curious species is native only to Monterey County, California. It is easily distinguished by its flat, bristle-pointed needles 1–2 inches long, its ovoid, non-resinous bud ¾–1 inch long, and its 3–4 inch cone with its spiny, long-exserted bracts.

a. Fruiting branch, x ⅔.
b. Seed, x ⅔.
c. Cone, x 1.

PINACEAE

REDWOOD

Sequoia sempervirens (D. Don) Endl.

HABIT. This handsome tree reaches greater heights than any other in the world, commonly rising 200–275 feet in height and from 8–12 feet in diameter (max. 367 by 20 feet); crown short and narrowly conical; bole clear and straight; often tight circles of young trees are found around old stumps, due to the ability of the tree to crown sprout.

LEAVES. Spirally arranged, flattened, and decurrent; on lower branches ½–1 inch long, linear, appearing 2-ranked, acute tips, short petioles; on leaders and fertile branches ¼–½ inch long, awl-shaped to needle-shaped, in several ranks and thickly clothing the twigs; dark yellow-green above with two bands of stomata below; persistent several years and falling with twigs.

FLOWERS. Monoecious; solitary; male oblong, of several spirally arranged bracts containing stamens; female of 15–20 spirally arranged, peltate scales, each bearing 3–12 erect ovules; ovuliferous bract and scale partially fused.

FRUIT. Woody, ovoid, pendent cone; ¾–1 inch long; red-brown; with wrinkled, peltate scales; maturing in one season. Seed: ⅟₁₆ inch long, light brown, laterally 2-winged with wings as broad as seed, 2–9 seeds on each scale.

TWIG. Slender, greenish, smooth. Winter buds: small, globose, covered by numerous, imbricated, acute scales.

BARK. 6–12 inches thick; fibrous; red-brown to cinnamon-brown; deeply furrowed.

WOOD. Important; light clear red weathering to dark red; soft and weak; very durable; used for lumber, dimension stock, tanks, shingles, and other products. A single tree yielded 480,000 board feet.

SILVICAL CHARACTERS. Very tolerant; growth rapid; maturity reached in 400 to 1,800 years; reproduces vigorously by stump sprouts as well as producing large numbers of seed; deep, wide-spreading lateral root system; remarkably free from enemies.

HABIT. Restricted to the fog belt in the Coast Ranges from the Santa Lucia Mountains near Carmel, California, to southern Oregon; the dominant species in this narrow belt; in pure stands or mixed with Douglas-fir, Sitka spruce, grand fir, western hemlock, and hardwoods.

a. Fruiting branch, x ⅔.

b. Upper crown twig, x ⅔.

c. Seed, x ⅔.

PINACEAE

Giant Sequoia. Bigtree

Sequoia gigantea (Lindl.) Decne. [*Sequoia washingtoniana*
(Winsl.) Sudw.] (*Sequoia wellingtonia* Seem.)

HABIT. The most massive and probably the oldest of all living things; commonly reaching a height of 250–280 feet and a diameter of 10–15 feet (max. 293 by 37 feet); crown scraggly and open; bole clear with short thick branches.

LEAVES. Spirally arranged; ¼–½ inch long; ovate to lanceolate; appressed or spreading, but thickly clothing the twig; rigid; sharp-pointed; decurrent at base; blue-green; turning brown in 2 to 3 years, but persisting for several years.

FLOWERS. Similar to redwood, but female with 25–40 scales.

FRUIT. Woody, ovoid-oblong, pendent cones; 2–3½ inches long; red-brown; peltate, wrinkled scales; reaching full size first year, but not maturing until second year; unique in that seed may be retained in cone up to 20 years while peduncle lives and grows and cone looks like young cone. Seed: ¼ inch long; light brown; laterally 2–winged with wings broader than seed; 2–9 seeds on each scale.

TWIG. Slender; leaf-covered. Winter buds: Small, naked.

BARK. 12–24 inches thick; fibrous cinnamon-red; furrowed between broad, rounded ridges.

WOOD. Unimportant; similar to redwood, but brittle; impractical to log because of size.

SILVICAL CHARACTERS. Intermediate in tolerance; growth rapid; probably the oldest living thing, attaining ages of 4,000–5,000 years; reproduction sparse, mineral soil needed for seed germination; tree does not sprout; wide-spreading lateral root system; no natural enemies aside from lightning and fire and no tree is known to have died from old age, insects, or fungal attack.

HABITAT. Native only in some 32 groves of varying extent found along the western middle slopes of the Sierra Nevada mountains of California; in former geologic periods this genus was widely scattered through the forests of the Northern Hemisphere; generally associated with sugar, ponderosa, and Jeffery pines, white and red fir, and incense-cedar.

a. Fruiting branches, x 1

b. Section of cone showi
   seeds, x 1.

c. Seed, x 1.

PINACEAE

BALDCYPRESS

Taxodium distichum (L.) Rich.

HABIT. A large and important tree, 100–120 feet high and 3–5 feet in diameter (max. 150 by 17 feet); young crown narrowly pyramidal, becoming irregular and flattened with age; bole tapered with fluted butt; peculiar conical structures known as knees arise from roots on wetter sites.

LEAVES. Spirally arranged; deciduous (lateral twigs falling, with attached leaves; on lower branches ½–¾ inch long, linear, appearing 2–ranked; on fertile branches about ½ inch long, appressed, and nearly scalelike; yellow-green.

FLOWERS. Monoecious; male cones in drooping panicles, each composed of 6–8 stamens; female subglobose, of several spirally arranged, peltate scales each bearing 2 erect ovules.

FRUIT. Woody, subglobose, pendent cone; ¾–1 inch in diameter; brown; of several wrinkled, peltate scales; maturing in one year and usually disintegrating at maturity. Seed: ¼ inch long, brown, irregularly 3–angled and 3–winged, with 2 seeds to each scale.

TWIG. Terminal twigs bearing axillary buds and persistent; lateral twigs deciduous with needles still attached. Winter buds: small, subglobose, with several imbricated scales.

BARK. Variable; thin and scaly to fibrous and 1½ inches thick; red-brown to ash-gray.

WOOD. Important; variegated in color from light to dark brown; moderately heavy, hard, and strong; very durable; used for construction lumber, siding, caskets, shingles, etc.

SILVICAL CHARACTERS. Intolerant; growth rather slow on wet sites; attains age of 1,000–3,000 years; reproduces well from seed and stump sprouts vigorously; shallow, wide-spreading roots; surprisingly windfirm even on wet, unstable soils; wood of old trees riddled with pecky rot.

HABITAT. Typical in swamps; in pure stands or with water tupelo, sweetgum, and other bottomland hardwoods.

* * *

A closely related, unimportant, smaller tree, *Taxodium distichum* var. *nutans* (Ait.) Sweet, the pondcypress, differs from baldcypress in having smaller scalelike to needle-shaped leaves which are closely appressed. This is found in bogs and along ponds from southern Virginia to Louisiana. *Taxodium mucronatum* Ten., the Montezuma baldcypress of Mexico, which enters southern Texas, differs from other species in having persistent needles.

[93]

a. Male flowers, x ½.

b. Fruiting branch, x ½.

c. Seed, x 1.

PINACEAE

Incense-cedar

Libocedrus decurrens Torr.

HABIT. A medium-sized tree 80–120 feet high and 3–4 feet in diameter (max. 186 by 8 feet); tapering, often fluted trunk covered for up to half its length with lustrous, irregular foliage.

LEAVES. Small, scalelike; whorled in 4's; facial leaves flattened; the lateral keeled and almost ensheathing facial leaves; oblong-ovate; ⅛–½ inch long; persistent 3–5 years; glandular; aromatic when crushed; fronds usually in a vertical plane.

FLOWERS. Monoecious; terminal; male oblong, golden, with 12–16 decussate 4-celled anthers; female oblong, yellow-green, of 6 scales, the inner 2 each bearing 2 erect ovules.

FRUIT. Leathery, pendent cones; ¾–1½ inches long; oblong; 6-scaled, with 2 becoming greatly enlarged and spreading at maturity; maturing in one season. Seed: ⅓–½ inch long, in pairs on fertile scales, unequally laterally winged, straw-colored.

TWIGS. Slender; flattened; leaf-covered; in long sprays which are more often in a vertical plane than in a horizontal plane. Winter buds: minute, naked, inconspicuous.

BARK. Thin, smooth to scaly, and gray-green on young stems, becoming 3–8 inches thick, yellow-brown to cinnamon-red, fibrous, and deeply furrowed on old trees.

WOOD. Chief source of pencil stock; would be highly important for many uses except for prevalence of pecky rot; sapwood white; heartwood reddish, soft, fragrant.

SILVICAL CHARACTERS. Tolerant; growth rather slow; maturity reached in about 300 years; reproduction abundant and vigorous; moderately deep lateral root system; fire and pecky rot caused by *Polyporus amarus* cause extensive damage.

HABIT. Transition zone; altitudinal range 1,000–9,000 feet; on cool, moist soils; in mixed stands with sugar, ponderosa, Jeffrey, and white pine, white fir, and Douglas-fir.

WESTERN REDCEDAR
AND
NORTHERN WHITE-CEDAR

a. Branchlet with cones, x 1.

b. Seeds, x 1.

WESTERN REDCEDAR

NORTHERN WHITE-CEDAR

PINACEAE

WESTERN REDCEDAR. GIANT ARBORVITAE
Thuja plicata Donn

HABIT. A large tree, 150–200 feet high and 4–8 feet in diameter (max. 250 by 16 feet); tapering, fluted trunk; irregular crown of horizontal or drooping branches.

LEAVES. Small, scalelike; persistent 2–5 years; decussate the facial leaves flattened, grooved; the lateral leaves rounded or keeled; lustrous dark yellow-green.

FLOWERS. Monoecious; terminal; dark brown; male with 3–6 pairs of decussate stamens; female 8–12 scaled.

FRUIT. Leathery or sub-woody erect cones; ½ inch long; ovoid-oblong; maturing in one season; scales 8–12 (only 6 being fertile), thin, spine-tipped. Seed: ⅛ inch long, brown, with lateral wings each about as wide as seed.

TWIGS. Slender; flattened; leaf-covered in long drooping sprays. Winter buds: minute, naked, inconspicuous.

BARK. Thin (½–1 inch); fibrous; narrow interlacing ridges; cinnamon-red to gray-brown on old trunks.

WOOD. Widely used where durability rather than strength is required; sapwood white; heartwood reddish, soft, fragrant; shingles, siding, interior trim, boats, poles, etc.

SILVICAL CHARACTERS. Tolerant; growth rather rapid; trees over 1,000 years old reported; reproduction generally plentiful; shallow, wide-spreading root system; fire and pecky heart rot cause serious damage.

HABITAT. Transition and Canadian zones; altitudinal range 2,000–7,000 feet in Rocky Mountains; on rich soils with abundant moisture; in mixed coniferous stands.

* * *

NORTHERN WHITE-CEDAR. EASTERN ARBORVITAE
Thuja occidentalis L.

Aside from its eastern distribution, this species differs from *Thuja plicata* by only minor characters, the cones having but 4 fertile scales and the leaves being dull green and usually glandular-pitted. This small tree grows on a variety of sites and is typical of swampy areas. It is not important, although used to some extent for posts and poles. The oriental arborvitae, *T. orientalis* L., is widely planted and perhaps naturalized. It is easily distinguished from the native species by the vertical disposition of the leaf sprays, the thick cone scales, and the wingless seed.

PINACEAE

The Cypresses and White-cedars

Characteristics of the Genera *Cupressus* L. and

Chamaecyparis Spach

HABIT. Evergreen, resinous, pyramidal trees (sometimes shrubs); clear tapering trunks; and dense crowns of stout, erect, or horizontal branches.

LEAVES. Small, scalelike, (often awl-shaped on leading shoots); ovate; with slender, spreading, or appressed tip; thickened, rounded, and often glandular on the back; persistent 3–6 years; decussate (in pairs alternately crossing at right angles); becoming brown and woody before falling; margins smooth to finely serrate.

FLOWERS. Monoecious, minute, terminal; male oblong of numerous decussate stamens each bearing 2–6 subglobose anthers; female of 4–14 peltate decussate scales, each with 2–20 erect, basal ovules; bract and ovuliferous scale wholly fused.

FRUIT. Subglobose, leathery to woody, erect cone; maturing in 1–2 seaons; cone scales peltate, thick, often with a central boss or mucro which is a remnant of flower scales. Seed: 1–20 in several rows on each scale, erect, with lateral wings.

TWIGS. Slender, quadrangular or flattened, leaf-covered. Winter buds: minute, naked, inconspicuous.

WOOD. Strongly aromatic; light brown to yellow heartwood; pale yellow sapwood; very durable.

SILVICAL CHARACTERS. Tolerant; usually slow-growing.

GENERAL. The genus *Chamaecyparis* is considered by many authors to be but a section of the genus *Cupressus* and because of their similarity they are described together here. The chief differences between them are described in the key on the next page. Six species of *Cupressus* and three species of *Chamaecyparis* are native to the United States.

KEY TO THE SPECIES OF CUPRESSUS AND CHAMAECYPARIS

1. Cone woody, 6–16-scaled, ½–1½ inches diameter, ripening 2nd year, with 6–20 seeds per scale; branchlets round or 4-angled; leaves fringed with narrow translucent border visible with lens...........
   ....CUPRESSUS, The CYPRESS.
   2. Leaves glaucous, pale blue to silvery gray-green; cone 6–8-scaled, ¾–1¼ inches diameter.
      3. Leaves acute, glandular; twigs gray; Arizona to Texas and Mexico.. *Cupressus arizonica* Greene, Arizona Cypress, p. 101.
      3. Leaves obtuse; twigs bright red; southern and lower California and Mexico..
         ....*Cupressus guadalupensis* S. Wats., Tecate Cypress.
   2. Leaves dark or bright green.
      4. Leaves conspicuously glandular-pitted on back; cone 6–8-scaled, ½–1 inch diameter.
         5. Cones with prominent horn-like umbos; rare; Oregon and California *Cupressus macnabiana* A. Murr., McNab Cypress.
         5. Cones with short-conical umbos; southern Oregon and northern California.......*C. bakeri* Jeps., Modoc Cypress
      4. Leaves without glands or obscurely glandular.
         6. Cones 6–8-scaled, ½–¾ inch diameter; California (Mendocino County) *Cupressus goveniana* Gord., Gowen Cypress.
         6. Cones 8–14-scaled, ⅞–1½ inches diameter.
            7. Branchlets and boss of cone scales thick; California.....
               ......*Cupressus macrocarpa* Hartw., Monterey Cypress.
            7. Branchlets and boss of cone scales thin; planted ornamental.....*Cupressus sempervirens* L., Italian Cypress
1. Cone leathery to semi-fleshy, 4–10-scaled, ¼–½ inch diameter, ripening in 1 or 2 years, with 2 seeds (rarely 5) per scale; twigs somewhat flattened; leaves entire. CHAMAECYPARIS, The WHITE-CEDAR
   8. Branchlets not arranged in conspicuous horizontal planes; leaves green on both sides; bark on mature trees thin; cones with 4–6 scales; lateral and facial leaves nearly equal in size.
      9. Branchlets slender; leaves about 1/16 inch long, usually glandular; cones ¼ inch diameter, maturing in 1 year, 1–2 seeds per scale; heartwood light-brown; Atlantic Coast from Maine to Mississippi...................*Chamaecyparis thyoides* (L.) B.S.P., Atlantic White-cedar, p. 105.
      9. Branchlets stout; leaves about ⅛ inch long, often without glands; cones ¼–½ inch diameter, maturing in 2 years, 2–4 seeds per scale; heartwood clear yellow; Pacific Northwest....
         Chamaecyparis nootkatensis (D. Don) Spach, Alaska-cedar, p. 105.
   8. Branchlets arranged in conspicuous horizontal planes; cones with 10 scales; leaves with glaucous or whitish marks below; heartwood light brown.
      10. Bark on mature trees thick and furrowed; leaves conspicuously glandular on the back and indistinctly marked with white streaks below, lateral much larger than facial; Oregon and California, also widely planted.....*Chamaecyparis lawsoniana* (A. Murr.) Parl., Port Orford-cedar, p. 103.
      10. Bark on mature trees thin; leaves without glands or glands indistinct, but with distinct white markings below; Japanese ornamentals widely planted in the United States.
         11. Leaves closely appressed, obtuse to acute, the lateral much larger than the facial, conspicuous Y-shaped white mark below; cone ⅛–½ inch diameter......*Chamaecyparis obtusa* (S. & Z.) Endl., Hinoke White-cedar, p. 103.
         11. Leaves loosely appressed, acuminate, the lateral slightly larger than the facial, conspicuous white patches below; cone ¼ inch diameter....*Chamaecyparis pisifera* (S. & Z.) Endl., Sawara White-cedar, p. 103.

a. Seeds, x ¾.

b. Branchlet with cones, x ¾.

c. Male flower bud in autumn.

d. Different form of cone, x ¾.

e. Opened cone, x ¾.

PINACEAE

Arizona Cypress

Cupressus arizonica Greene

HABIT. Under favorable conditions a tree 50–60 feet high and 1–2½ feet in diameter (max. 80 by 4 feet); trunk short, limby, sharply tapering; crown dense, sharply conical.

LEAVES. Scalelike, pointed, ⅟₁₆ inch long; silvery gray-green; dying and turning red-brown the second year and falling about 4 years later; commonly without glands or pits on back; giving off a skunklike odor when bruised.

FLOWERS. Male oblong, yellow; female subglobose.

FRUIT. ¾–1 inch in diameter, subglobose, dark red-brown on stout stalks; of 6–8 peltate scales, each with stout, incurved, prominent boss; maturing during second summer and remaining on tree many years. Seed: 6–20 on each scale ⅟₁₆–⅛ inch long, oblong to triangular, deep red-brown; thin, narrow, lateral wings.

TWIGS. 4-angled, dark gray, loose-scaly bark with smooth, reddish inner bark visible below. Winter buds: minute, inconspicuous, naked.

BARK. Loose-scaly on young trunks and branches, showing smooth reddish inner bark below; on old trunks 1¼ inches thick, fibrous, deeply furrowed and ridged, dark red-brown.

WOOD. Slightly aromatic: durable; heartwood light brown; sapwood straw-colored; soft and light, splitting easily; used locally for fence posts, mine timbers, etc.

SILVICAL CHARACTERS. Tolerant throughout life; growth slow; trees seldom over 400 years old; reproduction generally scanty, although seed produced every year.

HABITAT. Transition zone; altitudinal range from 4,500–8,000 feet; best growth on moist, gravelly, north slopes and benches, but hardy on dry, sterile, rocky sites.

* * *

Five similar but unimportant species are native to the Pacific Coast. These are separated in the key on page 99. The distinctions between these are minor and it is often difficult to identify the species. These species, together with the Italian cypress, are commonly planted as ornamentals in warmer sections of the United States.

a. Fruiting branch, x 1.
b. Seed, x 1.
c. Seed, x 2.

PINACEAE

PORT-ORFORD-CEDAR

Chamaecyparis lawsoniana (A. Murr.) Parl.

HABIT. A large, handsome tree 140–180 feet high and 4–6 feet in diameter (max. 225 by 16 feet); boles clear and often buttressed; crown short-conical, with many branches.

LEAVES. Scalelike; blunt; 1/16 inch long; entire; yellow-green to blue-green; turning brown after 2–3 years, but persisting for several years; glandular; forming flat, horizontal, feathery sprays.

FLOWERS. Male oblong, bright red; female subglobose.

FRUIT. 1/3 inch in diameter; globose; red-brown; abundant; of 6–8 decussate, peltate scales, each with thin, acute, reflexed boss; maturing in 1–2 years; persistent on twig after seed released. Seed: 2–5 on each scale, 1/8 inch long, ovoid, chestnut-brown, with 2 broad lateral wings.

TWIGS. Slender; flattened; leaf-covered. Winter buds: minute, naked, inconspicuous.

BARK. 6–10 inches thick, red-brown to silver-brown, fibrous, and furrowed on old trunks; young bark thin and scaly.

WOOD. Important; aromatic; very durable; pale brown; light; easily worked; used for battery separators, Venetian blinds, boats, aircraft, and other uses; cut far exceeds growth.

SILVICAL CHARACTERS. Moderately tolerant; growth moderate; maturity reached in 300-350 years, but often living for more than 500 years; reproduction aggressive; free from insect and fungal enemies, though damaged by fire.

HABITAT. Altitudinal range from sea level to 5,000 feet; requires abundant soil and atmospheric moisture; in pure stands or mixed with numerous conifers.

* * *

Two Japanese species are widely planted as ornamentals:

1. The Sawara white-cedar, *Chamaecyparis pisifera* (S. & Z.) Endl., is a narrow, pyramidal tree of fairly rapid growth which is easily identified by its acuminate leaves which are obscurely glandular and dark green above and have conspicuous white lines below. The cones are 1/4 inch or less in diameter, and consist of 10–12 scales.

2. The Hinoki white-cedar. *Chamaecyparis obtusa* (S. & Z.) Endl., is a tree with broad, pyramidal crown, characterized by obtuse leaves which are dark green above and not glandular and with conspicuous white lines below. The cones are 1/3–1/2 inch in diameter, and consist of 8–10 scales.

ALASKA YELLOW-CEDAR

a. Seed, x 1 and 2.

b. Fruiting branchlet, x 1.

ATLANTIC WHITE-CEDAR

a. Mature fruit closed, x 1.

b. Fruit open, x 1.

c. Section through cone showing seed location, x 1.

d. Fruiting branchlet, x 1.

PINACEAE

ALASKA-CEDAR
Chamaecyparis nootkatensis (D. Don) Spach

HABIT. A medium-sized tree 60–90 feet high and 2–3 feet in diameter (max. 130 by 6 feet); clear, buttressed, often fluted bole; crown conical, of drooping branches.

LEAVES. Scalelike; acute; ⅛ inch long; blue-green to gray-green; persistent 2–3 years; usually without glands; sprays appearing limp and wilted.

FLOWERS. Male bright yellow; female subglobose, brown.

FRUIT. ¼–½ inch in diameter; globose; purple to red-brown; of 4–6, decussate, peltate, bossed scales; maturing in 2 years. Seed: 2–4 on each scale, ¼ inch long, broad wings.

TWIGS. Rather stout; pendulous. Winter buds: minute.

BARK. Thin, gray-brown, fibrous, and furrowed on old trunks; young bark thin and scaly.

WOOD. Moderately important; durable; heartwood clear yellow; used for boats, trim, blinds, etc.

SILVICAL CHARACTERS. Intermediate in tolerance; growth slow; ages over 600 years attained; reproduction sparse; lateral roots.

HABITAT. Sea-level (Alaska) to timber line; moist sites; pure stands or mixed with many conifers.

* * *

ATLANTIC WHITE-CEDAR. SOUTHERN WHITE-CEDAR
Chamaecyparis thyoides (L.) B.S.P.

This tree of the Atlantic seaboard differs from the other native species by the following characters:

HABIT. Small to medium-sized (max. 120 by 5 feet); bole clear, cylindrical; crown conical with drooping branches.

LEAVES. 1/16–⅛ inch long; blue-green; keeled and glandular.

FRUIT. ¼ inch in diameter; globose; purple to red-brown; reflexed boss; somewhat fleshy; maturing in 1 year. Seed: 1–2 on each scale, ⅛ inch long.

BARK. Thin; gray to red-brown; fibrous; furrowed.

WOOD. Similar to northern white-cedar; used for posts and poles.

SILVICAL CHARACTERS. Moderately tolerant; growth slow; reproduction vigorous; shallow, lateral roots.

HABITAT. Swamps and bogs in the Coastal plains; pure stands or mixed with many species.

PINACEAE

The Junipers

Characteristics of the Genus *Juniperus* L.

HABIT. Evergreen, aromatic small trees or shrubs.

LEAVES. Persistent for several years, sessile, aromatic; needle-like or awl-shaped on young growth; of three types on older growth; (1) ternate, spreading, and entirely needle-like or subulate; (2) decussate, appressed, decurrent, and entirely scalelike; (3) a combination of the preceding types.

FLOWERS. Dioecious (rarely monoecious); minute and inconspicuous; male yellow, solitary, of numerous ternate or decussate stamens; female of 3–8 decussate or ternate pointed scales, some or all bearing 1 or 2 ovules.

FRUIT. A berry-like, succulent, indehiscent cone, formed by coalescence of flower scales; subtended by persistent flower bracts; maturing in 1–3 years. Seed: 1–21 in cone, ovoid, unwinged, marked at base by a scar (hilum).

BUDS. Small, naked and covered by leaves (scaly in dwarf juniper).

BARK. Thin, soft, fibrous, and shreddy (brittle, thick and divided into nearly square plates in alligator juniper).

WOOD. Durable; weak; close-grained; aromatic; heartwood red-purple to brown; sapwood whitish.

SILVICAL CHARACTERS. Exceedingly variable; mostly intolerant; slow-growing; long-lived; seed disseminated by birds or mammals; deep lateral roots.

GENERAL. This genus contains 40–60 species widely scattered through the Northern Hemisphere, with 13 species native to the United States. Only *J. virginiana* is of any commercial importance, although several other species form conspicuous parts of the vegetation. Two appear as small shrubs:

(1) The dwarf juniper, *Juniperus communis* L., while circumpolar and extending through most of the United States and Canada, attains tree size only in New England and southern Illinois; this species has ternate leaves, ⅓–½ inch long, which are all needle-like, scaly buds, and axillary flowers; the prostrate, high mountain form has been designated *J. communis* var. *montana* Ait. (*J. communis* var. *sibirica* Rydb.).

(2) The prostrate juniper, *J. horizontalis* Moench, entering the United States from the north, differs from dwarf juniper in having closely appressed, decussate leaves, ⅛–¼ inch long. This species often forms dense creeping mats.

KEY TO THE SPECIES OF JUNIPERS

1. Leaves all needle-like or awl-shaped, ⅛–½ inch long, ternate; buds scale, ⅛ inch long; usually a small shrub, rarely a small tree . . . . *J. communis*, **Common Juniper**, p. 106.
1. Leaves on mature branches usually scalelike, ⅛ inch long or less, opposite, (on young or vigorous shoots often needle-like); buds indistinct, naked.
   2. Trunk bark in thick, squarish plates; fruit red-brown, ½ inch diameter, usually 4-seeded, ripening in 2 years; heartwood brown; southwest . . . . *J. deppeana*, **Alligator Juniper**, p. 113.
   2. Trunk bark fibrous and shreddy.
      3. Fruit bright red to red-brown beneath, whitish bloom; western.
         4. Fruit bright red (rarely copper-colored) ¼ inch diameter, 1-seeded; heartwood brown; western Texas and New Mexico . . . . *J. pinchotii*, **Pinchot Juniper**, p. 113.
         4. Fruit dull red-brown or copper-colored; heartwood brown.
            5. 4–12 seeds per fruit; drooping branches; southern Texas and Mexico . . . . . . *J. flaccida*, **Drooping Juniper**, p. 113.
            5. 1 (rarely 2) seeds per fruit; branches seldom drooping.
               6. Fruit ¼–¾ inch diameter; seed completely enclosed; fruit maturing in 2 years; heartwood brown.
                  7. Leaves in whorls of 3's, rarely opposite; seed marked at base by light-colored hilum; California . . . . . . *J. californica*, **California Juniper**, p. 115.
                  7. Leaves opposite, rarely in 3's; seed marked to middle by conspicuous hilum; Rocky Mountains . . . . *J. osteosperma*, **Utah Juniper**, p. 113.
               6. Fruit ⅛–⅛ inch diameter; seed marked at base by hilum; fruit maturing in 1 year; Nevada to Colorado and south to Texas and Arizona . . . . *J. monosperma*, **One-seed Juniper**, p. 111.
      3. Fruit bluish to blue-black, 1–3 seeded.
         8. Leaf margin smooth; heartwood distinctly reddish.
            9. Fruit maturing in 2 years; western . . . . *J. scopulorum* **Rocky Mountain Juniper**, p. 111.
            9. Fruit maturing in 1 year; eastern.
               10. Fruit 1/24–1/12 inch diameter, drooping branches, South Carolina to eastern Texas . . . . *J. silicicola*, **Southern Redcedar**, p. 109.
               10. Fruit ¼–⅛ inch diameter, branches erect or spreading . . . . . . *J. virginiana*, **Eastern Juniper**, p. 109.
         8. Leaf margin minutely fringe-toothed (under hand lens); heartwood brownish.
            11. Fruit with 2–3 thick-shelled seeds; maturing in 2 years; Northwest and Pacific Coast . . . . *J. occidentalis*, **Western Juniper** p. 115.
            11. Fruit and 1–2 thin-shelled seeds, maturing in 1 year.
               12. Seed 1 (rarely 2), pale brown; leaves gray-green; Nevada to California and south . . . . *J. monosperma*, **One-seed Juniper**, p. 111.
               12. Seed 1–2; dark brown; leaves blue-green; Missouri to Texas and Mexico . . *J. ashei*, **Ashe Juniper**, p. 113.

a. Branchlet with awl-shaped leaves, x

b. Tip of branchlet, showing awl-sha
leaves, enlarged.

c. Fruiting branchlet with scale-like lea
x 1.

d. Tip of branchlet, showing scale-
leaves, enlarged.

PINACEAE

Eastern Redcedar

Juniperus virginiana L.

HABIT. A small to medium-sized tree 30–40 feet high and 1–2 feet in diameter (max. 100 by 4 feet); crown dense, irregular, pyramidal; numerous ornamental varieties widely planted.

LEAVES. The scalelike leaves decussate, closely appressed, dark green, acute, ⅟₁₆ inch long, smooth margined, glandular; the awl-shaped, juvenile leaves often ternate, sharp-pointed, ¼–½ inch long.

FLOWERS. Dioecious, or rarely monoecious.

FRUIT. Glaucous, dark blue, and berry-like; ¼–⅓ inch in diameter; subglobose; maturing in 1 year. Seed: 1–2 (rarely 3–4) in each cone, angled and acute, requiring 2–3 years to germinate.

TWIGS. Slender, 4–angled. Winter buds: naked, minute, leaf covered.

BARK. Thin (⅛–¼ inch); red-brown; fibrous, exfoliating into long, narrow strips.

WOOD. Bright red, often streaked with white; aromatic; durable; easily worked; moderately heavy and hard; weak; used for chests, trim, pencils, and posts.

SILVICAL CHARACTERS. Intermediate in tolerance; growth slow; maximum age about 300 years; deep, lateral roots; reproduction abundant and vigorous; often disfigured by "cedar apples" caused by *Gymnosporangium juniperi*.

HABITAT. Adapted to a variety of sites, but typical on poor, dry soils; in pure stands or mixed with hardwoods such as oaks and hickory.

* * *

Southern Redcedar

Juniperus silicicola (Small) Bailey (*Juniperus lucayana* Britt.)

This species is very similar to eastern redcedar, but can be distinguished by its very small fruit (1/12–1/24 inch in diameter), and very slender, pendulous branches. It also differs from eastern redcedar in that it is found on wet, swampy sites from South Carolina to eastern Texas.

Rocky Mountain Juniper

a, b. Variable number of seed in fruit,
x 1 and x 2.
c. Branchlet with ripe fruit, x 1.

One-seed Juniper

a. Seeds, x 1 and x 2.
b. Branchlet with fruit, x 1.

PINACEAE

Rocky Mountain Juniper

Juniperus scopulorum Sarg.

HABIT. From a bushy shrub on exposed sites to a tree 40–55 feet high and 15–30 inches in diameter; trunk often dividing near the ground; crown typically irregular and rounded.

LEAVES. ⅛ inch long; acute or acuminate; pale to dark green; obscurely glandular on back; smooth margins.

FLOWERS. Dioecious.

FRUIT. Glaucous; blue; ¼–⅓ inch in diameter; maturing in 2 years. Seed: 1–2 per cone, angled, acute, grooved.

WOOD. Heartwood dull red or bright red and streaked with white; sapwood thick and white; durable.

HABITAT. Upper Sonoran and Transition zones; largest distribution of any western juniper; very drouth resistant; in pure stands or mixed with pinyon, ponderosa pine, etc.

* * *

One-seed Juniper

Juniperus monosperma (Engelm.) Sarg.

HABIT. A small tree or shrubby as a result of large branches leaving trunk at or below root collar.

LEAVES. ⅛ inch long; acute; gray-green; denticulately fringed; usually glandular.

FLOWERS. Dioecious.

FRUIT. Glaucous; copper-colored (rarely blue); ⅛–¼ inch long; maturing in one year. Seed: 1 (rarely 2) in each cone; ovoid.

WOOD. Heartwood yellow-brown to red-brown; sapwood white; durable; rather heavy and hard; used for posts and fuel.

HABITAT. Upper Sonoran zone; growing on dry, rocky slopes; in pure stands or with pinyon and ponderosa pines.

GENERAL. A related Southwestern form with a single seed exposed at the apex and formerly given specific rank as open-seed juniper, *J. gymnocarpa* (Lemm.) Cory, is now considered a form of *J. monosperma*.

Utah Juniper

a. Narrow side of seeds, x 1
   and x 2.
b. Broad side of seeds, x 1
   and x 2.
c. Branchlet with ripe fruit,
   x 1.

Alligator Juniper

a. Variable forms and numbers of seed
   in fruit, x 1 and x 2.
b. Branchlet with ripe fruit, x 1.

PINACEAE

Utah Juniper

Juniperus osteosperma (Torr.) Little
[*Juniperus utahensis* (Eng.) Lemm.]

HABIT. A spreading shrub or small tree; trunk single, or many-stemmed just above the ground; crown rounded.

LEAVES. ⅛ inch long, acute, pale yellow-green, minutely toothed, usually glandular.

FLOWERS. Usually monoecious, sometimes dioecious.

FRUIT. Glaucous; red-brown; ¼–¾ inch long; maturing in 2 years. Seed: 1 (rarely 2) in each cone; ovoid; sharply angled; acute; marked to the middle by a conspicuous hilum.

WOOD. Heartwood light yellow-brown; sapwood thick and white; very durable; used locally for fuel and fence posts.

HABITAT. Upper Sonoran zone; on dry, rocky slopes; in pure stands or with one-seed juniper, pinyon, and desert shrubs.

* * *

Alligator Juniper

Juniperus deppeana Steud. (*Juniperus pachyphloea* Torr.)

HABIT. A spreading shrub or small tree; crown broad.

LEAVES. ⅛ inch long, acute, blue-green, minutely toothed, conspicuously glandular.

FLOWERS. Monoecious.

FRUIT. Glaucous; dark red-brown; ⅓–½ inch long; maturing in 2 years. Seed: 1–4 (usually 4) in each cone; distinctly grooved; conspicuously swollen on back.

BARK. Very characteristic; ½–4 inches thick; red-brown; deeply furrowed into square plates 1–2 inches across.

WOOD. Heartwood brown; durable; used locally.

HABITAT. Upper Sonoran and Transition zones; drouth resistant; commonly mixed with nut pines and oaks.

* * *

Three species enter this region in west Texas:

1. Ashe Juniper, *J. ashei Buch.*, with blue-green leaves and brown seed.

2. Drooping Juniper, *J. flaccida* Schl., with drooping branches.

3. Pinchot Juniper, *J. pinchotii* Sudw. in Texas and southeastern New Mexico with bright red fruit.

SIERRA JUNIPER

a. Branchlet with ripe fruit, x 1.

b, c, d. Variable number of seed to a fruit, x
and x 2.

CALIFORNIA JUNIPER

(a) Seed, x 2; (b) Fruiting branchlet, x 1.

PINACEAE

Western Juniper. Sierra Juniper.

Juniperus occidentalis Hook.

HABIT. A bushy shrub or small tree; short, straight trunk; broad, rounded crown, extending nearly to ground.

LEAVES. ⅛ inch long; acute or acuminate; gray-green; conspicuously glandular-pitted on back; denticulately fringed.

FLOWERS. Dioecious.

FRUIT. Glaucous; blue-black; ¼–⅓ inch in diameter; maturing in 2 years. Seed: 2–3 in each cone; ovoid, acute.

WOOD. Heartwood pale brown tinged with red; sapwood white and thick; exceedingly durable; used locally for posts.

HABITAT. Upper Sonoran to Hudsonian zones; on exposed, dry, rocky, mountain slopes; usually in pure, open stands.

* * *

California Juniper

Juniperus californica Carr.

HABIT. A small tree or shrubby as a result of large branches leaving the trunk near the ground.

LEAVES. — inch long; acute; yellow-green; conspicuously glandular on back; fringed on the margins.

FLOWERS. Dioecious.

FRUIT. Red-brown; glaucous; ⅜–¾ inch long; maturing in 2 years. Seed: 1–2 in each cone; obtuse.

WOOD. Heartwood pale brown tinged with red; thin, white sapwood; durable; used locally for posts.

HABITAT. Upper Sonoran zone; on desert and mountain slopes; with pinyon and chaparral.

a. Sterile branchlet, x ⅔.
b. Fruiting branchlet, x 1.
c. Section of twig, x 2.

TAXACEAE

CALIFORNIA TORREYA. CALIFORNIA NUTMEG

Torreya californica Torr. [*Tumion californicum*
(Torr.) Greene]

HABIT. A rare, small tree 15–70 feet high and 1–2 feet in diameter; clear, often malformed bole; crown pyramidal, with slender, spreading branches.

LEAVES. Persistent many years; linear-lanceolate; spirally arranged, appearing 2-ranked; 1–3½ inches long; acuminate and often bristle-tipped; flat; rigid; dark green and lustrous above; pale below, with 2 narrow, distinct bands of stomata; petioled; decurrent.

FLOWERS. Dioecious; male solitary, consisting of numerous stamens in whorls of 4; female in pairs, ¼ inch long, the ovule surrounded by and finally enclosed in fleshy sac.

FRUIT. Drupe-like; a single seed with a woody outer coat completely enclosed in a thin, fleshy, green to purple envelope; ellipsoidal; 1–1½ inches long; maturing in 2 years, but requiring additional year before germinating.

TWIGS. Slender, drooping. Winter buds: small, ovoid, acute; of few overlapping, shining, opposite scales.

BARK. Thin (⅓–½ inch); gray-brown; in narrow, scaly ridges.

WOOD. Unimportant; soft; light clear yellow.

SILVICAL CHARACTERS. Tolerant; growth slow; long-lived; reproduction sparse, but stumps sprout vigorously; lateral roots.

HABITAT. Dependent on moist sites; in pure, dense thickets or mixed with hardwoods.

* * *

FLORIDA TORREYA. STINKING-CEDAR

Torreya taxifolia Arn. [*Tunion taxifolium* (Arn.) Greene

This is a rare, small, handsome tree found only along the bluffs of the Apalachicola River in Florida and southern Georgia. It differs from the western species in having needles slightly rounded on the back and about 1½ inches long.

Branchlet with fruit, x 1.

TAXACEAE

PACIFIC YEW. WESTERN YEW

Taxus brevifolia Nutt.

HABIT. A small tree or large shrub, 20–50 feet high and 1–2 feet in diameter; limby, often fluted or malformed trunks; large, open, conical crown, with long, slender, drooping branches; a sprawling shrub near timber line.

LEAVES. Persistent 5–12 years; linear-lanceolate; spirally arranged, appearing 2-ranked; ½–1 inch long; sharp-pointed; petiolate; green above, paler beneath.

FLOWERS. Dioecious, solitary, axillary, surrounded by scales of bud; male in globose heads of 6–14 stamens, yellowish; female single, greenish, the apical scale bearing a solitary erect ovule with a basal disk.

FRUIT. A single, erect, ovoid-oblong seed with a hard, bony shell; ⅓ inch long; exposed at apex, but partially or entirely surrounded by, but free from, the thickened, scarlet, fleshy aril-like disk of the flower; maturing in one season.

TWIGS. Slender, drooping. Winter buds: small, ovoid, obtuse; of numerous overlapping scales.

BARK. Very thin (¼ inch), scaly, dark red-purple.

WOOD. Heavy, hard, strong; durable; heartwood bright orange to rose-red; sapwood thin, yellow; used for bows, canoe paddles, fence posts, and turned articles.

SILVICAL CHARACTERS. Most tolerant forest tree of northwest; growth slow; maturity reached in 250–350 years; reproduction scanty; deep, wide-speading roots; stumps sprout.

HABITAT. Transition to Hudsonian zone; altitudinal range from 2,000–8,000 feet; on deep, moist soils; in small groups or as an occasional understory tree in mixed forests.

* * *

FLORIDA YEW

Taxus floridana Nutt.

This is a rare, small, bushy tree found only along the bluffs of the Apalachicola River in Florida. It differs from Pacific yew in having dark green, falcate needles, ¾–1 inch long.

SALICACEAE

The Poplars and Cottonwoods

Characteristics of the Genus *Populus* L.

HABIT. Mostly large, fast-growing, deciduous trees.

LEAVES. Alternate; simple; turning yellow before falling in autumn; petioles mostly long and often laterally compressed; stipules present, falling as leaves unfold.

FLOWERS. Regular; dioecious; both sexes in drooping aments; appearing from separate buds, before the leaves; individual flowers solitary, apetalous, inserted on broad, cup-shaped disk, subtended by dilated, lobed, and often laciniate scale or bract; staminate with 4 to many stamens; pistillate, a single, 1-celled, usually sessile ovary with 2–4 placentas and 2–4 stigmas.

FRUIT. A 1-celled, 2–4-valved capsule containing numerous seeds. Seed: small, tufted with long silky hairs, extremely buoyant; vitality transient and must germinate within few days.

TWIGS. Pith homogeneous, stellate in cross section. Winter buds: terminal present, covered by several scales.

BARK. Astringent; light-colored; deeply furrowed or smooth.

WOOD. Light; soft; weak; diffuse-porous; not durable; heartwood light brown; used for pulp, veneer, and lumber.

SILVICAL CHARACTERS. Intolerant; fast-growing; short-lived; reproduction widespread and abundant; stumps and roots sprout vigorously; extensive, wide-spreading root systems.

GENERAL. This genus contains about 35 species scattered over the northern Hemisphere and in Northern Africa; 9 species and several hybrids are native to North America, and 2 European species have become naturalized.

* * *

KEY TO THE SPECIES OF POPLARS AND COTTONWOODS

1. Twigs, buds, petioles, and lower surfaces of leaves white tomentose; widely planted and naturalized.
    2. Leaves irregularly sinuate-dentate or palmately 3–5 lobed, base usually rounded or flat..........*P. alba*, White Poplar, p. 123.
    2. Leaves toothed, not lobed, base heart-shaped.................
    ....*P. canescens*, Gray Poplar, p. 123.
1. Twigs, buds, petioles, and leaves hairy or glabrous at maturity.
    3. Leaf petiole round in cross section, leaf base round or heart-shaped.
        4. Leaves broadly ovate, 4–7 inches long and nearly as broad, densely hairy when they unfold, but becoming glabrous; Atlantic Coast, southeastern and central states.............
        ....*P. heterophylla*, Swamp Cottonwood, p. 125.
        4. Leaves ovate to lanceolate, ⅛ or more longer than broad.

5. Leaves lanceolate to ovate-lanceolate, 2–4 inches long; petioles short (less than ⅓ length of blade); buds ¼–¾ inch long, resinous; Rocky Mountains.......................
.........*P. angustifolia*, Narrowleaf Cottonwood, p. 129.
5. Leaves ovate to ovate-lanceolate; petioles at least ½ as long as leaf blade.
  6. Leaves 3–6 inches long, margins finely toothed; buds ¾–1 inch long, very resinous and aromatic.
    7. Capsule 3-valved, hairy; stigmas 3; 40–60 purple stamens; Pacific region............................
    ....*P. trichocarpa*, Black Cottonwood, p. 127.
    7. Capsule 2-valved, glabrous; stigmas 2; 20–30 pink stamens; northern North America..................
    ....*P. balsamifera*, Balsam Poplar, p. 127.
  6. Leaves 2–4 inches long, margins coarsely toothed; buds ½–¾ inch long, slightly resinous, not aromatic; Rocky Mts...*P. X acuminata*, Lanceleaf Cottonwood, p. 129.
3. Leaf petiole definitely flattened laterally.
  8. Leaves broadly ovate to suborbicular, clearly defined translucent border, 1–3 inches long, base rounded; buds almost nonresinous; capsules 2-valved, thin-walled; 6–12 stamens.
    9. Leaves finely toothed, glabrous; buds glabrous; Atlantic to Pacific...........*P. tremuloides*, Quaking Aspen, p. 123.
    9. Leaves with few coarse teeth; buds hairy; eastern.........
    ....*P. grandidentata*, Bigtooth Aspen, p. 123.
  8. Leaves deltoid to rhombic-ovate, with clearly defined translucent border, 2–7 inches long; buds resinous; capsules 3- or 4-valved (2-valved in Black and Lombardy Poplars) thickwalled; 12–60 stamens.
    10. Leaves rhombic-ovate (rarely deltoid), long acuminate, base wedge-shaped or rounded, hybrids or naturalized trees widely planted through North America.
      11. Leaves longer than broad, 2–6 inches long, coarsely toothed...*P. X canadensis*, Carolina Poplar, p. 125.
      11. Leaves about as long as broad, 2–4 inches long, finely toothed.
        12. Tree with wide-spreading, stout branches........
        ....*P. nigra*, Black Poplar, p. 123.
        12. Columnar tree with erect branches narrow, spinelike crown.*P. nigra italica*, Lombardy Poplar, p. 123.
    10. Leaves deltoid in shape, 2–4 inches long; native trees.
      13. Leaves with glands at point where petiole and blade meet; margins ciliate, with numerous teeth.
        14. Leaves thick, very broad and truncate at base; twigs thick.
          15. Buds glabrous; leaves finely toothed, eastern..
          ...*P. deltoides*, Eastern Cottonwood, p. 125.
          15. Buds slightly hairy, leaves coarsely toothed; Great Plains to Rocky Mountains...........
          ....*P. sargentii*, Plains Cottonwood, p. 125.
        14. Leaves thin, often rounded or wedge-shaped at base; twigs slender; Texas.....................
        ....*P. palmeri*, Palmer Cottonwood, p. 125.
      13. Leaves without glands at point where petiole and blade meet; margins not ciliate, with usually less than 15 teeth on a side.
        16. Pedicels longer than capsules; leaves with no more than 10 teeth on a side; Colorado, New Mexico, west Texas and Mexico......................
        P. fremontii wislizenii, Rio Grande Cottonwood,
        16. Pedicels shorter than capsules; leaves with more than 10 teeth on a side; New Mexico west to California *P. fremontii*, Fremont Cottonwood, p. 125.

[121]

QUAKING ASPEN

a. Winter twig, x 2.

b. Leaf, x 1.

c. Staminate flower, enlarg

d. Pistillate flower, enlarge

e. Fruiting branchlet, x ½

BIGTOOTH ASPEN

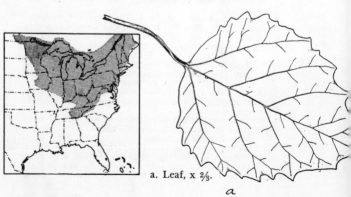

a. Leaf, x ⅔.

SALICACEAE

QUAKING ASPEN. POPLAR

Populus tremuloides Michx.

HABIT. A small tree 50–60 feet high and 1–2 feet in diameter; loose, rounded crown with slender branches.

LEAVES. Semiorbicular or broadly ovate; 1½–3 inches in diameter; yellow-green; apex acute; base rounded; finely crenate-serrate with glandular teeth; thin and firm; glabrous; petioles flattened, 1½–3 inches long.

FRUIT. Capsules narrowly conical; ¼ inch long; curved; 2-valved; gray-hairy. Seed; light brown, 1⁄32 inch long.

TWIGS. Slender; round; bright red-brown and lustrous, becoming gray. Winter buds; terminal ¼–½ inch long, conical, sharp-pointed, red-brown, sometimes slightly resinous.

BARK. Smooth; green-white to cream-colored.

SILVICAL CHARACTERS. Canadian and Hudsonian zones; reproducing vigorously on cut-over or burned-over areas and forming a protective canopy for more tolerant species.

* * *

BIGTOOTH ASPEN

Populus grandidentata Michx.

This medium-sized tree differs from quaking aspen in having coarsely sinuate-toothed leaves 2–5 inches long, stout twigs, and puberulous, dusty-gray buds ⅛ inch long.

* * *

The following European forms have become naturalized in parts of the United States. Their distinguishing features appear in the key:

1. White poplar, *P. alba* L., is a large, widely planted tree.
2. Gray poplar, x *P. canescens* (Ait.) Sm., is a hybrid of *alba* x *tremula*.
3. Black poplar, *P. nigra* L., is a wide-spreading tree.
4. Lombardy poplar, *P. nigra* var. *italica* Muenchh., is a hybrid clon of narrow columnar crown and ascending branches which is widely planted.

[123]

a. Twig with winter buds, x ½.
b. Twig with leaves, x ⅗.
c. Fruit, x ½.

SALICACEAE

Eastern Cottonwood

Populus deltoides Bartr.

HABIT. This important eastern species is a large tree 60–100 feet high and 3–5 feet in diameter (max. 175 by 11 feet); broad, open crown; large, spreading branches.

LEAVES. Broadly deltoid; 3–6 inches long; apex acuminate; coarsely crenate-serrate, teeth glandular; glabrous; petiole flattened, 1½–3 inches long, with 2 glands at apex.

FRUIT. Capsules ovoid, ⅓ inch long; in catkins 8–12 inches long. Seed: light brown, hairy, about 1/16 inch long.

TWIGS. Stout; yellow-brown; angular; glabrous. Winter buds: ¾ inch long, conical, acute, shiny brown, resinous.

BARK. Yellow-green and smooth on young trunks, becoming thick ash-gray, and furrowed.

* * *

Five other cottonwoods and 2 hybrids having the deltoid leaves and other characters similar to *P. deltoides* are native and distinguished in the key:

1. Fremont cottonwood, *P. fremontii* S. Wats., in the southwest.
2. Rio Grande cottonwood, *P. fremontii* var. *wislizenii* S. Wats. in the southwest.
3. Swamp cottonwood, *P. heterophylla* L., in the east differs in having a rounded petiole.
4. Palmer cottonwood, *P. palmeri* Sarg., in western Texas.
5. Plains cottonwood, *P. sargentii* Dode, in the Great Plains.

   P. x conadensis (Alt.) Sm., the Carolina poplar, (*P. deltoides* x *nigra*) is extensively planted in cities.

   P. x parryi Sarg. (*P. fremontii* x *trichocarpa*) in California.

Black Cottonwood

a. Leaf and bud, x ½.
b. Fruit (capsule), x 1.
c, d, e. Staminate flower.
c. Fringed scale, x 2.
d. Stamens on disc, x 2.
e. Single stamen, x 4.
f, g, h. Pistillate flower (after Longyear).
f. Single flower, x 2.
g. Cross section of ovary with stigmas attached.
h. Fringed scale, x 2.

Balsam Poplar

(a) Twig and bud, x ½;   (b) Leaf, x ½.

SALICACEAE

Black Cottonwood

Populus trichocarpa Torr. & Gray

HABIT. The largest of American poplars and the largest broad-leaved tree in the Pacific Northwest; long, clear, cylindrical trunk; crown open, rounded.

LEAVES. Ovate to ovate-lanceolate; 5–6 inches long and 3–4 inches wide; apex acute to long-acuminate; base rounded or slightly cordate; margin finely crenate; leathery; dark green above, silver-white to pale green below; petioles round, long.

FRUIT. Capsules subglobose; ⅓ inch long; 3-valved; hairy.

TWIGS. Moderately slender; round or slightly angled; red-brown at first, becoming glabrous and dark gray. Winter buds: terminal ¾ inch long, ovoid, orange-brown, covered by fragrant, yellow-brown resin.

BARK. Smooth and greenish on young stems; becoming pale gray, 1–2½ inches thick, deeply and sharply furrowed.

* * *

Balsam Poplar

Populus balsamifera L. (*Populus tacamahacca* Mill.)

HABIT. A medium-sized tree seldom over 60–80 feet high and 1–3 feet in diameter; open, narrow crown.

LEAVES. Broadly ovate to ovate-lanceolate; 3–6 inches long and 2–4 inches broad; apex acute to acuminate; base rounded or cordate; finely crenate-serrate; thin and firm; dark green above, much paler below; petioles round, slender, long.

FRUIT. Capsules ovoid; ¼–⅓ inch long; 2-valved; glabrous; short-stalked. Seed: light brown, 1/12 inch long.

TWIGS. Moderately stout; round; red-brown. Winter buds: terminal 1 inch long, ovoid, chestnut-brown, saturated by fragrant, amber-colored resin.

BARK. On young trunks smooth and green-brown; on large trunks deeply furrowed and gray-black.

GENERAL The variety *subcordata* Hylander differs from the species in having leaves which are usually broader, with pubescent petioles. Balm-of-Gilead, a widely planted ornamental tree in the Northeast, is a clon from a single pistillate tree of this variety.

NARROWLEAF COTTONWOOD

(a) Twig with leaves, x ⅔;   (b) Different form of leaf, x ⅔;
(c) Twig with winter buds, x ⅔.

LANCELEAF COTTONWOOD

a. Twig with winter buds, x ⅔.

b. Twig with leaves, x ⅔.

SALICACEAE

NARROWLEAF COTTONWOOD

Populus angustifolia James

HABIT. A medium-sized tree 50–70 feet high and 12–20 inches in diameter; crown pyramidal with slender, erect branches.

LEAVES. Lanceolate to ovate-lanceolate; 2–4 inches long and ½–1½ inches wide; apex long-tapering; finely to coarsely serrate; thin and firm; bright yellow-green above, paler below; petioles short (less than ⅓ length of blade), slender, somewhat flattened on upper side.

FRUIT. Capsules broadly ovoid; ¼ inch long; 2-valved.

TWIGS. Slender; round; yellow-green, becoming ash-gray. Winter buds: terminal ¼–¾ inch long, slender, long-pointed, chestnut-brown, very resinous and somewhat aromatic.

BARK. Light yellow-green; ¾–1 inch thick; smooth except near base of old trees where it is divided by shallow furrows.

* * *

LANCELEAF COTTONWOOD

Populus X acuminata Rydb.

HABIT. A medium-sized tree about 40 feet high and 1–2 feet in diameter; rounded crown with large branches.

LEAVES. Rhombic-lanceolate to ovate; 2–4 inches long and ¾–2 inches wide; apex acuminate; base usually cuneate; coarsely crenate-serrate; rather thick; dark green above, dull green below; petioles nearly round, slender, 1–3 inches long.

FRUIT. Capsules oblong-ovoid; about ⅓ inch long; thin-walled; acute; 3- or rarely 2-valved; on short, slender stalks.

TWIGS. Slender; round or slightly 4-angled; pale yellow-brown. Winter buds: terminal about ⅓–¾ inch long, narrow, acuminate, light chestnut-brown, rather resinous.

BARK. Nearly white and smooth on young trunks; on old trees gray-brown, ½ inch thick, deeply divided into flat ridges.

GENERAL. This tree is now generally regarded as a hybrid between *P. angustifolia* and *P. sargentii* or *P. fremontii*.

SALICACEAE

The Willows

Characteristics of the Genus *Salix* L.

HABIT. Shrubs or less frequently trees; latter often with several trunks from greatly extended rootstalk.

LEAVES. Alternate; simple; commonly lanceolate; margins entire or toothed; pinnately veined; sessile or short-petioled; stipules small and soon falling, except on vigorous shoots where they are leaflike and persistent.

FLOWERS. Regular; dioecious; in terminal and axillary aments, appearing with or before the leaves; individual flowers solitary, apetalous, on glandlike disk, subtended by pubescent, entire to dentate, deciduous or presistent scale or bract; staminate with 1-2 or 3-12 stamens inserted on base of bract; pistillate a single, 1-celled, sessile or stalked ovary, containing 4-8 ovules on each of 2 placentas, style short, terminating in 2 short, 2-parted stigmas.

FRUIT. A 1-celled, 2-valved, acuminate capsule. Seed: small, dark brown, tufted with long, silky hairs, bouyant, of transient vitality.

TWIGS. Slender to stout; round; tough; often easily separated at junction with branch; marked by elevated leaf scars; pith homogeneous, terete. Winter buds; terminal absent; lateral covered by single, caplike scale.

BARK. Astringent; scaly; variously colored.

WOOD. Light; soft; weak; usually brittle; durable in some species; heartwood pale brown, often tinged with red; used to small extent for athletic goods and charcoal.

SILVICAL CHARACTERS. Intolerant; fast-growing; remarkable vitality and sprouting vigorously from stumps or cuttings; usually swamp or moisture-loving plants.

GENERAL. This genus contains about 170 species scattered over the Northern Hemisphere, with about 100 species native to North America; identification of the various species is difficult; 38 native and 4 naturalized species have been listed as occasionally reaching tree size in North America, but only 15 of these native species are commonly trees, and included in the key with the naturalized species.

KEY TO THE TYPICAL TREE SPECIES OF WILLOWS

1. Stamens 3 to 12; filaments free; flower bracts deciduous.
    2. Leaves green below; petioles eglandular at base.
        3. Capsule hairy; twigs yellow-gray; Southwest . . . .
            . . . . *S. gooddingii* Ball. Goodding Willow
        3. Cap. glabrous; twigs red *S. nigra* Marsh., Black Willow, p. 133.
    2. Leaves pale or bluish below; ovary and capsules glabrous.
        4. Petioles without glands at base of lead.
            5. Twigs easily separable; flower bracts entire.
                6. Leaves 4–5 inches long, narrowly lanceolate to lanceolate;
                    petioles under ½ inch; Southeast . . . .
                    . . . . *S. caroliniana* Michx., Coastal Plain Willow
                6. Leaves 2½–4 inches long, lanceolate to ovate-lanceolate;
                    petioles ½–¾ inch long; northern and central . . . .
                    . . . . *S. amygdaloides* And., Peachleaf Willow, p. 133.
            5. Twigs firmly attached; flower bracts toothed; southwest.
                7. Leaves silver-white below; capsules short-stalked; stamens
                    usually 3 . . *S. bonplandiana* H. B. K., Bonpland Willow
                7. Leaves glaucous or yellow-hairy below; capsules long-
                    stalked; stamens 4–6; Southwest . . . .
                    . . . . *S. laevigata* Bebb, Red Willow
        4. Petioles glandular; twigs separable; flower bracts toothed;
            throughout west . . . . *S. lasiandra* Benth, Pacific Willow
1. Stamens 2.
    8. Widely planted and naturalized ornamentals; capsules glabrous.
        9. Tree with distinctive "weeping" habit; leaves glabrous; capsules
            sessile . . . . *S. babylonica* L., Weeping Willow
        9. Branches not drooping; capsule short-stalked.
            10. Leaves with silky hairs on both sides; twigs green to bright
                yellow . . . . *S. alba* L., White Willow
            10. Leaves nearly glabrous; twigs brownish . . . .
                . . . . *S. fragilis* L., Crack Willow
    8. Native species which are often shrubby and seldom planted.
        11. Bracts deciduous, yellowish; filaments free, more or less hairy;
            stipe of ovary much shorter than bract.
            12. Leaves ⅛–1⅛ inches long, linear; stigmas linear; south-
                western . . . . *S. taxifolia* H. B. K., Yewleaf Willow
            12. Leaves over 1⅛ inches long, mostly linear-lanceolate;
                stigmas short.
                13. Leaves white-hairy below; stipules minute or want-
                    ing; throughout west *S. exigua* Nutt., Coyote Willow
                13. Leaves nearly glabrous below; stipules large, deciedu-
                    ous; throughout North America . . . .
                    . . . . *S. interior* Rowlee, Sandbar Willow
        11. Bracts persistent, darker; filaments glabrous.
            14. Ovary and capsule glabrous; bracts dark brown.
                15. Leaves acute or rounded, thin; filaments united at
                    base; western . . . . *S. lasiolepis* Benth., Arroyo Willow
                15. Leaves acuminate, thick and leathery; filaments free.
                    16. Leaves 1½–2 inches long, oblanceolate; twigs
                        glabrous; western . . . .
                        . . . . . . *S. mackenzieana* Barr., Mackenzie Willow
                    16. Leaves 4–6 inches long, narrow-lanceolate; twigs
                        hairy; central United States . . . .
                        . . *S. eriocephaia* Michx., Missouri River Willow
            14. Ovary and capsule hairy.
                17. Stipe of ovary longer than light, hairy flower bracts;
                    through North America . . . .
                    . . . . *S. bebbiana* Sarg., Bebb Willow
                17. Stipe shorter than brown, hairy flower bracts; western
                    . . . . *S. scouleriana* Barr., Scouler Willow

BLACK WILLOW

(a) Winter twig, x ⅔; (b) Twig, enlarged; (c) Leaf, x ⅔;
(d) Staminate flowers, x ⅔; (e) Pistillate flowers, x ⅔.

PEACHLEAF WILLOW

(a) Twig with leaves, x ⅔; (b) Fruit, x ⅔; (c) Pistillate flower, x 4; (d) S
flower, x 4.

SALICACEAE

BLACK WILLOW

Salix nigra Marsh.

HABIT. A small to large tree (max. 120 by 4 feet); trunk often divided; crown broad and open with stout branches.

LEAVES. Lanceolate; 3–6 inches long; acuminate; finely serrate; thin; bright green above, paler beneath; petiole short.

FRUIT. Capsules ovoid-conic; ¼ inch long; short-stalked; glabrous. Seed: minute, hairy-tufted.

BARK. Nearly black; thick; deeply divided into furrows separating thick, scaly ridges.

SILVICAL CHARACTERS. Intolerant; fast-growing; stream banks and lake shores; with mixed hardwoods.

GENERAL. This is the largest American willow and the only one important for its wood products. It is used for lumber, veneer, pulp, charcoal and artificial limbs.

* * *

PEACHLEAF WILLOW

Salix amygdaloides Anderss.

HABIT. A tree rarely 60–70 feet high and 2 feet in diameter; trunk single, columnar; rather narrow, rounded crown.

LEAVES. Lanceolate to ovate-lanceolate; 2–5 inches long; acuminate; finely serrate; thin and firm; light green above, pale and glaucous below; petioles slender, ½–¾ inch long.

FRUIT. Capsules globose-conic; ¼ inch long; long-stalked; glabrous; light yellow-red. Seed: minute, hairy-tufted.

BARK. Brown, often tinged with red; ½–¾ inch thick; divided by irreglar furrows into broad, flat, connecting ridges.

SILVICAL CHARACTERS. Intolerant; moist sites along banks of streams.

GENERAL. This willow is the only species native to the Rocky Mountain region which is typically a tree.

JUGLANDACEAE

THE WALNUTS

Characteristics of the Genus *Juglans* L.

HABIT. Small to large handsome trees; crowns broad and open; stout, ascending branches.

LEAVES. Alternate; pinnately compound; deciduous; native species with 9–23 sessile, oblong-lanceolate, finely serrate, acute to acuminate leaflets.

FLOWERS. Monoecious; apetalous; appearing with or after the leaves; staminate in preformed aments, with 8–40 stamens; pistillate in spikes of 2–8 flowers, each with a 2-celled ovary and 2 divergent, plumose stigmas.

FRUIT. A drupe-like nut encased in a semifleshy, indehiscent husk; maturing in one year; nut thick-shelled, containing solitary, 2–4 lobed, sweet, oily, edible seed.

TWIGS. Stout; round; with characteristic chambered pith. Winter buds: terminal present, few-scaled. Leaf scars: conspicuous, with three U-shaped bundle scars.

WOOD. Dark-colored; durable; diffuse-porous; valuable.

SILVICAL CHARACTERS. Intolerant; deep taproot; nuts disseminated largely by rodents or streams.

GENERAL. Of the six native species only the two eastern are of commercial importance and treated separately. The four southwestern species are distinguished in the key. They are:

1. California Walnut, *Juglans californica* S. Wats.

2. Hinds Walnut, *Juglans hindsii* Jeps.

3. Arizona Walnut, *Juglans major* (Torr.) Heller.

4. Little Walnut, *Juglans microcarpa* Berl. (*J. rupestris* Engelm.)

The Persian or English walnut, *Juglans regia* L., is widely planted in warmer parts of the country and is included in the key. The variety with thin-shelled nuts is commonly marketed and the wood is widely used under the name of Circassian walnut.

KEY TO THE SPECIES OF WALNUTS

1. Leaves with 9–29 toothed leaflets; nut with thick, bony partitions; native species.
  2. Fruit ovoid-oblong, in clusters of 3–5; band of pale hair separating leaf scar from bud; leaflets 11–17, oblong-lanceolate; heartwood light brown, soft; eastern. . . . .*J. cinerea*, Butternut, p. 137.
  2. Fruit globose, solitary or in pairs; buds not separated by hairy band from leaf scar; heartwood dark brown, hard.
    3. Fruit 1½–2 inches in diameter.
      4. Nut deeply ridged; 15–23 leaflets; eastern. . . . .
      . . . .*J. nigra*, Black Walnut, p. 137.
      4. Nut smooth or faintly grooved; 15–19 leaflets; California. . .
      . . . .*J. hindsii*, Hinds Walnut, p. 134.
    3. Fruit 1–1½ inches long; nut grooved; leaflets 9–13 (rarely to 19), oblong-lanceolate; Colorado, New Mexico, and Arizona. . .
    . . . .*J. major*, Arizona Walnut, p. 134.
    3. Fruit ½–¾ inch long; nut grooved.
      5. Leaflets 17–23, narrow-lanceolate; Oklahoma, Texas, and New Mexico. . . . .*J. microcarpa*, Little Walnut, p. 134.
      5. Leaflets 11–15 (rarely to 19), oblong-lanceolate; California. . . . .*J. californica*, California Walnut, p. 134.
1. Leaves with 5–9 (rarely to 13), entire or nearly entire leaflets; fruit globose, 1½–2 inches in diameter; nut wrinkled, with thin partitions; widely planted in warm areas. . . .*J. regia*, English Walnut, p. 134.

*   *   *

MYRICACEAE

Waxmyrtle. Bayberry
Myrica L.

Three species of this usually shrubby genus may form small trees. This genus is easily distinguishable by its simple, alternate, aromatic, persistent leaves, which bear minute, resinous dots; dioecious or monoecious flowers in aments; small, globose, drupaceous fruit, covered with wax and containing a thick-walled nut; slender twigs without terminal buds and with scaly lateral buds; thin, smooth, whitish to gray bark. The fruit wax is used in making candles.

1. Southeastern species; flowers dioecious.
  2. Leaves oblanceolate, coarsely toothed, yellow-green with conspicuous orange glands; fruit ⅛ inch in diameter, coated with thick, blue wax; coastal plain from New Jersey to Florida, west to Arkansas and Texas. .*Myrica cerifera* L., Southern Waxmyrtle,
  2. Leaves oblong-obovate, dark green.
    3. Leaves entire, glabrous; fruit ⅛–½ inch in diameter thinly coated with white wax; Florida to Mississippi. . . . .
    . . . .*Myrica inodora* Bartr., Odorless Bayberry
    3. Leaves toothed, glabrous or pubescent below, fruit ⅛ inch in diameter thickly coated with wax; coastal plain New Jersey to Louisiana. . .*Myrica heterophylla* Raf., Evergreen Bayberry
1. Pacific coast species; flowers monoecious; leaves 2–4 inches long, oblanceolate to oblong-lanceolate, remotely toothed, with minute black glands below; fruit, ¼ inch in diameter, purple, papillose, thinly coated with gray wax; coastal areas in Pacific states. . . . .
. . . .*Myrica californica* Cham., Pacific Waxmyrtle,

BLACK WALNUT

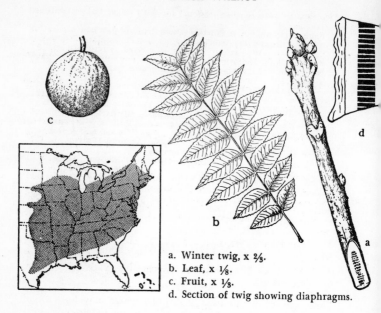

a. Winter twig, x ⅔.
b. Leaf, x ⅛.
c. Fruit, x ⅓.
d. Section of twig showing diaphragms.

BUTTERNUT

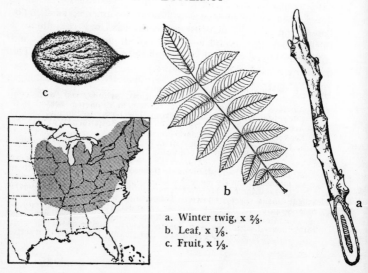

a. Winter twig, x ⅔.
b. Leaf, x ⅛.
c. Fruit, x ⅓.

JUGLANDACEAE

Black Walnut

Juglans nigra L.

HABIT. A tree 60–90 feet high and 2–3 feet in diameter (max. 150 by 6 feet); trunk straight and clear; crown broad and open.

LEAVES. 1–2 feet long with 15–23 leaflets; leaflets 3–4 inches long, ovate-lanceolate, finely serrate, yellow-green, glabrous above and hairy below.

FRUIT. Globose; 1½–2 inches in diameter; solitary or in clusters of 2–3; husk thick, yellow-green, pubescent; nut shell corrugated.

TWIGS. Stout, light brown; leaf scar obcordate, without downy pad at top; chambered pith buff colored with thin diaphragms. Winter buds: terminal ⅓ inch long, ovoid, blunt, hairy, lateral buds smaller, often superposed.

BARK. Thick; dark brown to nearly black; deep, narrow furrows.

WOOD. Heavy; hard; strong; very valuable and important.

SILVICAL CHARACTERS. Fast growing; long-lived; on fertile, moist soils; in mixed stands; reproduction depends largely on rodents.

* * *

Butternut

Juglans cinerea L.

HABIT. A tree 30–60 feet high and 1–2 feet in diameter (max. 110 by 3 feet); trunk short; crown broad and open.

LEAVES. 1–2½ feet long with 11–17 leaflets; leaflets 2–4 inches long, oblong-lanceolate, serrate, yellow-green, rugose above and hairy below.

FRUIT. Oblong-ovoid; 1½–2½ inches long; solitary or in clusters of 2–5; husk green-brown, sticky, glandular-hairy; nut shell deeply corrugated.

TWIG. Stout, green to red-brown; leaf scar straight across top with dense hairy pad at top; chambered pith dark chocolate-brown with thick diaphragms. Winter buds: terminal ½–¾ inch long, conical, flattened, hairy; lateral buds smaller, rusty-tomentose.

BARK. Rather thick; light gray; smooth on young trunks, becoming shallowly furrowed with broad ridges.

WOOD. Rather light and soft; light brown; substitute for walnut.

SILVICAL CHARACTERS. Fast growing; short-lived; varied sites; in mixed stands.

JUGLANDACEAE

The Hickories

Characteristics of the Genus *Carya* Nutt.

HABIT. Medium-sized trees with clear straight trunks and open spreading crowns.

LEAVES. Alternate; pinnately compound; deciduous; leaflets 3–17, nearly sessile, ovate to obovate, finely serrate, tips acute to acuminate, and bases inequilateral.

FLOWERS. Monoecious; apetalous; appearing after the leaves; staminate in 3-branched aments, with 3–10 stamens; pistillate in spikes of 2–10 flowers, each with a 1-celled ovary and 2 sessile stigmas.

FRUIT. Nut enclosed in a semi-woody, partly dehiscent, 4-valved husk; maturing in one year; nut shell thin to thick, hard, ribbed, smooth to rugose; sweet to bitter.

TWIGS. Mostly rather stout; round; pith solid. Winter buds: terminal present, much larger than laterals, with imbricated or valvate scales.

BARK. Smooth and gray on young trunks, becoming scaly or rough; very hard and compact.

WOOD. Highly important; very heavy, hard, and strong; light colored; not durable; semi ring-porous; used for handles, tools, etc.

SILVICAL CHARACTERS. Moderately intolerant; slow growing, long-lived; taproot system; varied moist sites.

GENERAL. Twelve species are recognized in the United States (some authors recognize 19 species); several, together with numerous varieties and hybrids, are difficult to identify. Eight species come under the group known as "true hickories," which are characterized by numerous, imbricated bud scales, 3–9 leaflets, and essentially unwinged fruit husks; and four species are classified as "pecan hickories," which are characterized by 4–6 valvate bud scales, 5–17 (mostly more than 7) often falcate leaflets, and fruit husks which are typically broadly winged at the sutures.

KEY TO THE SPECIES OF HICKORIES

1. Bud naked or with 4–6 valvate scales; leaflets 7–17, usually lanceolate, often falcate, about of same size; fruit husk winged. **Pecans**
2. Nuts about twice as long as broad, sweet, thin-shelled; buds brown, covered with yellow hairs; leaflets 9–17; bark thick, furrowed; Illinois to Alabama and Texas *C. illinoensis*, **Pecan**, p. 145.
2. Nuts about as long as broad; leaflets 7–13; bark scaly.
   3. Leaflets 7–9 (rarely 5–11), ovate-lanceolate to obovate; buds brown, hairy; nut sweet, with thick, hard shell; South Carolina to Arkansas and south.....................................
   ....*C. myristicaeformis*, **Nutmeg Hickory**, p. 145.
   3. Leaflets lanceolate to ovate-lanceolate; nut bitter.
      4. Leaflets 7–13 (usually 9–11); buds red-brown; Virginia to Illinois and south.....*C. aquatica*, **Water Hickory**, p. 145.
      4. Leaflets 7–9 (usually 7); buds bright yellow; Quebec to Minnesota and south.....................................
      ....*C. cordiformis*, **Bitternut Hickory**, p. 145.
1. Bud with more than 6 overlapping scales; leaflets 3–9, the uppermost largest; husk usually without wings; nut thick-shelled, sweet (except in pignut hickory). **True Hickories**
5. Terminal buds ½–1½ inches long; twigs thick; fruit 1–2½ inches long.
   6. Bark on old trunks shaggy with loose plates; fruit husk ¼–½ inch thick; upper 3 leaflets conspicuously larger than others; twigs and petioles glabrous to hairy.
      7. Leaflets usually 7 (rarely 5–9), hairy below; twigs pale orange, hairy; shell very thick; New York to Kansas and south...........*C. laciniosa*, **Shellbark Hickory**, p. 141.
      7. Leaflets usually 5 (rarely 7), glabrous or slightly hairy below; twigs red-brown, usually glabrous; Quebec to Minnesota and south.......*C. ovata*, **Shagbark Hickory**, p. 141.
   6. Bark on old trunks close; fruit husk ⅛–¼ inch thick; leaflets 5–9, of about same size; twigs and petioles often woolly; Massachusetts to Nebraska and south...........................
   ....*C. tomentosa*, **Mockernut Hickory**, p. 143.
5. Terminal buds ¼–½ inch long; twigs moderately thick to slender; fruit ¾–1½ inches long; Bark on old trunks close; fruit husk 1/12–1/4 inch thick.
   8. Winter buds and leaves glabrous or pale hairy.
      9. Buds, leaves, and petioles essentially glabrous; husk of fruit very thin (1/12–1/8 inch); leaflets 5 (rarely 3–7); nut bitter, shell ridged from base to apex; husk obovoid; Maine to Minnesota and south...*C. glabra*, **Pignut Hickory**, p. 143.
      9. Winter buds and leaves with silvery or pale hairs; husk of fruit ⅛–¼ inch thick; leaflets 7 (rarely 5–9).
         10. Leaves covered with silvery scales in spring; petiole and rachis hairy; fruit ellipsoidal to globose; Virginia to Tennessee and south...........................
         ....*C. pallida*, **Sand Hickory**, p. 143.
         10. Leaves woolly in spring; petioles glabrous; fruit obovoid; Arkansas to Texas and Mississippi...................
         ....*C. leiodermis*, **Swamp Hickory**, p. 143.
   8. Buds, twigs, and leaves red-hairy; leaflets 5–7.
      11. Fruit obovoid; Florida *C. floridana*, **Scrub Hickory**, p. 143.
      11. Fruit subglobose, obovoid, or pyriform; Indiana to Kansas, Texas, and Louisiana...*C. texana*, **Black Hickory**, p. 143.

a. Winter twig, x 1.
b. Portion of twig, enlarged.
c. Leaf, x 1/3.
d. Flowering branchlet, x 1/2.
e. Staminate flower, enlarged.
f. Pistillate flower, enlarged.
g. Fruit, x 1/2.

JUGLANDACEAE

Shagbark Hickory

Carya ovata (Mill.) K. Koch [*Hicoria ovata* (Mill.) Britt.]

HABIT. A tree 60–80 feet high and 1–2 feet in diameter (max. 120 by 4 feet); narrow, open crown and large branches.

LEAVES. 8–14 inches long with 5 (rarely 7) leaflets; leaflets obovate to ovate-lanceolate, the terminal 5–7 inches long and usually much longer than the lateral; finely serrate margins; thick, dark green and glabrous above, yellow-green and usually glabrous below.

FRUIT. Globose to ellipsoidal; 1–2½ inches long (mostly about 1½ inches); husk ¼–½ inch thick, completely dehiscent; nut 4-ribbed with thick shell and sweet seed.

TWIGS. Stout, gray to red-brown, more or less hairy. Winter buds; terminal ½–¾ inch long, broadly ovoid, with 3–4 visible, overlapping, brown, pubescent, loosely fitting scales.

BARK. Very characteristic on mature trunks, ¾–1 inch thick, gray, breaking into thin plates 1–3 feet long which are free at one or both ends and give tree typical shaggy appearance.

SILVICAL CHARACTERS. This important tree has a varied habitat, being typically mixed with oak on upland slopes in the north, while in the south it is commonly on moist alluvial soils with several hardwoods.

* * *

Shellbark Hickory

Carya laciniosa (Michx.) Loud. [*Hicoria laciniosa* (Michx.) Sarg.]

This species has similar shaggy bark and differs from shagbark hickory in having usually 7 leaflets which are velvety below, orange twigs, and somewhat larger fruit (1¾–2½ inches long) with a 4–6 ribbed nut. Range from New York to Nebraska, south to northern Louisiana, and east to eastern Tennessee.

a. Winter twig, x 1.
b. Leaf, x 1/3.
c. Flowering branchlet, x 1/2.
d. Staminate flower, enlarged.
e. Pistillate flower, enlarged.
f. Fruit, x 1/2.

JUGLANDACEAE

MOCKERNUT HICKORY

Carya tomentosa Nutt. [*Hicoria alba* (L.) Britton]

[*Carya alba* (L.) Nutt.]

HABIT. A tree 50–70 feet high and 1–2½ feet in diameter (max. 100 by 4 feet); broad, open crown with large branches.

LEAVES. 8–12 inches long with 7–9 (rarely 5) leaflets; leaflets lanceolate to obovate-oblanceolate, the terminal 4–7 inches long and somewhat larger than the lateral; finely to coarsely serrate margins; thick, dark yellow-green and glabrous above, paler and hairy below, glandular resinous and fragrant.

FRUIT. Globose to obovoid; 1½–2 inches long; husk ⅛–¼ inch thick, splitting nearly to the base; thick shell; sweet seed.

TWIGS. Stout, gray to red-brown, hairy. Winter buds: terminal ½–¾ inch long, subglobose, red-brown.

BARK. Thick, firm, dark gray, with shallow furrows and low, interlacing ridges on mature trunks.

SILVICAL CHARACTERS. Typical of well-drained upland slopes; associated with oak and other hardwoods.

* * *

PIGNUT HICKORY

Carya glabra (Mill.) Sweet

Pignut Hickory differs from mockernut in having 5 (rarely 7) essentially glabrous leaflets; fruit usually about 1 inch long, pyriform or obovoid, with a thin husk (under ⅛ inch) splitting only part way to the base; and an unribbed nut with sweet seed. Eastern States except for Coastal Plain and far north.

* * *

Four other unimportant species of "true hickories" have furrowed and firm to scaly bark and are distinguished in the key They are:

1. Scrub Hickory, *Carya floridana* Sarg., on dry Florida hills.

2. Swamp Hickory, *Carya leiodermis* Sarg., on wet sites in Arkansas, Texas, Louisiana, and Mississippi.

3. Sand Hickory, *Carya pallida* (Ashe) Engl. & Graebn., on dry sites from Virginia and Tennessee to Florida and Alabama.

4. Black Hickory, *Carya texana* Buckl., on dry uplands from Indiana to Kansas, to Louisiana and Texas.

a. Winter twig, x 1.

b. Leaf, x ⅓.

c. Flowering branchlet, x ½.

d. Staminate flower, enlarged.

e. Pistillate flower, enlarged.

f. Fruit, x 1.

JUGLANDACEAE

BITTERNUT HICKORY

Carya cordiformis (Wang.) K. Koch [*Hicoria cordiformis* (Wang.) Britt.]

HABIT. A tree 50–75 feet high and 1–2 feet in diameter (max. 100 by 3 feet); broad, open crown with slender ascending branches.

LEAVES. 6–10 inches long with 7–11 leaflets; leaflets lanceolate to oblong-lanceolate, the terminal 3–6 inches, slightly larger than lateral, finely to coarsely serrate margins, bright green and glabrous above, paler below.

FRUIT. Subglobose; about 1 inch long; husk thin (less than ⅛ inch) with yellow-green, scurfy pubescence, splitting half way to base; 4-winged above middle; nut smooth, thin-shelled, bitter.

TWIGS. Rather stout; green to gray-brown. Winter buds: terminal ⅓–¾ inch long, flattish, long-pointed, sulfur-yellow, scurfy-pubescent, with valvate scales.

BARK. Thick, firm, gray, with shallow furrows and ridges.

SILVICAL CHARACTERS. Adapted to variety of sites; the most abundant and uniformly distributed of the hickories; with mixed hardwoods.

* * *

There are three other native species of "pecan hickories:"

Pecan, *Carya illinoensis* (Wang.) K. Koch (*Carya pecan* Engl. & Graebn.), famed for its nuts, is the largest of the hickories (max. 180 by 6 feet). This species is characterized by having 9–17 lanceolate, usually falcate leaflets; fruit ellipsoidal, 1–2½ inches long, with thin dark brown husk, splitting from apex to base; nut nearly smooth with sweet seed; and buds ¼–½ inch long, yellow-brown, and scurfy. The Mississippi River Valley from southern Wisconsin to Texas and Alabama and widely planted through the South.

* * *

Water Hickory, *Carya aquatica* (Michx.) Nutt., is similar to pecan but differs in having a smaller (1½ inches long) fruit, with a thin nearly black, husk that splits half way to the base and an obovoid, 4-ribbed nut with a bitter seed. In swamps from Virginia to Texas and north to Illinois.

* * *

Nutmeg Hickory, *Carya myristicaeformis* (Michx.) Nutt., is a rather rare tree with 5–9 ovate-lanceolate leaflets and an ellipsoidal, 4-winged fruit 1½ inches long, with a very thin husk that splits to the base. In swamps or moist sites from South Carolina to Oklahoma and south to Alabama and Texas.

BETULACEAE

The Birches

Characteristics of the Genus *Betula* L.

HABIT. Small to medium-sized graceful trees and shrubs; crown on young trees narrow, pyramidal, symmetrical; branches short and slender, more or less erect on young trees and becoming horizontal or pendulous on older trees.

LEAVES. Alternate; simple; deciduous; mostly ovate to triangular; acute to acuminate; serrate, dentate, or lobulate; deciduous; petioled; stipules fugacious; scarious.

FLOWERS. Regular; monoecious; apetalous; appearing before or with leaves; staminate in 1–3 clustered, long, pendulous aments produced early the previous season, every bract with 3 individual flowers, each of 4 stamens adnate to a 4-parted calyx; pistillate in solitary, small, slender aments appearing on ends of spurlike lateral branches below the staminate flowers, individual flowers naked, in clusters of 3, and subtended by 3-lobed bract.

FRUIT. Small, compressed, laterally winged nutlet; in erect or pendent strobiles; scales deciduous from persistent cone axis at maturity, releasing the nutlets; maturing in fall of first year (one species maturing in spring).

TWIGS. Slender; round; marked by horizontal lenticels and small leaf scars; spur shoots with paired leaves commonly present on old growth; pith small, round, homogeneous. Winter buds: terminal absent, lateral with imbricated scales; twig lengthening by one of upper lateral buds.

BARK. Smooth, papery (or in Sweet Birch furrowed); resinous; marked by horizontally elongated lenticels; often peeling off in thin, papery layers.

WOOD. Strong, heavy, and hard; diffuse-porous; light-colored; some species highly valued for timber.

SILVICAL CHARACTERS. Mostly fast-growing and short-lived; adapted to planting on poor, sandy or boggy soil; many used for ornamental planting because of handsome foliage and showy bark; lateral root systems.

GENERAL. This genus contains about 40 species of trees and shrubs scattered through the Northern Hemisphere; the European white birch (*Betula pendula* Roth.) and especially its cut-leaf, weeping variety (*dalecarlica* Schn.) are often planted in this country; eleven species are native to North America, 7 of which form trees.

KEY TO THE SPECIES OF BIRCHES

1. Leaves with 9–12 pairs of veins; fruit erect, oblong-ovoid; wing not as broad as nutlet; twigs with wintergreen flavor; important eastern timber species.
    2. Bark dark, furrowed, not separating into papery layers; bracts of fruit glabrous...............*B. lenta*, **Sweet Birch,** p. 153.
    2. Bark dirty-yellow, separating into thin papery layers; bracts of fruit hairy..........*B. alleghaniensis*, **Yellow Birch,** p. 151.
1. Leaves with 8 or less pairs of veins (7–9 in River Birch); fruit oblong or cylindric; twigs without wintergreen flavor.
    3. **Bark red-brown to chestnut-brown.**
        4. Bark separating freely into papery layers; fruit erect; wing much narrower than nutlet; eastern.....................
        ....*B. nigra*, **River Birch,** p. 151.
        4. Bark not separating into papery layers; fruit pendent; wing broader than nutlet; western.
            5. Fruit ½–¾ inch long; leaves wedge-shaped at base; western Canada and Alaska..........................
            ....*B.* x *eastwoodiae*, **Yukon Birch,** p. 155.
            5. Fruit 1–1¼ inches long; leaves usually rounded at base; western United States and southwestern Canada.......
            ....*B. occidentalis*, **Water Birch,** p. 155.
    3. Bark distinctly white in color.
        6. Bark chalky-white, not separating freely into papery layers; leaves triangular or rhombic, bright green; Delaware and Pennsylvania to eastern Canada........................
        ....*B. populifolia*, **Gray Birch,** p. 153.
        6. Bark lustrous, pink-white, separating freely into papery layers; leaves usually ovate to oval.
            7. Young twigs hairy and nearly non-glandular; bracts of fruit with middle lobe much longer than lateral lobes; Northern transcontinental...........................
            ....*B. papyrifera*, **Paper Birch,** p. 149.
            7. Young twigs glabrous and resinous-glandular; bracts of fruit with middle lobe not longer than lateral lobes.
                8. Leaves hairy along veins on lower surface; small tree from Vermont north to east Canada...............
                ....*B. caerulea-grandis*, **Blueleaf Birch,** p. 149.
                8. Leaves strictly glabrous; a handsome, widely cultivated, Eurasian tree; often with pendulous branches and lobed leaves.. *B. pendula*, **European Birch,** p. 146.

a. Winter twig, x 1.
b. Portion of twig, enlarged.
c. Leaf, x 1.
d. Flowering branchlet, x ½.
e. Staminate flower, enlarged.
f. Bract with pistillate flowers, enlarged.
g. Fruiting branchlet, x ½.
h. Nutlet, x 5.

BETULACEAE

Paper Birch

Betula papyrifera Marsh.

HABIT. A tree 60–70 feet high and 2–3 feet in diameter (max. 120 by 4 feet); old trees with open crowns and short, pendulous branches.

LEAVES. Ovate; 2–5 inches long; coarsely, irregularly, and usually doubly serrate; dull dark green and glabrous above, light yellow-green, black-glandular and glabrous or puberulous below.

FRUIT. Strobiles cylindrical, pendant, on slender peduncles, 1–1½ inches long; scales about as long as broad, puberulous; nutlet narrower than wings.

TWIGS. At first green, hairy, and marked by scattered, orange-colored, oblong lenticels; becoming dark orange-brown and lustrous; not aromatic. Winter buds: ¼ inch long, obovoid, acute, dark chestnut-brown, glabrous.

BARK. Cream-white; separating into thin, papery layers; marked by long, narrow, raised lenticels; inner bark orange.

WOOD. Moderately important; used for pulp, lumber, turned articles, and fuel.

SILVICAL CHARACTERS. Canadian zone; intolerant; short-lived; spreading roots; reproduction vigorous, taking over extensive areas following fire; rich or sandy soils.

GENERAL. Six varieties have been differentiated and are included in the distribution map:

1. *commutata* (Reg.) Fern. from Idaho to Washington and British Columbia.
2. *cordifolia* (Reg.) Fern. from Labrador to Minnesota and New York.
3. *humilis* (Reg.) F. & R. in western Canada and Alaska.
4. *kenaica* (Evans) Henry in Alaska.
5. *montanensis* (But.) Sarg. in Montana and Idaho.
6. *subcordata* (Rydb.) Sarg. from Idaho to Oregon and western Canada.

* * *

Blueleaf Birch, Betula *caerulea-grandis* Blanchard, is a small tree found in Nova Scotia, Maine, and Vermont. It is characterized by ovate, blue-green leaves and pink-white bark which is not papery or exfoliating but slightly.

[149]

YELLOW BIRCH

a. Winter twig, x 1.
b. Portion of twig, enlarged.
c. Leaf, x ½.
d. Flowering branchlet, x ½.
e. Fruiting branchlet, x ½.
f. Fruit, x 10.

YELLOW BIRCH · RIVER BIRCH

BETULACEAE

Yellow Birch

Betula alleghaniensis Brit. (*Betula lutea* Michx.)

HABIT. A tree 60–80 feet high and 1–2 feet in diameter (max. 100 by 4 feet); with rounded, open crown and pendulous branches.

LEAVES. Ovate to oblong-ovate; 3–5 inches long; sharply doubly serrate; rounded, inequalateral base; dull, dark green and glabrous above, paler below; slightly aromatic; with 9–11 pairs of veins.

FRUIT. Strobiles ovoid, erect, nearly sessile, 1–1½ inches long; scales hairy, longer than broad with wide lateral lobes, tardily deciduous; nutlet about as broad as wing.

TWIGS. Smooth; lustrous; yellow-brown to dark brown; with slight wintergreen taste (source of oil of wintergreen). Winter buds: lateral ¼ inch long, ovate, acute, chestnut-brown, ciliate on scale margins.

BARK. Thin; dirty yellow to bronze colored; separating horizontally into thin, papery, curled strips.

WOOD. Very important, supplying about 75 per cent of birch lumber; used for furniture, flooring, veneer, etc.

SILVICAL CHARACTERS. Intermediate in tolerance; maturity reached in about 150 years; growth rather rapid; reproduction vigorous; shallow roots; restricted to cool, moist sites; in mixtures with conifers and hardwoods.

* * *

River Birch

Betula nigra L.

This unimportant species is a medium-sized tree typical of stream banks. It is quite similar to yellow birch in appearance and silvical characters and differs from it in the following ways:

LEAVES. Rhombic-ovate and often lobed; base wedge-shaped; more or less hairy below; with 5–9 pairs of veins.

FRUIT. Unique in that it matures in May or June; strobiles oblong, erect, on stout peduncles; scales with narrow, hairy, erect lobes.

TWIGS. Red-brown; hairy at first; not aromatic. Winter buds: ¼ inch long, woolly through summer.

BARK. Thin; salmon-pink to red-brown; separating into thin, papery, curled strips; furrowed and scaly at base of old trees.

[151]

a. Winter twig, x 1.
b. Portion of twig, enlarged.
c. Leaf, x ½.
d. Flowering branchlet, x ½.
e. Staminate flower, enlarged.
f. Bract with pistillate flowers, enlarge
g. Fruiting branchlet, x ½.
h. Fruit, enlarged.

SWEET BIRCH   GRAY BIRCH

BETULACEAE

Sweet Birch

Betula lenta L.

HABIT. A medium-sized tree 50–75 feet high and 1–2 feet in diameter (max. 80 by 4½ feet); rounded, open crown with pendulous branches.

LEAVES. Ovate to oblong-ovate; 2½–4 inches long; usually singly serrate; heart-shaped or unequally rounded at base; dull, dark green and glabrous above, paler below; strongly aromatic; with 9–11 pairs of veins.

FRUIT. Strobiles oblong-ovoid, erect, nearly sessile, 1–1½ inches long; scales glabrous, longer than broad, with wide lateral lobes; nutlet about as broad as wing.

TWIGS. Smooth; lustrous; light red-brown; with strong wintergreen taste (source of oil of wintergreen). Winter buds: ¼ inch long, conical, acute, red-brown, divergent.

BARK. ½–¾ inch thick; nearly black; not papery; breaking into irregular, thin, scaly plates; smooth on young trees.

WOOD. Important and similar to yellow birch.

SILVICAL CHARACTERS. Intermediate in tolerance; maturity reached in about 150 years; growth rather slow; reproduction not abundant; typical on moist sites, but hardy on poor, dry soils; a scattered tree with mixed hardwoods.

* * *

Gray Birch

Betula populifolia Marsh.

This unimportant, small tree is typical on poor sites in the Northeast. In its silvical characters it is similar to paper birch.

LEAVES. Triangular to rhombic; long-pointed; doubly serrate; with 5–9 pairs of veins; petioles slender, elongated.

FRUIT. Strobiles cylindrical, pendant, on slender peduncles; scales about as long as broad with recurved lateral lobes; nutlet slightly narrower than wing.

TWIGS. Resinous-glandular; red-yellow; not aromatic. Winter buds: ¼ inch long, ovoid, chestnut-brown, gummy.

BARK. Thin; gray-white; close and firm; not papery or exfoliating very slightly; black, triangular patches below branches.

a. Twig with leaves and fruit, x 1.

b. Staminate aments, x ½.

c. Scale of fruit, x 4.

BETULACEAE

Water Birch. Red Birch

Betula occidentalis Hook. (Betula fontinalis Sarg.)

HABIT. A shrub or small tree 20–25 feet high and 12–14 inches in diameter; broad, open crown with ascending branches; frequently in crowded, dense thickets.

LEAVES. Ovate; 1–2 inches long and ¾–1 inch wide; acute or acuminate; sharply and often doubly serrate; sometimes slightly lobed; thin and firm; glabrous; dark dull green above, pale yellow-green and minutely glandular below; turning dull yellow in autumn; petioles stout, ⅓–½ inch long, light yellow, glandular-dotted; stipules bright green, slightly ciliate.

FRUIT. Strobiles cylindrical, pendant (rarely erect) long-stalked, 1–1¼ inches long; scales ciliate; nutlet slightly narrower than wing.

TWIGS. At first light green and glandular, becoming dark red-brown; marked by horizontal lenticels. Winter buds: ¼ inch long, ovoid, acute, very resinous, chestnut-brown.

BARK. Thin (¼ inch); smooth; lustrous dark bronze; marked by pale horizontal lenticels, becoming on old trunks 6–8 inches long and ¼ inch wide.

WOOD. Rather light and soft; strong; heartwood light brown; sapwood thick, light-colored; not important; used locally for fencing and fuel.

SILVICAL CHARACTERS. Upper Sonoran and Transition zones; intolerant; shallow root system; reproduction abundant in moist, mineral soil; generally along borders of streams in moist mountain valleys and cañons.

* * *

Yukon birch, *Betula* X *eastwoodiae* Sarg., a hybrid of *B. glandulosa* and *B. papyrifera* is a small tree or shrub found in swampy sites in northern Alberta and the Yukon. It is characterized by broadly ovate to elliptic leaves 1–1½ inches long; pendulous, cylindric strobiles ¾ inch long, with glabrous scales longer than broad; and close, chestnut-brown bark not readily separating into papery scales. The bog or resin birch, *Betula glandulosa* Michx., is a shrubby circumpolar form of cold sites.

BETULACEAE

The Alders

Characteristics of the Genus *Alnus* B. Ehrh.

HABIT. Deciduous shrubs or small to medium-sized trees.

LEAVES. Alternate; simple; usually serrate or dentate; pinnately veined; falling without change of color; petioled; stipules fugacious, ovate, acute, scarious.

FLOWERS. Regular; monoecious; apetalous; mostly appearing before or with leaves (rarely opening in autumn); in 1–3 flowered cymes; formed during previous season; staminate in long, pendulous aments, every scale bearing 3–6 flowers, each flower subtended by 3–5 bractlets and composed of 4-parted calyx and 4 (rarely 1–3) stamens; pistillate in erect, stalked, ovoid or oblong aments, appearing below staminate flowers, individual flowers in pairs, composed of a naked ovary surmounted by 2 stigmas and subtended by 2–4 bractlets.

FRUIT. Small, flat, chestnut-brown, wingless or laterally winged nutlet, bearing remnants of style at apex; in persistent, semi-woody strobiles, each scale bearing 2–4 nutlets.

TWIGS. Slender to moderately stout; round; reddish or tinged with red; marked by raised leaf scars and lenticles; pith homogeneous, triangular in cross section. Winter buds: terminal absent; lateral-stalked, 2–3-scaled, usually red; twig lengthening by one of upper lateral buds.

BARK. Astringent; mostly gray; smooth, except at the base of trunks of large trees.

WOOD. Light; soft; straight-grained; diffuse-porous; durable in water; heartwood red-brown; sapwood very thick and whitish.

SILVICAL CHARACTERS. Tolerant to intolerant; rather short-lived; shallow, spreading roots; on moist or wet sites, commonly along streams or on mountain slopes.

GENERAL. This genus contains about 30 species scattered through the cooler portions of the Northern Hemisphere and extending into the mountains of South America; 8 species attaining tree size are native to North America, although 7 of these are typically shrubs and only *Alnus rubra* is of commercial importance. The European alder, *Alnus glutinosa* (L.) Gaertn., has become naturalized in the eastern United States.

[156]

KEY TO THE SPECIES OF ALDERS

1. Buds sessile, 3–6 scaled, dark purple; pistillate ament enclosed in bud during winter; leaves ovate, lobulate, usually irregularly singly toothed; Alaska to California and east to Montana........
.................*Alnus sinuata* (Reg.) Rydb., **Sitka Alder**, p. 161.

1. Buds stalked, 2–3 scaled; pistillate ament appearing in fall (sometimes enclosed during winter in red alder).

   2. Leaves with 8–15 pairs of veins.

      3. Leaves lobulate, doubly toothed; buds reddish.

         4. Wing of nut broad; leaves ovate to elliptic, often red-hairy below, slightly revolute; important tree; Alaska to California and east to Idaho........................
         ....*Alnus rubra* Bong., **Red Alder**, p. 159.

         4. Wing of nut reduced to narrow border; leaves neither red-hairy nor revolute; shrubs or rarely small trees to 30 feet.

            5. Twigs marked with orange lenticels; Rocky Mountains and Pacific Coast from Yukon to Mexico.......
            ....*Alnus tenuifolia* Nutt., **Thinleaf Alder**, p. 161.

            5. Twigs marked with white lenticels; Newfoundland to Saskatchewan, south to Pennsylvania and Nebraska, also in Europe and Asia.........................
            ...*Alnus rugosa* (D. R.) Spr., **Speckled Alder,** p. 161.

      3. Leaves finely to coarsely toothed.

         6. Western shrubs or small trees; leaves coarsely toothed.

            7. Leaves oval or ovate; Idaho to Washington and south to lower California...............................
            ....*Alnus rhombifolia* Nutt., **White Alder**

            7. Leaves oblong-lanceolate; New Mexico and Arizona, south into Mexico..............................
            ....*Alnus oblongifolia* Torr., **Arizona Alder**

         6. Eastern shrubs, rarely small trees; leaves finely toothed.

            8. Leaves with straight veins; several pistillate catkins per bud; Maine to Minnesota and south to Florida and Texas...*Alnus serrulata* (Alt) Willd., **Hazel Alder**

            8. Leaves with arching veins; 1–3 pistillate catkins per bud; Delaware, Maryland, and Oklahoma..........
            ....*Alnus maritima* (Marsh.) Muhl., **Seaside Alder**

   2. Leaves with 5–6 pairs of veins, oval to orbicular, coarsely and doubly toothed; native to Eurasia but naturalized in the Northeastern States............. ....
   ....*Alnus glutinosa* (L.) Gaertn., **European Alder**

E'07

a. Twigs with leaves and fruit, x ¾.

BETULACEAE

RED ALDER

Alnus rubra Bong.

HABIT. A medium-sized tree 80–100 feet high and 1–3 feet in diameter (max. 130 by 5 feet); clear trunk; crown narrow and rounded with pendulous branches.

LEAVES. Ovate to elliptic; 3–6 inches long and 1½–3 inches wide; obtuse or rounded at base; apex acute; margins slightly crenately lobed with doubly dentate gland-tipped teeth; thick and firm; dark green and glabrate above, paler and rusty-pubescent below; petiole orange, round, grooved, ¼–¾ inch long.

FLOWERS. Preformed; the staminate aments 1¼ inches long, becoming 4–6 inches long, orange; opening in early spring, ⅓–½ inch long with dark red scales and bright red style.

FRUIT. Strobiles ½–1¼ inches long; woody; persistent; ovoid to oblong; on orange peduncles or rarely sessile; truncate scales with much thickened, rugose tips;; nutlet nearly circular with encircling membranous wing or 2 lateral wings.

TWIGS. Slender to rather stout; light green and tomentose at first, becoming bright red and lustrous during second year. Winter buds: lateral ⅓–⅔ inch long, stalked, dark red, with pale, scurfy pubescence.

BARK. Thin; smooth; nearly white to blue-gray outer bark and bright red-brown inner bark; sometimes roughened by small, warty excrescences; breaking into large, flat plates on old trees.

WOOD. Important (probably the most important hard-wood on the Pacific Coast); light; soft; with prominent rays; used for furniture, veneer, and novelties.

SILVICAL CHARACTERS. Intermediate in tolerance; rapid growth; short-lived, maturity being reached in 60–90 years; lateral roots; aggressive reproduction, often taking over burned or logged areas; on varied sites, but typical of stream banks; in pure or mixed stands.

THINLEAF ALDER

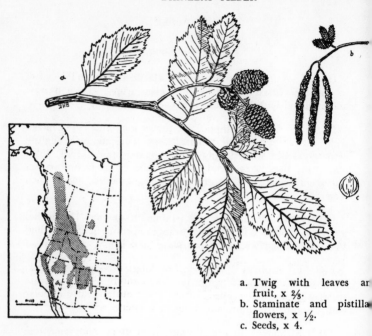

a. Twig with leaves and fruit, x 2/3.
b. Staminate and pistillate flowers, x 1/2.
c. Seeds, x 4.

SITKA ALDER

a. Twig with leaves and fruit, x 1.
b. Seed, x 3.

BETULACEAE

Thinleaf Alder. Mountain Alder

Alnus tenuifolia Nutt.

HABIT. A shrub or small tree occasionally 30 feet high and 6–8 inches in diameter; crown narrow and round-topped.

LEAVES. Ovate-oblong; 2–4 inches long; slightly, acutely and laciniately lobed; doubly serrate; thin and firm; dark green and glabrous above, pale yellow-green below.

FRUIT. Nut nearly circular; wing reduced to thin, membranaceous border; strobiles ⅓–½ inch long, obovoid-oblong; scales truncate, much thickened, 3-lobed at apex.

TWIGS. Slender; marked by few, large orange-colored lenticels. Winter buds; stalked, ¼–⅓ inch long, bright red, puberulous.

BARK. Thin; smooth; red-brown.

SILVICAL CHARACTERS. Tolerant when young, becoming intolerant with age; on banks of mountain streams; the common alder of the Rocky Mountain region; closely related and considered by some authors to be a synonym of the eastern speckled alder, *Alnus rugosa*.

* * *

Sitka Alder

Alnus sinuata (Regel) Rydb. (*Alnus sitchensis* Sarg.)

HABIT. A shrub or small tree rarely 40 feet high and 7–8 inches in diameter; crown narrow and open.

LEAVES. Ovate; 3–6 inches long; acute; usually divided into numerous, short, lateral lobes; sharply and doubly serrate; membranaceous; yellow-green above, pale below.

FRUIT. Nut oval, about as wide as its wings; strobiles ½–¾ inch long and about ⅓ inch wide; truncate scales thickened at apex; on slender peduncles; in elongated, leafy panicles.

TWIGS. Slender; large, pale lenticels. Winter buds: sessile, ½ inch long, acuminate, dark purple, finely pubescent.

BARK. Thin; blue-gray; bright red inner bark.

SILVICAL CHARACTERS. Tolerant when young, becoming intolerant with age; in moist flats and along stream borders.

a. Winter twig, x 1.

b. Portion of twig, enlarged.

c. Leaf, x ½.

d. Flowering branchlet, x ½.

e. Staminate flower, enlarged.

f. Pistillate flower, enlarged.

g. Fruit, x ½.

BETULACEAE

EASTERN HOPHORNBEAM

Ostrya virginiana (Mill.) K. Koch

HABIT. A small tree 20–40 feet high and 8–18 inches in diameter (max. 65 by 3 feet); with rounded crown and slender, pendulous, often contorted branches.

LEAVES. Alternate; simple; oblong-ovate; 3–5 inches long with 11–15 pairs of veins; deciduous; acuminate; sharply doubly serrate margins; thin and tough; dull dark green above, paler and somewhat hairy below.

FLOWERS. Regular; monoecious; perianth absent; appearing with leaves; staminate in long, drooping, cylindrical aments in clusters of 3, each flower containing 3–14 stamens crowded on a hairy receptacle; pistillate in erect, loose, paired aments, each flower enclosed in a hairy, sac-like involucre.

FRUIT. Small (¼ inch), 1-celled, 1-seeded, ovoid, flat, unwinged nut; enclosed in enlarged (1 inch), pale, membranaceous, involucre of flower; in loose, suspended strobiles 1–1½ inches long, resembling clusters of hops.

TWIGS. Slender; round; red-brown becoming dark brown. Winter buds: terminal absent, lateral ⅛–¼ inch long, ovoid, acute, with characteristic longitudinal striations on the bud scales which have a greenish base and brown top.

BARK. Thin; gray-brown; broken into small, shaggy plates which give it characteristic shreddy appearance.

WOOD. Very heavy, hard, and strong; unimportant; resembling hickory and known as ironwood; little used.

SILVICAL CHARACTERS. Tolerant; slow-growing; lateral roots; varied sites, but typical on dry slopes.

* * *

KNOWLTON HOPHORNBEAM

Ostrya knowltonii Cov.

This rare, local tree is found in mountains and canyons of western Texas, southeastern New Mexico, northern Arizona, and southeastern Utah. It differs from *O. Virginiana* in having leaves 1–2 inches long with 5–8 pairs of veins.

[163]

a. Winter twig, x 1.

b. Portion of twig, enlarged.

c. Leaf, x 1.

d. Flowering branchlet, x ½.

e. Staminate flower, enlarged.

f. Pistillate flower, enlarged.

g. Fruit, x ½.

BETULACEAE

American Hornbeam. Bluebeech

Carpinus caroliniana Walt.

HABIT. A large shrub or small bushy tree rarely 40 feet high and 1 foot in diameter; trunk characteristically fluted; crown close and flat-topped with slender, zigzag branches.

LEAVES. Alternate; simple; ovate to oval; 2–4 inches long; deciduous; acuminate; sharply doubly serrate; thin and tough; dull dark green above, paler below.

FLOWERS. Regular; monoecious; perianth absent; appearing with leaves; staminate in aments 1½ inches long, with green, hairy scales, each flower with 3–20 stamens; pistillate in loose aments ½–¾ inch long, with green, hairy scales, each bearing 2 pistils with scarlet styles.

FRUIT. Small (⅓ inch), 1-seeded, ovoid, flat, brown, unwinged nut; attached to base of halbard-shaped, leafy involucre; in loose strobiles.

TWIGS. Slender; round; pale green at first, becoming lustrous and red-brown. Winter buds: terminal absent, lateral ⅛ inch long, rusty brown, acute, scaly, usually 4-sided in cross section.

BARK. Thin; smooth; blue-gray; often mottled with light or dark patches; with fluted trunk an unmistakable character.

WOOD. Heavy; hard; strong; unimportant.

SILVICAL CHARACTERS. Tolerant; slow-growing; lateral root; on varied sites but prefers moist soil.

* * *

Hazelnut

Corylus L.

Three shrubby species are native to North America and one of these, *Corylus cornuta* var. *californica* (A. OC.) Sharp, may occasionally reach tree size in California. The other two species are small eastern shrubs known for their edible nuts, American Hazelnut (*C. americana* Walt.) and Beaked Hazelnut (*C. cornuta* Marsh. var. *cornuta*). The Giant Filbert, *Corylus maxima* Mill., of southern Europe is planted in warm parts of the United States. The hazelnuts are characterized by deciduous, alternate, simple, oval to ovate, doubly serrate leaves; scaly lateral buds; and an ovoid nut surrounded by a leafy, toothed involucre.

a. Winter twig, x 1.
b. Portion of twig, enlarged.
c. Leaf, x 1.
d. Flowering branchlet, x ¾.
e. Staminate flower, enlarged.
f. Pistillate flower, enlarged.
g. Bur, opened, x 1.
h. Nut, x 1.

FAGACEAE

AMERICAN BEECH

Fagus grandifolia Ehrh.

HABIT. A beautiful, medium-sized tree 60–80 feet high and 2–3 feet in diameter (max. 120 by 5½ feet); clear straight trunk; compact, rounded crown with slender, spreading branches.

LEAVES. Alternate; simple; deciduous; elliptical to oblong-ovate; 2½–6 inches long; penniveined; coarsely serrate with sharp teeth; acuminate; thin; dark blue-green above and yellow-green and lustrous below; short-petioled.

FLOWERS. Monoecious; apetalous; appearing after the leaves open; staminate in globose heads 1 inch in diameter, each with a 4–8-lobed calyx and 8–16 stamens; pistillate in 2–4-flowered spikes, each with a 4–5-lobed calyx, a 3-celled ovary, and 3 styles.

FRUIT. A triangular, edible nut ½–¾ inch long; 2–3 completely enclosed in a woody, 4-parted bur or involucre covered with weak, unbranched spines; maturing in one year.

TWIGS. Slender; round; lustrous; olive green, becoming ash-gray; occasionally zigzag; pith round. Winter buds: terminal present, ¾–1 inch long, slender, lance-shaped, acuminate, with numerous, imbricated scales, a very distinctive feature.

BARK. Thin; close; smooth; light blue-gray; often mottled; similar in appearance on old and young trunks.

WOOD. Important; strong, heavy, and hard; diffuse-porous; light in color; not durable; used for flooring, handles, furniture, etc.

SILVICAL CHARACTERS. Very tolerant; rather fast growing; long-lived, attaining an age of about 400 years; shallow, lateral roots; reproduction good; roots sprout vigorously; on moist sites; in mixture with numerous hardwoods.

GENERAL. This genus contains about 10 species scattered through the Northern Hemisphere, with only one native to North America. In the southern part of its range, American beech passes into the variety *caroliniana* (Loud.) Fern. & Rehd., which differs in having short-ovate, thicker leaves. The important European beech, *Fagus sylvatica* L., is a commonly planted ornamental; the variety *atropunicea* West. with dark bronze-purple leaves; the variety *pendula* Loud. with the weeping habit of drooping branches; and the variety *laciniata* Vig. with deeply cut leaves are familiar shade trees.

a. Winter twig, x 1.
b. Leaf, x ½.
c. Flowering branchlet, x ½.
d. Staminate flower, enlarged.
e. Pistillate flower, enlarged.
f. Prickly bur, opened, x ½.
g. Nut, x ½.

FAGACEAE

AMERICAN CHESTNUT

Castanea dentata (Marsh.) Borkh.

HABIT. A handsome tree 60–90 feet high and 2–4 feet in diameter (max. 120 by 10 feet); frequently divided trunk; broad, open crown with large, horizontal branches.

LEAVES. Alternate; simple; deciduous; oblong-lanceolate; 5½–8 inches long; penniveined coarsely serrate with sharp, glandular teeth; acuminate; thin; yellow-green; glabrous.

FLOWERS. Monoecious; apetalous; appearing after the leaves; in staminate and bisexual aments; the staminate aments in 3–7-flowered cymes, each flower with 10–20 stamens; the pistillate flowers solitary or in clusters of 2–3.

FRUIT. A rounded, flattened, chestnut-brown, edible nut ½–1 inch long; 2–3 nuts completely enclosed in a 2–4 valved, globose bur, 2–2½ inches in diameter and covered with prickly, sharp, branched spines; maturing in one year.

TWIGS. Rather stout; round; lustrous; chestnut-brown; glabrous; pith stellate. Winter buds; terminal absent, lateral ovoid, acute, brown ¼ inch long, with 2–3 visible scales.

BARK. Thick; gray-brown; furrowed, with broad, flat ridges.

WOOD. Important; rather weak and soft; very durable; ring-porous; used for furniture, poles, posts, ties, and tannin.

SILVICAL CHARACTERS. Intermediate in tolerance; fast growing; long-lived; taproot; stump sprouts vigorously; threatened with extinction by chestnut blight, a fungal bark disease; varied sites; with mixed hardwoods.

* * *

THE CHINKAPINS

Four other species of *Castanea* form small trees or shrubs in the southern states. These are known as Chinkapins and differ from chestnut in having hairy or woolly leaves, woolly twigs and buds, and smaller, single-seeded burs.

1. Leaves silky hairy to nearly glabrous below, 3–4 inches long; spines on bur scattered and short; North Carolina to Arkansas and south......*C. alnifolia* var. *floridana* Sarg., **Florida Chinkapin**
1. Leaves woolly below
  2. Spines on bur crowded and slender.
    3. Leaves 5–9 inches long, bristle-tipped; Missouri, Arkansas, and Oklahoma.......*C. ozarkensis* Ashe., **Ozark Chinkapin**
    3. Leaves 3–6 inches long with short rigid teeth; N. J. to Mo. and south......*C. pumila* (L.) Mill., **Alleghany Chinkapin**
  2. Spines on bur scattered, short, and stout; leaves 2–3 inches long; Coastal Plain, Virginia to Texas....................
........................*C. ashei* Sudw., **Ashe Chinkapin**

a. Leafy twig, x ⅔.
b. Flowering twig, x ⅔.
c. Fruit, x ⅔.

FAGACEAE

Golden Chinkapin

Castanopsis chrysophylla (Dougl.) A. DC.

HABIT. A small to medium-sized tree 60–80 feet high and 1–2 feet in diameter (max. 125 by 3½ feet), a large shrub in Washington; trunk clear and straight; dense, rounded crown with stout, spreading branches.

LEAVES. Alternate; simple; persistent 2–3 years; lanceolate to oblong-ovate; 2–6 inches long; penniveined; entire and often revolute; usually acuminate; thick and leathery; dark green and lustrous above; covered with small golden-yellow scales below.

FLOWERS. Monoecious; apetalous; appearing after the leaves; in staminate and bisexual aments; the staminate aments in 3-flowered cymes, each flower with 10–12 stamens; the pistillate flowers solitary or in clusters of 2–3, with 3-celled ovaries.

FRUIT. A rounded, broadly ovoid, yellow-brown nut ½ inch long; 1–2 nuts enclosed in a 4-valved, globose bur 1–1½ inches in diameter and covered with prickly, dense, unbranched spines; maturing in 2 years.

TWIGS. Rather slender; rigid; round; covered at first with golden-yellow scales, becoming scurfy and red-brown; pith stellate. Winter buds: terminal present, ovoid, ¼ inch long, light brown, with numerous overlapping scales.

BARK. Thick; dark red-brown; deeply furrowed with broad, scaly ridges.

WOOD. Unimportant; intermediate in strength and hardness; ring-porous; occasionally used for lumber.

SILVICAL CHARACTERS. Tolerant; growth rather rapid; long-lived, reaching 500 years; taproot in early life, giving way to deep lateral system; often in pure stands on poor, dry sites and as an understory tree in redwood and Douglas-fir stands.

GENERAL. There are about 30 Asiatic species of this genus, with only 2 species native to the west coast of the United States. *Castanopsis sempervirens* Dudl. is a small alpine shrub in California.

TANOAK

a. Leafy twig, x ½.
b. Fruit, x 1½.

FAGACEAE

Tanoak. Tanbark-oak

Lithocarpus densiflorus (Hook. & Arn.) Rehd.

HABIT. A medium-sized tree 70–90 feet high and 2–3 feet in diameter (max. 150 by 8 feet); trunk clear; crown rounded with ascending branches.

LEAVES. Alternate; simple; persistent 3–4 years; oblong to oblong-lanceolate; 3–5 inches long; penniveined; repand or dentate to entire-revolute; acute or rounded; thick; pale green and usually glabrous above; brown, woolly pubescent below in spring, becoming blue-white and nearly glabrous.

FLOWERS. Monoecious; apetalous; appearing after the leaves; in staminate and bisexual aments; staminate flowers crowded, each with 10 stamens; the pistillate flowers solitary with 3-celled ovary.

FRUIT. An oval, bitter, yellow-brown nut (acorn) ¾–1 inch long; enclosed at base in a shallow, tomentose, spiny, cuplike involucre, lined with a lustrous red pubescence; maturing in 2 years.

TWIGS. Stout; round; covered for 1–3 years with a thick tomentum of fascicled hairs, becoming red-brown and often with a glaucous bloom. Winter buds: terminal present; ovoid; obtuse; ¼ inch long; covered by a few tomentose scales.

BARK. Thick; red-brown; deeply furrowed with broad, rounded, scaly ridges; high in tannin content.

WOOD. Unimportant; hard and strong; ring-porous; little used.

SILVICAL CHARACTERS. Tolerant; growth moderate; maturity reached in 200–300 years; deep taproot system; typical on moist, well-drained sites; in mixture with conifers and hardwoods; coppices vigorously and reproduces well by seed.

GENERAL. There are about 100 Asiatic species of this genus found in warm climates. Only the one species is native to North America.

FAGACEAE

The Oaks

Characteristics of the Genus *Quercus* L.

HABIT. Deciduous or evergreen trees or shrubs; with astringent properties; pubescence of fascicled hairs.

LEAVES. Alternate; simple; deciduous or persistent; shape and size often variable on same tree; stipulate.

FLOWERS. Regular; monoecious; vernal; staminate in clustered aments, individual flowers with a 4–7-lobed calyx enclosing 6 (rarely 2–12) stamens; pistillate solitary or in 2 to many-flowered spikes, individual flowers with a 6-lobed calyx surrounding a 3-(rarely 4–5) celled ovary with 1–2 ovules in each cell, the whole partly enclosed in an involucre.

FRUIT. An acorn; 1-seeded by abortion; maturing in 1–2 years; partially enclosed by scaly cup (modified involucre).

TWIGS. Slender to stout; angled; pith homogeneous, stellate; marked by plate lenticels and semicircular lear scars. Winter buds: clustered at end of twig; terminal present; with many chestnut-brown scales imbricated in 5 ranks.

BARK. Scaly or dark and furrowed.

WOOD. Heavy; hard; strong; with prominent rays.

SILVICAL CHARACTERS. Varying from intermediate in tolerance (many white oaks) to intolerant (most red and live oaks); long-lived; generally with deep taproot systems; hybridizes frequently.

GENERAL. This is a variable genus and it is often difficult to distinguish between the species. Fifty-nine native species are recognized as reaching tree size; in addition there are numerous hydrids and varieties as well as many shrubby species. Five shrubby southwestern forms that are reported to become small trees in Texas, New Mexico, or Arizona are not keyed out. These are *Q. graciliformis* Mull., *Q. gravesii* Sudw., *Q. grisea* Liebm., *Q. havardii* Rydb., and *Q. laceyi* Small. The key distinguishes between the tree species and all oaks of importance are described and pictured in more detail. The native oaks logically break themselves down into 2 subgenera, the white oaks and the red oaks, each of which is further subdivided into 3 groups. A recent study indicates that all the live oaks should be placed under the red oak group on the basis of wood structure.

The English oak, *Quercus robur* L. is commonly planted. This oak has leaves which resemble white oak but are smaller (2½–5 inches long). It is further characterized by having the fruit borne on peduncles 1–3 inches long.

KEY TO THE SPECIES OF OAKS

I. Leaves turning brown in the fall of the first year, neither thick and leathery nor spiny-toothed.

    II. Leaves or leaf lobes not bristle-tipped; acorn maturing in 1 year, usually sweet; nut shell smooth on inside . WHITE OAKS

        III. Leaves deeply lobed or rarely entire . . . .
. . . . True White Oaks, p. 175.

        III. Leaves coarsely toothed or shallowly lobed . . . .
. . . . Chestnut Oaks, p. 176.

    II. Leaves or leaf lobes commonly bristle-tipped; acorn maturing in 2 years, usually bitter; nut shell woolly on inside . . . .
. . . . RED OAKS

        IV. Leaves lobed, rarely broadly ovate and entire . . . .
. . . . True Red Oaks, p. 176.

        IV. Leaves entire and mostly narrow . . . Willow Oaks, p. 178.

I. Leaves remaining green on the tree at least until the new leaves appear the following spring, usually thick and leathery, margins entire or spiny-toothed . . . . LIVE OAKS, p. 178.

TRUE WHITE OAKS

1. Eastern Species (east of the Rocky Mountains).
    2. Leaves entire or slightly lobed.
        3. Acorns enclosed only at base by thin cup.
            4. Acorn ¾–1 inch long; leaves mostly blue-green; shrubby; Western Texas and Oklahoma . . . .
Q. durandii var. *brevilobata* (Torr.) Palmer, **Bigelow Oak**
            4. Acorn ½–⅔ inch long; leaves yellow-green; large tree; South Carolina to Florida, west to Texas and Arkansas
. . . . *Q. durandii* Buckl., **Durand Oak**
        3. Acorns enclosed ¼–⅔ length in thick cup.
            5. Acorn ⅓–½ inch long; leaves blue-green; western Texas and Oklahoma . . . . *Q. mohriana* Buckl., **Mohrs Oak**
            5. Acorn ⅝ inch long; leaves yellow-green; South Carolina to Florida . . . . *Q. chapmanii* Sarg., **Chapman Oak**
    2. Leaves more or less deeply lobed.
        6. Acorns enclosed ½ or more of length in cup; leaves 5–9 lobed.
            7. Acorn cup conspicuously fringed on margin; leaves nearly divided in two by deep sinuses . . . .
. . . . *Q. macrocarpa*, **Bur Oak,** p. 181.
            7. Acorn cup not fringed and nearly covering acorn; leaves irregularly lobed . . . . . . *Q. lyrata*, **Overcup Oak,** p. 183.
        6. Acorns enclosed less than ½ of length in unfringed cup.
            8. Leaves regularly and usually deeply 7–9 lobed, glabrous below . . . . *Q. alba*, **White Oak,** p. 181.
            8. Leaves typically cross-shaped, 5-lobed, red-woolly below
. . . . *Q. stellata*, **Post Oak,** p. 183.

1. Western Species (Rocky Mountain and Pacific Coast regions).
    9. Leaves undulately lobed with acute lobes or entire, blue-green, 1–1½ inches long; acorn enclosed only at base in cup.
        10. Leaves not spiny-toothed; Colorado to Nevada and south
. . . . *Q. undulata* Torr., **Wavyleaf Oak**
        10. Leaves spiny-toothed; Texas to Arizona . . . .
. . . . *Q. pungens* Liebm., **Sandpaper Oak**

9. Leaves pinnately and usually deeply lobed with rounded lobes.

   11. Acorns under ¾ inch long, enclosed for ½ or more of its length in cup; leaves yellow-green, 3–7 inches long, usually shrubby; Rocky Mountain region north to Wyoming and Nevada.................*Q. gambelii*, **Gambel Oak**, p. 185.

   11. Acorns ¾ of an inch long or longer, enclosed for less than ½ their length in cup; Pacific Coast species.

      12. Acorns 1–2¼ inches long, slender; deep, cup-like bowl; leaves 2½–3 inches long; California................ ....*Q. lobata*, **California White Oak**, p. 187.

      12. Acorns ¾–1½ inches long, ovoid; very shallow cup.

         13. Leaves dark yellow-green, 3–6 inches long; petioles hairy, ½–1 inch long; British Columbia to California....*Q. garryana*, **Oregon White Oak**, p. 187.

         13. Leaves blue-green, 2–4 inches long; shallowly lobed to sinuately toothed to entire; petioles woolly, ¼–½ inch long; California.................... ....*Q. douglasii*, **Blue Oak**, p. 185.

Chestnut Oaks (Eastern Trees)

1. Fruit long-stalked (1–4 inches); leaves coarsely sinuate-toothed to shallowly lobed, with 6–8 pairs of veins..................... ....*Q. bicolor*, **Swamp White Oak**, p. 191.

1. Fruit short-stalked or sessile; leaves coarsely toothed.

   2. Leaves with 9–17 pairs of veins; large trees.

      3. Leaves woolly below and dark green above at maturity; acorn 1–1½ inches long, enclosed for ⅓ its length in thick cup...........*Q. michauxii*, **Swamp Chestnut Oak**, p. 189.

      3. Leaves more or less hairy below and yellow-green above; acorn enclosed for ⅓–½ its length in thin cup.

         4. Leaves with rounded teeth; acorn 1–1½ inches long; cup on short stalk (¼–½ inch long)................. ....*Q. prinus*, **Chestnut Oak**, p. 189.

         4. Leaves with sharp teeth; acorn ½–1 inch long; cup sessile or nearly so....*Q. muehlenbergii*, **Chinkapin Oak**, p. 191.

   2. Leaves with 3–8 pairs of veins and usually sharp teeth; acorn ⅖–⅗ inch long, enclosed for ½ its length in thick cup; shrubby or rarely a small tree; Mass. to N. C. and west to Nebr. and Texas.............*Q. prinoides* Willd., **Dwarf Chinkapin Oak**

True Red Oaks

1. California and Oregon species; leaves usually 7-lobed; scales of fruit cup loosely imbricated.................................. ....*Q. kelloggii*, **California Black Oak**, p. 201

1. Eastern Species (not reaching the Rocky Mountain region).

   2. Leaves deeply lobed.

      3. Leaves white- to red-woolly below.

         4. Leaves usually 5-lobed, 2–5 inches long; Maine to North Carolina and Kentucky *Q. ilicifolia* Wangenh., **Bear Oak**

4. Leaves of 2 forms, either 3-lobed at apex or deeply 5–11 lobed, 6–8 inches long.................................
.... *Q. falcata*, **Southern Red Oak,** p. 195.

3. Leaves green below.

5. Leaves dull, 7–11 lobed, with sinuses extending about ½ way to midrib; acorn enclosed in cup-shaped to shallow (var. *maxima*) cup..*Q. rubra*, **Northern Red Oak,** p. 193.

5. Leaves lustrous, mostly 5-7 lobed, sinuses extending more than ½ way to midrib.

6. Acorn cup shallow, covering only the base of the acorn.

7. Leaves 6–8 inches long; acorns ¾–1¼ inches long, oblong.......*Q. shumardii*, **Shumard Oak,** p. 195.

7. Leaves 2½–6 inches long; acorn not over ½ inch long.

8. Leaves 4–6 inches long; acorn hemispheric, ½ inch long.........*Q. palustris*, **Pin Oak,** p. 199.

8. Leaves 2½ inches long; acorn ellipsoidal to globose, ⅓–½ inch long; only in Georgia.....
.... *Q. georgiana* Curtis., **Georgia Oak**

6. Acorn cup covering at least the basal ¼ of acorn.

9. Acorn cup with loosely imbricated scales, forming a free margin on rim; winter buds woolly or red hairy.

10. Leaves usually 7-lobed; winter buds tomentose .... *Q. velutina*, **Black Oak,** p. 193.

10. Leaves usually 5-lobed; winter buds rusty pubescent......*Q. laevis*, **Turkey Oak,** p. 201.

9. Acorn cup with tightly imbricated scales; winter buds not woolly or red hairy.

11. Buds white hairy; acorn with rings near apex, ½–1 inch long *Q. coccinea*, **Scarlet Oak,** p. 197.

11. Buds not white hairy; acorn without rings.

12. Acorn ellipsoidal, ½–¾ inch long; Lake states...............................
Q. ellipsoidalis, **Northern Pin Oak,** p. 199.

12. Acorn oblong, ¾–1¼ inches long; lower Mississippi Valley......................
.... *Q. nuttallii*, **Nuttall Oak,** p. 199.

2. Leaves 3-lobed at apex or entire.

13. Mature leaves distinctly hairy below.

14. Leaves gray to rusty woolly below, of two types; acorn ½ inch long, enclosed for ⅓ or less of length in thin cup.......... *Q. falcata*, **Southern Red Oak,** p. 195.

14. Leaves tawny hairy below and scurfy; acorn ¾ inch long, enclosed for ⅓–½ its length in thick cup.......
.... *Q. marylandica*, **Blackjack Oak,** p. 197.

13. Mature leaves glabrous and green below; acorn enclosed for ⅓ or less of length in thin cup.

15. Leaves rounded at base; acorn ¼–⅓ inch long; Georgia, Florida, Alabama, and Arkansas..........
.................*Q. arkansana* Sarg., **Arkansas Oak**
15. Leaves wedge-shaped at base; acorn ⅓–⅔ inch long
.....................*Q. nigra*, **Water Oak**, p. 203.

WILLOW OAKS (EASTERN SPECIES)

1. Leaves mostly linear-lanceolate, glabrous to woolly below; acorn ⅓–½ inch long, green-brown.....*Q. phellos*, **Willow Oak**, p. 203.
1. Leaves mostly oblong-lanceolate to oblong-obovate.
    2. Leaves white woolly below; North Carolina to Florida and Texas.....................*Q. incana*, **Bluejack Oak**, p. 205.
    2. Leaves glabrous to hairy below.
        3. Leaves hairy below; acorn dark chestnut-brown, ½–¾ inch long..............*Q. imbricaria*, **Shingle Oak**, p. 205.
        3. Leaves essentially glabrous below; acorn nearly black, ½ inch long.
            4. Leaves elliptical to oblong-ovate, nearly evergreen......
.....................*Q. laurifolia*, **Laurel Oak**, p. 205.
            4. Leaves variable, spatulate to obovate to linear, sometimes lobed, deciduous..........*Q. nigra*, **Water Oak**, p. 203.

LIVE OAKS

1. Southeastern Live Oaks.
    2. Shell of nut glabrous on inside, acorn maturing in 1 year, on long stalks; leaves 2–5 inches long.........................
.........................*Q. virginiana*, **Live Oak**, p. 207.
    2. Shell of nut woolly on inside, acorn maturing in 2 years, short-stalked; leaves ½–2 inches long; So. Carolina to Florida and Miss.....................*Q. myrtifolia* Willd., **Myrtle Oak**
1. Western Live Oaks.
    3. California Live Oaks.
        4. Shell of nut glabrous on inside, acorn maturing in 1 year.
            5. Leaves about ¾ inch long; usually a shrub; through California.......*Q. dumosa* Nutt., **California Scrub Oak**
            5. Leaves 1–3 inches long; southwestern California.......
..............*Q. engelmannii* Greene, **Engelmann Oak**
        4 Shell of nut woolly on inside, acorn maturing in 2 years (except California Live Oak).
            6. Acorn ¾–1½ inches long, narrow; more than ½ covered by thin cup.....*Q. wislizenii*, **Interior Live Oak**, p. 211.
            6. Acorn less than ½ covered by cup.
                7. Acorn ¾–1½ inches long, narrow; leaves glabrous to hairy below..*Q. agrifolia*, **California Live Oak**, p. 211.
                7. Acorn ½–2 inches long, oblong to ovoid; leaves woolly below.
                    8. Leaves oblong-lanceolate; restricted to islands off coast of southern California...................
..........*Q. tomentella* Engelm, **Island Live Oak**
                    8. Leaves oblong-ovate; Washington to California and Arizona...*Q. chrysolepis*, **Canyon Live Oak**, p. 213.

3. Southwestern Live Oaks (West Texas to Arizona, south into Mexico).

9. Acorn shell glabrous on inside, light brown on outside, nut maturing in 1 year.

   10. Fruit in long-stalked clusters of 2 or more; leaves broadly obovate, yellow hairy below.............................
.................*Q. reticulata* H. & B., **Netleaf Oak**

   10. Fruit sessile or nearly so, single or paired; leaves oblong to ovate.

      11. Leaves glabrous below, 1–2 inches long; acorn enclosed about ⅓ length in cup slightly fringed at rim.....*Q. oblongifolia*, **Mexican Blue Oak,** p. 207.

      11. Leaves hairy below; acorn enclosed about ½ its length in unfringed cup.

         12. Leaves ½–1 inch long; acorn ½–⅔ inch long; Arizona........*Q. toumeyi* Sarg., **Toumey Oak**

         12. Leaves 1–4 inches long; acorn ¾–1 inch long; Arizona and New Mexico...................
......*Q. arizonica*, **Arizona White Oak,** p. 209.

9. Acorn shell woolly on inner surface.

   13. Acorn maturing in 1 year, dark brown to nearly black; leaves nearly glabrous below........................
.....................*Q. emoryi*, **Emory Oak,** p. 209.

   13. Acorn maturing in 2 years, light brown; leaves woolly below.

      14. Leaves lanceolate to elliptic, persistent until second spring......*Q. hypoleucoides*, **Silverleaf Oak,** p. 213.

      14. Leaves oblong-ovate to elliptic, persistent 3–4 years
.........*Q. chrysolepis*, **Canyon Live Oak,** p. 213.

WHITE OAK

a. Fruit, x 1.
b. Leaf, x ⅓.
c. Winter twig, x 1.
d. Staminate flower, enlarged.
e. Pistillate flower, enlarged.

BUR OAK

a. Fruit, x 1.
b. Leaf, x ⅓.
c. Flowering branchlet, x ½.

White Oak

Quercus alba L.

HABIT. A medium-sized tree 80–100 feet high and 3–4 feet in diameter (max. 150 by 9 feet); crown rounded with heavy branches.

LEAVES. Deciduous; oblong to obovate; 5–9 inches long; 7–9 (rarely 5)-lobed, with lobes either broad with shallow sinuses or narrow with deep sinuses extending nearly to the midrib; apex of lobes rounded; thin and firm; bright green and glabrous above and paler below.

FRUIT. Maturing in fall of first year; sessile or short-stalked; inner surface of nut shell glabrous; acorn ½–¾ inch long, light brown, oblong, enclosed for about ¼ its length in bowl-like cup with thickened warty scales; kernel sweet.

TWIGS. Rather stout; reddish. Winter buds: terminal ⅛ inch long, ovoid to globose, obtuse, red-brown, glabrous.

BARK. Light ashy gray; typically irregularly plated with loose plates, but sometimes furrowed with narrow ridges.

WOOD. The most important species of oak; heavy, hard, and strong; heartwood light brown and quite durable; used for furniture, cooperage, finish, ties, etc.

SILVICAL CHARACTERS. Intermediate in tolerance; rather slow growing; long-lived, attaining ages of 600 years.

* * *

Bur Oak

Quercus macrocarpa Michx.

HABIT. A handsome medium-sized tree 60–80 feet high and 2–3 feet in diameter (max. 170 by 7 feet); crown rounded with large, heavy branches.

LEAVES. Deciduous; oblong to obovate; 6–12 inches long; characteristically 5–9-lobed, with rounded lobes, the 2 center sinuses nearly dividing the leaf into 2 halves; thick; dark green and lustrous above, paler and hairy below.

FRUIT. Maturing in one year; sessile or long-stalked; acorn ⅗–2 inches long, ellipsoidal, brown, enclosed for ⅓ to all of its length in a characteristic fringe-margined cup; inner surface of nut shell glabrous; kernel sweet.

TWIGS. Stout; yellow-brown to gray; often with characteristic corky wings. Winter buds: ⅛–¼ inch long, hairy.

BARK. Thick; gray-brown; deeply furrowed and ridged.

WOOD. Important; similar to *Q. alba*.

SILVICAL CHARACTERS. Similar to *Q. alba;* moist bottomlands to dry hills in northwest; extending farthest west of eastern oaks.

POST OAK

a.

b.

a. Fruit, x 1.
b. Leaf, x ¾.

OVERCUP OAK

a.

b.

a. Fruit, x 1.
b. Leaf, x ¾.

FAGACEAE

Post Oak

Quercus stellata Wangenh.

HABIT. A small to medium-sized tree 40–50 feet high and 1–2 feet in diameter (max. 100 by 4½ feet), on poor sites a shrub; crown rounded with few large branches.

LEAVES. Deciduous; oblong to obovate; 4–6 inches long; typically deeply 5-lobed with the rounded middle lobes opposite giving a crosslike appearance; thick; dark green above, tomentose below.

FRUIT. Maturing in one year; sessile or nearly so; acorn ½–⅔ inch long, red-brown, oval, enclosed for ⅓ length in thin-scaled, bowl-shaped cup; shell glabrous inside; kernel sweet.

TWIGS. More or less tomentose. Winter buds: ⅛ inch long, hairy.

BARK. Red-brown; otherwise similar to *Q. alba*.

WOOD. Important; similar to *Q. alba*.

SILVICAL CHARACTERS. Similiar to *Q. alba;* site varies from dry sandy plains to moist river bottoms; a variable species with several varieties and hybrids.

* * *

Overcup Oak

Quercus lyrata Walt.

HABIT. A tree 40–60 feet high and 2–3 feet in diameter (max. 100 by 5 feet); crown open and rounded with large, crooked branches.

LEAVES. Deciduous; oblong to obovate; 6–10 inches long; deeply 5–9 lobed with broad irregular sinuses and rounded lobes, giving the leaf an irregular, deeply cut appearance; dark green above, paler below and glabrous or white-hairy.

FRUIT. Maturing in one year; sessile or nearly so; acorn ½–1 inch long, chestnut-brown, subglobose; nearly enclosed in a deep, thin cup with unfringed margin; shell glabrous inside; kernel sweet.

TWIGS. Rather slender, gray, usually glabrous. Winter buds: ⅛ inch long, mostly woolly.

BARK. Similar to *Q. alba*.

WOOD. Important; similar to *Q. alba*.

SILVICAL CHARACTERS. Similar to *Q. alba;* typical of wet, poorly drained clay soils.

Fruiting twig, x ⅔.

BLUE OAK

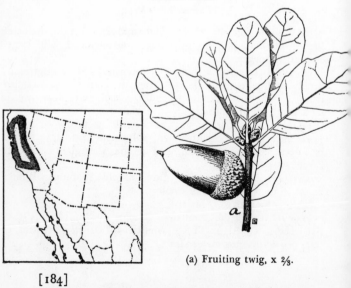

(a) Fruiting twig, x ⅔.

FAGACEAE

Gambel Oak

Quercus gambelii Nutt. (*Quercus utahensis* Rydb.) (*Quercus leptophylla* Rydb.) (*Quercus novomexicana* Rydb.)

HABIT. A shrub or small tree 25–35 feet high and 1 foot in diameter (max. 60 by 5 feet); crown open with thick, erect branches.

LEAVES. Deciduous; oblong to obovate; 2½–7 inches long; deeply 7–9 lobed with rounded lobes; thick; dark green above, paler and hairy below.

FRUIT. Maturing in one year; sessile or nearly so; acorn ⅗–¾ inch long; brown, ovoid; enclosed for about ¼–½ its length in thick-scaled, hairy cup; inner surface of nut shell glabrous.

TWIGS. Stout; orange-brown to red-brown; hairy. Winter buds: ⅛–¼ inch long, brown, hairy.

BARK. Similar to *Q. alba.*

WOOD. Unimportant; similar to *Q. alba;* used for fuel.

SILVICAL CHARACTERS. Similar to *Q. alba;* on dry foothills and canyon walls; the only abundant deciduous oak in the low Rocky Mountain forests; has been subdivided into several species by some authors.

* * *

Blue Oak

Quercus douglasii Hook. & Arn.

HABIT. A shrub to medium-sized tree 50–80 feet high and 2–3 feet in diameter; dense rounded crown.

LEAVES. Deciduous; oblong to obovate; 2–5 inches long; entire to sinuate-toothed to shallowly and irregularly 4–5 lobed; lobes and teeth rounded but often mucromate; dark blue-green above, paler and hairy below.

FRUIT. Maturing in one year; sessile or nearly so; acorn ¾–1¼ inches long, chestnut-brown, elliposoidal; enclosed at base in thin, shallow, hairy cup; inner surface of nut shell glabrous; kernel sweet.

TWIGS. Stout, red-brown. Winter buds: ⅛–¼ inch long, bright red.

BARK. Thin; gray; scaly; similar to *Q. alba.*

WOOD. Unimportant; similar to the red oaks and placed in that group by some authors.

SILVICAL CHARACTERS. Intolerant; on dry foothill sites.

CALIFORNIA WHITE OAK

a. Fruiting branch, x ⅔.

OREGON WHITE OAK

a. Fruiting branch, x ⅔.

FAGACEAE

California White Oak

Quercus lobata Nee

HABIT. The largest western oak, commonly 60–80 feet high and 3–5 feet in diameter (max. 125 by 9 feet); massive trunk dividing near the ground into large, spreading limbs; wide-spreading, drooping crown.

LEAVES. Deciduous; oblong to obovate; 2½–3½ inches long; deeply 7–11 lobed with rounded lobes; dark green and hairy above, pale and hairy below.

FRUIT. Maturing in one year; sessile or nearly so; acorn characteristic, 1¼–2¼ inches long, elongated-conic, green becoming brown; enclosed for ⅓ length in hairy cup with scales free at tip; inner surface of nut shell glabrous; kernel sweet.

TWIGS. Slender; gray to red-brown; hairy. Winter buds: ¼ inch long, orange-brown, ovoid, hairy.

BARK. Thick; light gray; scaly or broken into square plates.

WOOD. Unimportant; similar to *Q. alba.*

SILVICAL CHARACTERS. Similar to *Q. alba;* fast growing; fertile loams to poor dry soils.

* * *

Oregon White Oak

Quercus garryana Dougl.

HABIT. A tree 50–70 feet high and 2–3 feet in diameter (max. 120 by 8 feet); broad, compact crown with large branches.

LEAVES. Deciduous; oblong to obovate; 3–6 inches long; deeply 5–9 lobed with rounded lobes; thick and leather; dark · green above, paler and somewhat hairy below.

FRUIT. Maturing in one year; sessile or nearly so; acorn 1–1¼ inches long, ovoid; enclosed at base or to ⅓ of length in shallow cup with hairy, thickened scales; inner surface of nut shell glabrous; kernel sweet.

TWIGS. Stout; hairy and orange at first, becoming red-brown and glabrous. Winter buds: ⅓–½ inch long, densely woolly.

BARK. Similar to *Q. alba.*

WOOD. Unimportant; similar to *Q. alba.*

SILVICAL CHARACTERS. Similar to *Q. alba;* moist to dry sites; a low shrub in north and at higher altitudes.

CHESTNUT OAK

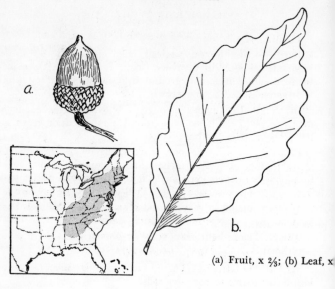

a.

b.

(a) Fruit, x ⅔; (b) Leaf, x

SWAMP CHESTNUT OAK

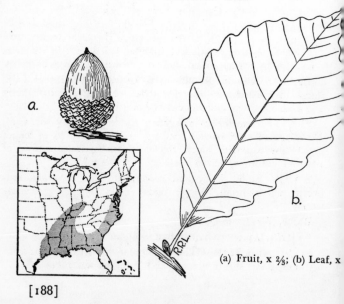

a.

b.

(a) Fruit, x ⅔; (b) Leaf, x

FAGACEAE

CHESTNUT OAK

Quercus prinus L. (*Quercus montana* Willd.)

HABIT. A medium-sized tree 50–70 feet high and 2–3 feet in diameter (max. 100 by 6½ feet); trunk often forking shortly above the ground into large ascending limbs; crown broad, open.

LEAVES. Deciduous; obovate to oblong-lanceolate; 4–9 inches long; coarsely serrate or crenate; yellow-green and lustrous above, paler and finely hairy below, petioles 1 inch long.

FRUIT. Maturing in one year; on short petioles; acorn 1–1½ inches long, ovoid, chestnut-brown, lustrous; enclosed for ½ or less of its length (sometimes only at base) in a thin, hairy cup; inner surface of nut shell glabrous; kernel sweet.

TWIGS. Stout; orange to red-brown. Winter buds: ¼–½ inch long, bright chestnut-brown, soft-hairy and ciliate.

BARK. Thick; dark red-brown to black; deeply furrowed with broad, rounded, scaly ridges; important source of tannin.

WOOD. Important; similar to *Q. alba.*

SILVICAL CHARACTERS. Similar to *Q. alba;* on poor, dry sites; in pure or mixed stands.

* * *

SWAMP CHESTNUT OAK

Quercus michauxii Nutt. (*Quercus prinus* L.)

HABIT. A medium-sized tree 60–80 feet high and 2–3 feet in diameter (max. 120 by 10 feet); straight, clear trunk; crown narrow, rounded, compact.

LEAVES. Deciduous; obovate; 5–8 inches long; coarsely dentate or crenate, often with gland-tipped teeth; dark green and lustrous above, silvery-white and hairy below, petioles ¾ inch long.

FRUIT. Maturing in one year; sessile or rarely stalked; acorn 1–1½ inches long, ovoid, bright brown; enclosed for ⅓ or less of its length in a thick, woolly cup with distinct wedge-shaped scales; inner surface of nut shell glabrous; kernel sweet.

TWIGS. Stout; orange to red-brown. Winter buds: ¼ inch long, ovoid, acute, red, thin hairy scales with pale margins.

BARK. Rather thick; ash-gray; scaly or irregularly furrowed with scaly, narrow ridges.

WOOD. Important; similar to *Q. alba.*

SILVICAL CHARACTERS. Similar to *Q. alba;* on moist to wet, often inundated, sites; in mixed stands.

Swamp White Oak

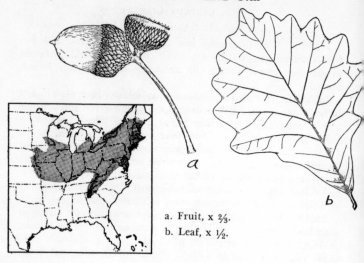

a. Fruit, x ⅔.
b. Leaf, x ½.

Chinkapin Oak

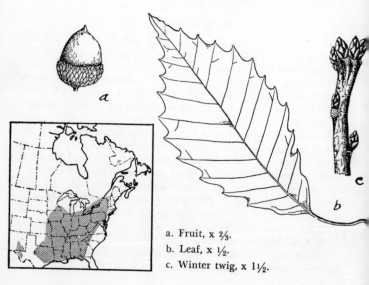

a. Fruit, x ⅔.
b. Leaf, x ½.
c. Winter twig, x 1½.

FAGACEAE

Swamp White Oak

Quercus bicolor Willd.

HABIT. A medium-sized tree 50–70 feet high and 2–3 feet in diameter (max. 100 by 5½ feet); trunk often limby; crown irregular, open.

LEAVES. Deciduous; obovate to oblong-obovate; 5–7 inches long; coarsely sinuate-crenate or dentate, or often shallowly and irregularly lobed; dark green and lustrous above, paler and slightly hairy to woolly below.

FRUIT. Maturing in one year; on characteristic stalks 1–4 inches long; acorn ¾–1¼ inches long, ovoid, light brown; enclosed for about ⅓ length in thick, light brown, fringed, hairy cup; inner surface of nut shell glabrous; kernel sweet.

TWIGS. Slender to rather stout; dark brown. Winter buds: ⅛ inch long, orange-brown, globose, nearly glabrous.

BARK. Thick; dark brown; deeply furrowed into blocky or long, scaly ridges; on younger parts separated into curly, papery scales.

WOOD. Moderately important; similar to *Q. alba*.

SILVICAL CHARACTERS. Similar to *Q. alba;* moist to wet sites.

* * *

Chinkapin Oak

Quercus muehlenbergii Engelm.

HABIT. A medium-sized tree 50–70 feet high and 1–3 feet in diameter (max. 160 by 4½ feet); narrow, rounded crown with rather short, ascending branches.

LEAVES. Deciduous; obovate to oblong-lanceolate; 4–7 inches long; coarsely serrate with gland-tipped teeth; thick; lustrous yellow-green above, paler and hairy below.

FRUIT. Maturing in one year; sessile or nearly so; acorn ½–¾ inch long, chestnut-brown to black, ovoid; enclosed for about ½ length in thin, hairy cup with small scales; inner surface of nut shell glabrous; kernel sweet.

TWIGS. Slender; orange to gray-brown; glabrous. Winter buds: ⅛ inch long, orange-brown, acute, conical.

BARK. Thin; ash-gray; roughly shallowly furrowed or scaly.

WOOD. Moderately important; similar to *Q. alba*.

SILVICAL CHARACTERS. Similar to *Q. alba;* often on dry sites.

Northern Red Oak

a. Fruit, x 1.
b. Leaf, x ½.
c. Flowering twig, x ½.
d. Staminate flower, enlarged.
e. Pistillate flower, enlarged.

Black Oak

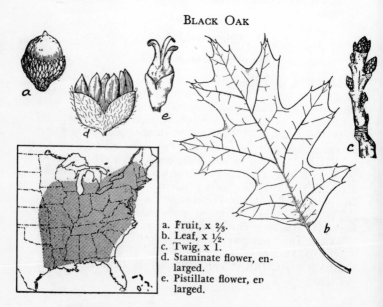

a. Fruit, x ⅔.
b. Leaf, x ½.
c. Twig, x 1.
d. Staminate flower, enlarged.
e. Pistillate flower, enlarged.

FAGACEAE

Northern Red Oak

Quercus rubra L. (*Quercus borealis* Michx.)

HABIT. A medium-sized tree 60–80 feet high and 2–4 feet in diameter (max. 150 by 6 feet); broad, rounded crown.

LEAVES. Deciduous; oblong to obovate; 5–9 inches long; 7–11 lobed with narrow sinuses extending half way to midrib; lobes toothed and bristle-tipped; dark green above, paler below; glabrous.

FRUIT. Maturing in 2 years; sessile or nearly so; acorn ½–1 inch long, pale brown, ovoid; enclosed at base or to ⅓ length in thick cup (the shallow cup form was known as var. *maxima*); inner surface of nut shell woolly; kernel bitter.

TWIGS. Stout; red-brown; lustrous. Winter buds: ¼ inch long.

BARK. Thick; nearly black; shallow furrows with wide, flat ridges; inner bark light red.

WOOD. Important; less strong and durable than *Q. alba*.

SILVICAL CHARACTERS. Moderately intolerant; sprouts vigorously; on moist sites; rather fast growing; in mixed stands; the variety *maxima* is no longer distinguished.

* * *

Black Oak

Quercus velutina Lam.

HABIT. A medium-sized tree 50–70 feet high and 2–3 feet in diameter (150 by 8 feet); irregular, rounded crown.

LEAVES. Deciduous; obovate to oblong; 5–9 inches long; 5–7 lobed with broad sinuses extending ⅔–⅞ of way to mid-rib; lobes toothed and bristle-tipped; dark green above, paler or coppery below with more or less scurfy pubescence.

FRUIT. Maturing in 2 years; sessile or nearly so; acorn ½–¾ inch long, red-brown, ovoid; enclosed for ⅓ or less in bowl-shaped cup of thin, loose, dull, woolly scales; inner surface of nut shell woolly; kernel bitter.

TWIGS. Stout; red-brown; glabrous. Winter buds; ¼–½ inch long, sharp-pointed, with woolly scales.

BARK. Thick; nearly black; deeply furrowed with narrow, scaly ridges; inner bark thick, yellow, very bitter.

WOOD. Important: similar to *Q. borealis*.

SILVICAL CHARACTERS. Moderately intolerant; similar to *Q. borealis;* on dry to good, moist sites.

[193]

SOUTHERN RED OAK

a. Fruit, x 1.
b. Leaf, x ¾.

SHUMARD OAK

a. Fruit, x 1.
b. Leaf, x ¾.

FAGACEAE

Southern Red Oak

Quercus falcata Michx. (*Quercus rubra* L. in part)

HABIT. A medium-sized tree 70–80 feet high and 2–3 feet in diameter (max. 120 by 7½ feet); large, rounded crown.

LEAVES. Deciduous; obovate to ovate; 5–10 inches long; lobed in 2 ways often found on same tree: (1). shallowly 3-lobed at apex, (2.) deeply and irregularly 5–7 lobed with falcate lobes; lobes bristle-tipped; dark green above, gray-green and white- or red-woolly below.

FRUIT. Maturing in 2 years; sessile or nearly so; acorn ½ inch long, orange-brown, subglobose; enclosed at base or to ⅓ length in thin, shallow cup with red-brown, hairy scales; inner surface of nut shell woolly; kernel bitter.

TWIGS. Stout; red-brown. Winter buds: ⅛–¼ inch long, red-brown.

BARK. Thick; nearly black; deeply furrowed with broad, scaly ridges (scaly in the important "cherry-bark" variety *pagodaefolia* Ell.); inner bark slightly yellow.

WOOD. Important (especially varieties); similar to *Q. borealis.*

SILVICAL CHARACTERS. Similar to *Q. velutina;* dry to wet sites.

* * *

Shumard Oak

Quercus shumardii Buckl.

HABIT. A large tree 80–100 feet high and 3–5 feet in diameter (max. 180 by 8 feet); open, wide-spreading crown.

LEAVES. Deciduous; obovate to oblong; 6–8 inches long; 5–7 lobed with sinuses extending more than half way to midrib; lobes toothed and bristle-tipped; dark green above, paler below; glabrous, except along midrib.

FRUIT. Maturing in 2 years; sessile or nearly so; acorn ¾–1¼ inches long, red-brown, ovoid; enclosed at base in thick, shallow cup with appressed scales; inner surface of nut shell woolly; kernel bitter.

TWIGS. Slender to stout; gray; glabrous. Winter buds: ¼ inch long, gray, ovoid, often angled.

BARK. Thick; deep, dark brown furrows, with scaly, pale gray ridges; on younger trees nearly black.

WOOD. Important; similar to *Q. borealis.*

SILVICAL CHARACTERS. Similar to *Q. velutina;* moist sites. Passing into the variety *texana* (Buckl.) Ashe in southern Oklahoma and central Texas.

SCARLET OAK

a. Fruit, x ⅔.
b. Leaf, x ½.
c. Twig, x 1.

BLACKJACK OAK

a. Fruit, x ⅔.
b. Leaf, x ½.
c. Flowering twig, x ½.

FAGACEAE

Scarlet Oak

Quercus coccinea Muenchh.

HABIT. A medium-sized tree 60–80 feet high and 1–3 feet in diameter (max. 100 by 4 feet); open, rounded crown.

LEAVES. Deciduous; obovate to oval; 3–7 inches long; deeply 5–9 lobed with wide circular sinuses; lobes toothed and bristle-tipped; bright, shiny green above, paler and glabrous below; turning brilliant scarlet in autumn.

FRUIT. Maturing in 2 years; sessile or nearly so; acorn ½–1 inch long, red-brown, subglobose, often with concentric rings near apex; enclosed for ½ length or less in thick cup with lustrous scales; inner surface of nut shell woolly; kernel bitter.

TWIGS. Slender; red-brown. Winter buds: ⅛–¼ inch long.

BARK. Similar to *Q. velutina*, but inner bark red, not bitter.

WOOD. Important; similar but inferior to *Q. borealis*.

SILVICAL CHARACTERS. Similar to *Q. velutina;* dry. sandy sites.

* * *

Blackjack Oak

Quercus marilandica Muenchh.

HABIT. A small, shrubby tree 20–30 feet high and ½–1 foot in diameter (max. 50 by 2½ feet); rounded, contorted crown.

LEAVES. Deciduous; variable, but typically obovate and more or less 3-lobed at the apex; 5–7 inches long; lobes entire or toothed, bristle-tipped; dark green and lustrous above, paler and surfy-pubescent below.

FRUIT. Maturing in 2 years; sessile or nearly so; acorn ¾ inch long, yellow-brown, subglobose; enclosed for ½ length in bowl-shaped cup with large, loose, red-brown, hairy scales; inner surface of nut shell woolly; kernel bitter.

TWIGS. Stout, red-brown. Winter buds: ¼ inch long, angled.

BARK. Thick; early black; divided into rough, square blocks.

WOOD. Unimportant; similar to *Q. borealis*.

SILVICAL CHARACTERS. Similar to *Q. velutina;* poor, dry sites.

Pin Oak

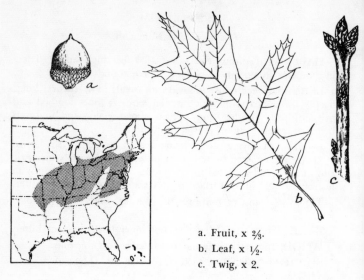

a. Fruit, x ⅔.
b. Leaf, x ½.
c. Twig, x 2.

Northern Pin Oak

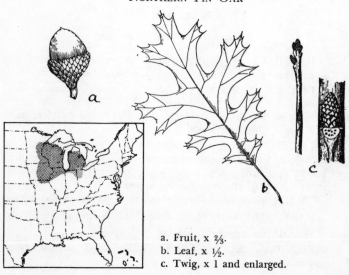

a. Fruit, x ⅔.
b. Leaf, x ½.
c. Twig, x 1 and enlarged.

FAGACEAE

Pin Oak

Quercus palustris Muenchh.

HABIT. A medium-sized tree 60–80 feet high and 1–3 feet in diameter (max. 120 by 6 feet); pyramidal crown with drooping lower branches which prune poorly.

LEAVES. Deciduous; obovate; 3–6 inches long; deeply 5–7 lobed with wide, rounded sinuses; lobes toothed and bristle-tipped; bright green and lustrous above, paler and glabrous below.

FRUIT. Maturing in 2 years; sessile or nearly so; acorn ½ inch long, hemispherical, light brown; enclosed at base in thin cup with red-brown, appressed, free-tipped scales; inner surface of nut shell woolly; kernel bitter.

TWIGS. Slender; red-brown. Winter buds: ⅛ inch long, red-brown.

BARK. Thick; gray-brown; long, smooth, finally scaly-ridged.

WOOD. Important; similar to *Q. borealis.*

SILVICAL CHARACTERS. Similar to *Q. velutina;* on moist sites; a common ornamental; is easily transplanted.

* * *

Northern Pin Oak

Quercus ellipsoidalis E. J. Hill

This species is similar to pin oak except for the ellipsoidal acorn ½–¾ inch long which is enclosed for ⅓–½ its length in bowl-shaped cup. From central Michigan and northern Ohio to eastern Iowa and southern Minnesota.

* * *

Nuttall Oak

Quercus nuttallii Palmer (*Quercus palustris* f. *nuttallii* Muller)

This species is similar to pin oak except for its oblong-ovoid acorn ¾–1¼ inches long which is enclosed for about ⅓ its length in a bowl-shaped cup and for the yellow axillary hairs on the lower surface of the leaf. Bottomlands of the Mississippi, Alabama, Tennessee, Missouri, Arkansas, Louisiana, Oklahoma, and Texas

CALIFORNIA BLACK OAK

a. Fruit, x 1.
b. Leaf, x 1.

TURKEY OAK

a. Fruit, x 1.
b. Leaf, x 1.

FAGACEAE

CALIFORNIA BLACK OAK
Quercus kelloggii Newb.

HABIT. A medium-sized tree 60–90 feet high and 2–4 feet in diameter (max. 130 by 9 feet); large, open, globose crown.

LEAVES. Deciduous; obovate; 3–8 inches long; deeply 5–7 lobed with rounded usually narrow sinuses; lobes usually toothed and bristle-tipped; dark yellow-green above, paler below; usually hairy.

FRUIT. Maturing in 2 years; short-stalked; acorn 1–1½ inches long, ellipsoidal, light chestnut-brown; enclosed for ⅓–¾ its length in bowl-shaped cup with thin, chestnut-brown, erose-margined scales; inner surface of nut shell woolly.

TWIGS. Slender to rather stout; red-brown. Winter buds: ¼ inch long, ovoid, chestnut-brown, ciliate on margins.

BARK. Thick, nearly black, divided by deep furrows into wide ridges; light brown and smooth on young stems.

WOOD. Unimportant; similar to *Q. borealis*.

SILVICAL CHARACTERS. Similar to *Q. velutina;* on dry, sandy soils.

* * *

TURKEY OAK
Quercus laevis Walt. (*Quercus catesbaei* Michx.)

HABIT. A small tree 20–30 feet high and 1–2 feet in diameter (max. 60 by 2½ feet); open, irregular crown.

LEAVES. Deciduous; variable and distinctive; 3–12 inches long (usually about 5); very deeply 3–5 lobed; lobes spreading and falcate, bristle-tipped; lustrous yellow-green above, paler below; glabrous except for tufts of red hairs in the axils of the veins.

FRUIT. Maturing in 2 years; short-stalked; acorn 1 inch long, oval, light brown; enclosed for about ⅓ its length in a thin, bowl-shaped, hairy cup; inner surface of nut shell woolly; kernel bitter.

TWIGS. Stout; red-brown; glabrous. Winter buds: ½ inch long, narrow, tapering, chestnut-brown, red-hairy.

BARK. Rather thick; nearly black; deeply furrowed with rough, scaly ridges.

WOOD. Unimportant; similar to *Q. borealis*.

SILVICAL CHARACTERS. Similar to *Q. velutina;* dry, sandy soils.

WILLOW OAK

a. Fruit, x 1.
b. Leaf, x 1.

WATER OAK

b.

a. Fruit, x 1.
b. Leaf, x 1.

FAGACEAE
WILLOW OAK
Quercus phellos L.

HABIT. A medium-sized tree 70–100 feet high and 2–4 feet in diameter (max. 130 by 7 feet); dense, rounded crown.

LEAVES. Deciduous; typically linear-lanceolate to ovate-lanceolate; 2–5 inches long; entire or wavy; acute with bristle tip; bright green above, paler and glabrous to hairy below.

FRUIT. Maturing in 2 years; sessile or nearly so; acorn not over ½ inch long, green-brown to yellow-brown, hemispherical; enclosed at base by shallow cup with thin, hairy, red-brown scales; inner surface of nut shell woolly; kernel bitter.

TWIGS. Slender; red-brown; glabrous. Winter buds: ⅛ inch long, sharp-pointed, chestnut-brown.

BARK. Rather thick, nearly black, and broken by deep furrows into rough ridges on old trunks; smooth and red-gray when young.

WOOD. Important; similar to *Q. borealis.*

SILVICAL CHARACTERS. Similar to *Q. velutina;* wet sites, commonly planted as ornamental.

* * *

WATER OAK
Quercus nigra L.

HABIT. A medium-sized tree 50–70 feet high and 2–3 feet in diameter (max. 125 by 6 feet); rounded, even crown.

LEAVES. Deciduous, though tardily so, as many remain green until later winter; extremely variable in shape, size, and margin; commonly spatulate, but also obovate to narrow-oblong; margin entire to shallowly 3-lobed at apex to deeply 5-7 lobed; 2–6 inches long; dull blue-green above, paler below; mostly glabrous.

FRUIT. Maturing in 2 years; sessile or nearly so; acorn ⅓–⅔ inch long, nearly black, subglobose; enclosed at base by shallow cup with thin, woolly scales; inner surface or nut shell woolly; kernel bitter, bright orange.

TWIGS. Slender; red-brown; glabrous. Winter buds: ⅛–¼ inch long, angled, sharp, with loose, red-brown scales.

BARK. Rather thin, gray-black, and broken by shallow furrows into wide, scaly ridges; smooth when young.

WOOD. Important; similar to *Q. borealis.*

SILVICAL CHARACTERS. Similar to *Q. velutina;* moist to wet sites; reproduces aggressively; common ornamental.

LAUREL OAK

(a) Fruit, x 1; (b) Leaf, x 1.

SHINGLE OAK

(a) Fruit, x 1; (b) Leaf, x ½.

FAGACEAE

Laurel Oak

Quercus laurifolia Michx.

HABIT. A medium-sized tree 50–70 feet high and 2–3 feet in diameter (max. 100 by 8 feet); dense, rounded crown.

LEAVES. Nearly evergreen, falling in early spring just before new leaves appear; elliptical to oblong-lanceolate; 2–4 inches long; entire or wavy, occasionally 3-lobed at apex; bristle-tipped; bright green above, paler below; glabrous.

FRUIT. Maturing in 2 years; sessile or nearly so; acorn 1/3–1/2 inch long, nearly black, hemispherical; enclosed at base by shallow cup with thin, red-brown, hairy scales; inner surface of nut shell woolly; kernel bitter.

TWIGS. Slender; red-brown; glabrous. Winter buds: 1/10–1/8 inch long, ovoid, pointed, with tight, bright red scales.

BARK. Thick, nearly black, deeply furrowed with broad, flat ridges; dark brown and smooth or scaly when young.

WOOD. Little used; similar to *Q. borealis.*

SILVICAL CHARACTERS. Similar to *Q. velutina;* moist sites; produces abundant seed corps; short-lived.

* * *

Shingle Oak

Quercus imbricaria Michx.

HABIT. A medium-sized tree 50–60 feet high and 2–3 feet in diameter (max. 4 feet); narrow, rounded crown.

LEAVES. Deciduous; oblong-lanceolate to oblong-obovate; and lustrous above, paler and hairy below.

FRUIT. Maturing in 2 years; usually short-stalked; acorn 1/2–3/4 inch long, chestnut-brown, ovoid; enclosed for 1/2 or less of length in bowl-shaped cup with thin, red-brown, appressed, hairy scales; inner surface of net shell woolly; kernel bitter.

TWIGS. Slender; green-brown. Winter buds: 1/8 inch long, brown.

BARK. Thick; gray-brown; shallowly furrowed and ridged.

SILVICAL CHARACTERS. Similar to *Q. velutina;* moist sites.

* * *

The bluejack oak, *Q. incana* Bartr., is a similar small tree of dry, sandy sites entending from Virginia to Florida and west to Texas. It is characterized by small elliptical leaves, blue-green above and white woolly below.

LIVE OAK

a. Leafy branch, x ⅔.
b. Different type of leaf, x ⅔.
c. Fruit, x ⅔.

MEXICAN BLUE OAK

(a) Leafy branch, x ⅔;   (b) Fruit, x ⅔.

FAGACEAE

Live Oak
Quercus virginiana Mill.

HABIT. A medium-sized tree 40–50 feet high and 3–4 feet in diameter (max. 80 by 11½ feet); trunk usually dividing near the ground into several large, horizontal limbs; crown dense and rounded with a span of 100–150 feet (max. 168 feet).

LEAVES. Persistent until new leaves appear; elliptical to oblong-obovate; 2–5 inches long; entire and wavy margin (rarely with few teeth); rounded tip; dark green above, paler and somewhat hairy below.

FRUIT. Maturing in one year; on stalks 1–5 inches long; acorn ¾–1 inch long, dark brown, ellipsoidal; enclosed for ⅓–½ its length in bowl-shaped cup with thin, red-brown, woolly scales; inner surface of nut shell glabrous; kernel sweet.

TWIGS. Slender; gray-brown; hairy. Winter buds: 1⁄16 inch long.

BARK. Rather thick; dark red-brown; shallowly furrowed with flat, scaly ridges.

WOOD. The only important live oak; diffuse porous; very heavy, hard, and strong; durable; used for ships, posts, etc.

SILVICAL CHARACTERS. Intolerant; typical of dry sites; long-lived; 3 varieties reach tree size.

* * *

Mexican Blue Oak
Quercus oblongifolia Torr.

HABIT. A shrub or small tree rarely 30 feet high and 18–30 inches in diameter; handsome, rounded crown.

LEAVES. Persistent until new leaves appear; ovate to elliptic; 1–2 inches long; entire or wavy with revolute margins (rarely coarsely toothed); blue-green above, paler and glabrous below.

FRUIT. Maturing in one year; sessile or rarely stalked; acorn ½–¾ inch long, chestnut-brown, ovoid to obovoid; enclosed for ⅓ length in bowl-like cup with thin, red-tipped, woolly scales; inner surface of nut shell glabrous; kernel sweet.

TWIGS. Slender; red-gray. Winter buds: 1⁄16–⅛ inch long, brown.

BARK. Thick; ash-gray; broken into nearly square, plate-like scales on old trunks.

SILVICAL CHARACTERS. Intolerant; on dry foothills.

ARIZONA WHITE OAK

a. Acorn, x 1.
b. Twig with leaves, x 1.
c. Different leaf forms, x 1.

EMORY OAK

a. Twig with leaves, x 1.
b. Fruit and leaf, x 1.

FAGACEAE

ARIZONA WHITE OAK

Quercus arizonica Sarg.

HABIT. A shrub or small tree rarely 60 feet high and 3 feet in diameter; handsome, round-topped crown with massive, contorted, nearly horizontal branches.

LEAVES. Persistent until appearance of new leaves; oblong-lanecolate to broadly ovate; 1–4 inches long (most about 2½); entire or with wavy, spiny teeth; revolute margin; dark blue-green above, paler and densely hairy below.

FRUIT. Maturing in one year; sessile or short-stalked; acorn ¾–1 inch long, chestnut-brown, oblong to obovoid; enclosed for ½ its length in deep cup with thick, corky, woolly, red-tipped scales; inner surface of nut shell glabrous; kernel sweet.

TWIGS. Stout; red-brown; red and hairy at first, becoming glabrous. Winter buds: ⅟₁₆ inch long, subglobose, brown, ciliate.

BARK. Rather thick; ash-gray; furrowed and scaly ridged.

SILVICAL CHARACTERS. Intolerant; on dry mountain slopes; the most common live oak in the Southwest.

* * *

EMORY OAK

Quercus emoryi Torr.

HABIT. A shrub or small tree rarely 60 feet high and 2–5 feet in diameter; round-topped, even crown with stout, drooping branches.

LEAVES. Persistent until appearance of new leaves; oblong-lanceolate; 1–2½ inches long; entire or remotely wavy toothed; leathery; dark green above, paler below; glabrous or slightly hairy.

FRUIT. Maturing in one year; sessile or nearly so; acorn ½–¾ inch long, nearly black, oblong to ovoid; enclosed for ⅓–½ its length in bowl-shaped cup with brown, hairy scales; inner surface of nut shell woolly; kernel sweet.

TWIGS. Slender; red and hairy at first, becoming dark brown and glabrous.

BARK. Thick; nearly black; deeply furrowed and scaly plated.

SILVICAL CHARACTERS. Intolerant; on dry foothills and mountains; very abundant; in pure or mixed stands; coppices freely; acorns important source of human and animal food.

INTERIOR LIVE OAK

a. Twig with leaves, x ⅔.
b. Twig with acorns, x ⅔.
c. Different shaped acorn, x ⅔.

CALIFORNIA LIVE OAK

a. Twig with leaves and acorns, x ¾

FAGACEAE

Interior Live Oak
Quercus wislizenii A. DC.

HABIT. Commonly shrubby though becoming a medium-sized tree 60–80 feet high and 2–4 feet in diameter (max. 100 by 6½ feet); wide, rounded crown with large spreading branches.

LEAVES. Persistent 2 years; lanceolate to broadly elliptic; 1–3 inches long (mostly about 1¼ inches); entire or with spiny teeth; leathery; glabrous; lustrous dark green above, paler below.

FRUIT. Maturing in 2 years; sessile or short-stalked; acorn 1–1½ inches long, chestnut-brown, slender-oblong, pointed; enclosed for ½ or less of its length in a bowl-shaped cup with thin, closely imbricated, ciliate scales; inner surface of nut shell woolly; kernel bitter.

TWIGS. Slender; dark brown. Winter buds: ⅛–¼ inch long, ovoid.

BARK. Thick; nearly black; deeply furrowed with scaly ridges.

SILVICAL CHARACTERS. Intolerant; slow growing; dry sites.

* * *

California Live Oak
Quercus agrifolia Née

HABIT. A medium-sized tree 50–75 feet high and 2–4 feet in diameter (max. 90 by 12½ feet); trunk dividing shortly above ground into several large, horizontal limbs which often rest on the ground; broad crown often 150 feet across.

LEAVES. Persistent until new leaves appear; oval or oblong to suborbicular; 1–3 inches long; margins entire to spiny toothed, revolute; leathery; lustrous dark green above, paler below; glabrous to hairy.

FRUIT. Maturing in one year; sessile or nearly so; acorn ¾–1½ inches long, chestnut-brown, slender-conic, pointed; enclosed for ⅓ of its length or only at base in bowl-shaped cup with thin, closely imbricated scales; inner surface of nut shell woolly; kernel bitter.

TWIGS. Slender; gray-brown. Winter buds: ¹⁄₁₆ inch long, globose.

BARK. Thick; nearly black; deeply furrowed with scaly ridges.

SILVICAL CHARACTERS. Intolerant; slow-growing; dry sites.

Canyon Live Oak

a. Twig with leaves, x ⅔.
b. Different form of leaves, x ⅔.
c. Acorn, x ⅔.

Silverleaf Oak

a. Twig with leaves and acorns, x ⅔.

FAGACEAE

Canyon Live Oak
Quercus chrysolepis Liebm.

HABIT. A shrub to medium-sized tree 60–80 feet high and 1–5 feet in diameter (max. 100 by 12 feet); usually dividing above the ground into large, horizontal branches; large, spreading crown; forming dense thickets on dry slopes.

LEAVES. Persistent 3–4 years; oblong-ovate to elliptic; 1–4 inches long; mostly entire on old trees and sinuate-dentate on young trees, or both forms appearing together; revolute margins; leathery; bright yellow-green and glabrous above; tawny-tomentose, becoming glabrous and blue-green below.

FRUIT. Maturing in 2 years; sessile or nearly so; acorn ½–2 inches long, chestnut-brown, ellipsoidal to ovate; enclosed at base in thick, shallow cup with hairy to golden-woolly scales; inner surface of nut shell woolly; kernel bitter.

TWIGS. Slender; brown to gray; woolly, sometimes becoming smooth. Winter buds: ⅛ inch, ovoid, acute, chestnut-brown.

BARK. Rather thick (¾–1½ inches); gray-brown, tinged with red; smooth except for small scales on old trunks.

SILVICAL CHARACTERS. Tolerant when young; long-lived; canyon walls to dry mountain slopes; passes into the variety *palmeri* (Engelm.) Sarg. in the Southwest.

* * *

Silverleaf Oak
Quercus hypoleucoides A. Camus (*Quercus hypoleuca* Engelm.)

HABIT. A shrub or small tree 20–30 feet high (rarely 60 feet) and 10–15 inches in diameter; narrow, rounded crown.

LEAVES. Persistent until appearance of new leaves; lanceolate to elliptic; 2–4 inches long; entire or with few coarse teeth near apex; revolute margins; leathery; dark yellow-green and lustrous above, woolly below.

FRUIT. Maturing in 2 years; sessile or short-stalked; acorn ½–⅔ inch long, chestnut-brown, ovoid; enclosed for ⅓ of its length in thick cup with thin, brown, silvery-hairy scales; inner surface of nut shell woolly; kernel bitter.

TWIGS. Stout; red-brown. Winter buds: ⅛ inch long, brown,

BARK. Rather thick (¾–1 inch); nearly black; deeply furrowed into broad, thick-scaled ridges.

SILVICAL CHARACTERS. Intolerant; on dry, low mountain sites.

ULMACEAE

THE ELMS

Characteristics of the Genus *Ulmus* L.

HABIT. Handsome trees often planted for shade or ornamental purposes; irregularly pinnate branching.

LEAVES. Alternate; simple; deciduous; lanceolate to obovate; stipulate; penniveined; simply or more commonly doubly serrate; 2-ranked; mostly unequal and oblique at the base and acuminate at the apex.

FLOWERS. Regular; perfect; small; in fasiccles or cymes; appearing before the leaves (in a few species not appearing until autumn); on slender, drooping pedicels; calyx 5–9 lobed; corolla absent; 4–6 stamens; ovary usually 1-celled by abortion, 1-ovuled, flattened, with a deeply 2-lobed style.

FRUIT. An oblong to suborbicular samara; maturing in the spring or autumn of the first year; surrounded at base by remnants of calyx; seed cavity compressed and surrounded by a thin papery wing which is commonly notched at the apex and tipped with the remnants of the persistent style.

TWIGS. Slender to stout; somewhat zigzag; with corky wings on some species; pith solid, round, Winter buds: terminal absent, lateral with overlapping scales.

BARK. Thick and furrowed; often with layers of 2 colors.

WOOD. Moderately important; heavy, hard, strong, and tough; ring-porous; not durable; difficult to split; specialized uses.

SILVICAL CHARACTERS. Rather tolerant trees; fast-growing; wide-spreading, lateral roots.

GENERAL. This genus contains about 20 species of trees scattered through the Northern Hemisphere; many are among our most important shade and ornamental trees. Six species are native to North America. Five exotic species which are commonly planted in this country are included in the key; of these *U. pumila*, which is widely grown in the central and western States, has been naturalized from Kansas to Minnesota.

KEY TO THE SPECIES OF ELMS

1. Leaves doubly serrate, unequal at base.
   2. Some of twigs with corky wings; fruit hairy, at least on margins; leaves not over 4 inches long.
      3. Buds and young twigs pale hairy; fruit appearing in spring, ovoid to suborbicular, hairy and ciliate, seed cavity not pronounced; leaves smooth above, hairy below; north from Kansas, Missouri, and Tennessee to Quebec and Ontario ....*U. thomasii*, **Rock Elm**, p. 219.
      3. Buds and young twigs glabrous or nearly so; fruit oblong, seed cavity pronounced; southern.
         4. Leaves 2–4″ long, acuminate, glabrous above, slightly hairy along veins below; fruit in fall, fringed on margin with long white hairs; Kansas and Illinois to Georgia and Oklahoma .... *U. serotina*, **September Elm**, p. 217.
         4. Leaves 1–2½″ long; fruit covered with long white hairs.
            5. Leaves acuminate, coarsely doubly toothed, smooth above and hairy below; fruit in spring; Indiana and Virginia to Kansas and south ....*U. alata*, **Winged Elm**, p. 217.
            5. Leaves rounded or acute at apex, unequally doubly toothed, almost singly toothed; roughened above and hairy below; fruit in fall; Arkansas to Mississippi and Texas .... *U. crassifolia*, **Cedar Elm**, p. 217.
   2. Twigs without corky ridges; fruit appearing in spring; seed cavity distinct.
      6. Fruit hairy or ciliate; buds glabrous or with rusty hairs; leaves usually 4–7″ long, rough on top.
         7. Buds with rusty hairs; fruit hairy over seed cavity; leaves rough on both surfaces; bark of trunk dark red-brown; Quebec to North Dakota and south to Florida .... *U. rubra*, **Slippery Elm**, p. 219.
         7. Buds glabrous; fruit hairy only on margin; leaves rough above; bark of trunk with alternating gray and brown layers; Newfoundland to Saskatchewan and south to Florida .... *U. americana*, **American Elm**, p. 217.
      6. Fruit glabrous; buds pale hairy or glabrous; European ornamentals.
         8. Twigs hairy; leaves rough above; petioles ⅛–¼″ long.
            9. Leaves 2–3″ long; petioles 1/6–1/4″ long; bark gray, furrowed; seed near apex of fruit .... *U. procera* Salisb., **English Elm**
            9. Leaves 3–6½″ long; petioles ⅛″ long; bark dark, remaining smooth many years; seed near center of fruit .... *U. glabra* Huds., **Wych Elm**
         8. Twigs glabrous; leaves 2–3″ long; smooth above; petioles ¼–½″ long . . *U. carpinifolia* Gled., **Smooth-leaved Elm**
1. Leaves ¾–3″ long, singly or nearly singly serrate, nearly equal at base, fruit glabrous; Asiatic ornamentals.
   10. Leaves ¾–2″ long, predominately rounded to acute at apex; fruit in fall, ovate, notched at apex .... *U. parvifolia* Jacq., **Chinese Elm**
   10. Leaves 1–3″ long, predominately acuminate to acute at apex; fruit in spring, suborbicular, with closed notch .... *U. pumila* L., **Siberian Elm**

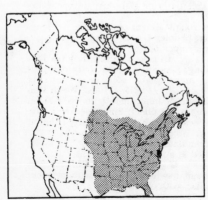

a. Winter twig, x 2.

b. Leaf, x ½.

c. Flowering branchlet, x ½.

d. Flower, enlarged.

e. Fruit, x 2.

ULMACEAE

American Elm. White Elm

Ulmus americana L.

HABIT. A handsome tree 75–100 feet high and 3–6 feet in diameter (max. 120 by 10 feet); open grown trees commonly dividing near the ground into several ascending limbs forming a vase-shaped crown; perhaps our most common ornamental species.

LEAVES. Oblong-obovate to oval; 4–6 inches long; coarsely doubly serrate; thick and firm; base conspicuously oblique; dark green and more or less rough above; paler below.

FRUIT. A smooth, oval to ovate samara ½ inch long, ciliate on margins and deeply notched at apex; seed cavity distinct; in long-stalked fasicles; maturing in late spring.

TWIGS. Slender; round; red-brown; hairy at first becoming glabrous. Winter buds: lateral ¼ inch long, chestnut-brown, acute.

BARK. Thick; ash-gray; variable, but typically diamond-shaped by furrows; alternate light and dark layers in outer bark.

WOOD. The most important of the elms.

SILVICAL CHARACTERS. Moderately tolerant; shallow-rooted; typical of moist sites, but hardy and widely planted on dry shelterbelts; seriously threatened by Dutch Elm disease; with mixed hardwoods.

* * *

Three unimportant elms are found in the Southeast; all of these are characterized by having corky wings on the twigs and small leaves. They are distinguished in the key.

1. Winged elm, *Ulmus alata* Michx., flowers and fruits in the spring; it is characterized by doubly serrate leaves 1–2½ inches long and hair-covered fruit ⅓ inch long with a distinct seed cavity.
2. Cedar elm, *Ulmus crassifolia* Nutt., flowers and fruits in the fall; it is characterized by nearly singly-toothed leaves 1–2½ inches long with rounded to acute apex and hair-covered fruit ⅓–½ inch long with a distinct seed cavity.
3. September elm, *Ulmus serotina* Sarg., flowers and fruits in the fall; it is characterized by acuminate leaves 2–4 inches long and fruit ciliate with white hairs.

[217]

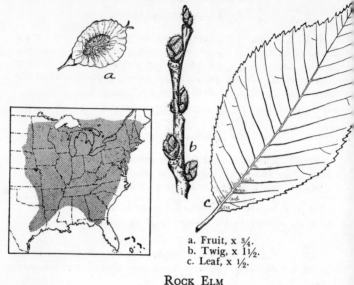

a. Fruit, x ¾.
b. Twig, x 1½.
c. Leaf, x ½.

ROCK ELM

a. Fruit, x ¾.
b. Twig, x 1 and enlarged.
c. Leaf, x ¾.

ULMACEAE

SLIPPERY ELM

Ulmus rubra Muhl. (*Ulmus fulva* Michx.)

HABIT. A medium-sized tree 40–70 feet high and 1–2 feet in diameter (max. 5 feet); clear trunk; rounded, open crown with spreading branches and ascending twigs.

LEAVES Oblong-obovate to oval; 4–7 inches long; coarsely doubly serrate; thick and firm; base conspicuously oblique; dark green and rough above; paler and rough below.

FRUIT. A suborbicular samara about ¾ inch long; seed cavity distinct, brown-woolly; wings and margins smooth; apex entire or nearly so; in short-stalked fascicles; maturing in spring.

TWIGS. Rather stout; ash-gray; rough. Winter buds: lateral ¼ inch long, nearly black, hairy.

BARK. Thick; dark red-brown; nearly parallel furrows; without alternate light and dark layers; inner bark mucilaginous.

SILVICAL CHARACTERS. Moderately tolerant; wide lateral roots; with mixed hardwoods; varied sites.

* * *

ROCK ELM. CORK ELM

Ulmus thomasii Sarg. (*Ulmus racemosa* Thomas)

HABIT. A handsome medium-sized tree 60–80 feet high and 2–3 feet in diameter (max. 100 by 5½ feet); trunk persisting into crown; narrow crown with drooping lower branches.

LEAVES. Obovate to oval; 2½–5 inches long; coarsely doubly serrate; thick and firm; base nearly equal; dark green and usually glabrous above; paler and slightly hairy below.

FRUIT. An obovate to oval samara ¾–1 inch long, hairy all over; seed cavity indistinct; apex shallowly notched; margins ciliate; in racemose cymes on long slender stalks; maturing in spring.

TWIGS. Rather stout; red-brown; usually developing corky wings. Winter buds: lateral ¼ inch long, brown, acute, downy-ciliate.

BARK. Thick; dark gray-brown; deeply and irregularly furrowed; alternate light and dark layers in outer bark.

SILVICAL CHARACTERS. Intermediate in tolerance; wide lateral roots; with mixed hardwoods; varied sites; poor reproduction.

ULMACEAE

The Hackberries

Characteristics of the Genus *Celtis* L.

HABIT. Shrubs or trees often planted for shade or ornamentals; irregularly pinnate branching.

LEAVES. Alternate; simple; lanceolate to ovate; acute or acuminate at apex; often oblique at base; serrate or entire margins; membranaceous or subcoriaceous; deciduous; mostly long petiolate; stipules thin, caducous, fugacious, enclosing leaf in bug.

FLOWERS. Regular polygamo-monoecious or rarely monoecious; minute; the staminate in fascicles toward the base of twig; above these the pistillate or perfect, solitary or in few-flowered fascicles; pedicellate; appearing soon after the unfolding of the leaves; calyx 4–5 lobed, green-yellow, deciduous; corolla absent; stamens as many as calyx lobes and opposite them; ovary 1-celled, ovoid, sessile, green and lustrous.

FRUIT. Subglobose or ovoid drupe; tipped with remnants of style; thick firm skin; thin, pulpy flesh; nutlet bony, thick-walled, reticulate-pitted; ripening in autumn and often remaining long after leaves fall. Seed: filling cavity in nutlet.

TWIGS. Round; unarmed or spinose. Winter buds: terminal absent; lateral small, scaly; branchlets prolonged by an upper lateral bud.

BARK. Usually gray and smooth, sometimes with conspicuous, corky, warty excrescenses.

WOOD. Rather heavy; fairly hard; not strong; odorless; ring-porous; moderately important; often sold as elm.

GENERAL. This genus consists of about 70 species scattered through the north temperate and tropical regions; 5 tree species and several varieties have been listed for the United States; native species often disfigured by gall-making insects distorting the buds and producing broomlike clusters of branchlets; this genus is in a confused state and needs revision; distributions have not been accurately determined.

KEY TO THE SPECIES OF HACKBERRIES

1. Fruit dark purple, on pedicels somewhat longer than leaf petioles; leaves 2½–4 inches long, usually sharply serrate with numerous teeth, green on both surfaces, without conspicuous reticulate veinlets on lower surface.......*C. occidentalis*, **Hackberry**, p. 223.
1. Fruit orange to red-brown to yellow; leaves entire or sparingly toothed.
    2. Fruit on pedicels much longer than leaf petioles; leaves 1½–3 inches long with conspicuous reticulate veinlets below.
        3. Leaves broadly ovate, green below; fruit yellow to orange-red..............*C. reticulata*, **Netleaf Hackberry**, p. 225.
        3. Leaves oblong-ovate, pale below; fruit dark red-brown; Texas.......*C. lindheimeri*, **Lindheimer Hackberry**, p. 223.
    2. Fruit on pedicels shorter or but little longer than leaf petioles; leaves without conspicuous reticulate veinlets below.
        4. Leaves mostly oblong-lanceolate, long-acuminate, 2–5 inches long; fruit yellow to orange-red........................ ....*C. laevigata*, **Sugarberry**, p. 225.
        4. Leaves ovate-lanceolate, short-acuminate, 1½–2½ inches long; fruit dark orange-red to red-purple................. ....*C. tenuifolia*, **Georgia Hackberry**, p. 223.

* * *

PLANERTREE. WATERELM

Planera aquatica Gmel.

This is a small, rare monotypic tree growing in swampy sites on the coastal plain and river valleys from North Carolina to Missouri and south. It is characterized by elmlike leaves which are 2–3¼ inches long and crenate-serrate and a peculiar prickly drupe ⅓ inch long which is covered with odd plates and processes.

a. Winter twig, x 1.

b. Portion of twig, enlarged.

c. Leaf, x ¾.

d. Flowering branchlet, x ½.

e. Staminate flower, enlarged.

f. Pistillate flower, enlarged.

g. Fruit, x 1.

ULMACEAE

HACKBERRY
Celtis occidentalis L.

HABIT. Occasionally shrubby, but often a rather large tree 100–120 feet high and 1–2 feet in diameter (max. 130 by 5 feet); crown rounded and of large, spreading branches.

LEAVES. Ovate to ovate-lanceolate; 2½–4 inches long; long-acuminate apex; obliquely rounded base; coarsely serrate or rarely almost entire; rather thin; light, dull green and rough above, slightly paler and pilose along veins below; turning light yellow in autumn; petioles ¼–½ inch long.

FRUIT. ⅓ inch in diameter; subglobose, ovoid, or obovoid; dark purple; on stems ½–¾ inch long; thick, tough skin; dark orange-colored flesh; oblong, pointed, light brown nutlet with prominently reticulated pit.

TWIGS. Slender; ridged; light brown, becoming darker; pubescent or glabrous; marked by pale, oblong lenticels; pith finely chambered at nodes. Winter buds: ¼ inch long, ovoid, pointed, pubescent, chestnut-brown.

BARK. Rather thick (1–1½ inches); dark brown; smooth, or more or less roughened by irregular wartlike excrescensces or by long ridges.

SILVICAL CHARACTERS. Intermediate intolerance; rapid growing; lateral roots; the largest and most handsome member of the genus; frequently planted in west because of drouth resistance; adapted to variety of sites, doing best on moist, rich soils, and stunted and scraggly on poor, dry sites.

* * *

LINDHEIMER HACKBERRY
Celtis lindheimeri Engelm.

This is a small tree native only to Texas and quite similar to netleaf hackberry. Identifying characters are included in the key.

* * *

GEORGIA HACKBERRY
Celtis tenuifolia Nutt. (Celtis pumila var. georgiana (Small) Sarg.)

This shrub or small tree is found on hills from New Jersey to Florida and Alabama and less commonly in Illinois, Missouri, Oklahoma, and Arkansas. Identifying characters are included in the key.

a. Twig with fruit and leaves, x ⅓.
b. Twig with winter buds, x ⅓.
c. Fruit, x 1.
d. Staminate flowers, x 1.

Netleaf Hackberry

a. Leaf, x ⅔.
b. Fruit, x 1.
c. Twig with fruit and leaves, x ⅓.

ULMACEAE

Sugarberry. Sugar Hackberry

Celtis laevigata Willd. (*Celtis mississippiensis* Bosc)

HABIT. A medium-sized tree 60–80 feet high and 2–3 feet in diameter (max. 5 feet); crown rounded with spreading branches.

LEAVES. Oblong-lanceolate; 2–5 inches long; acuminate apex; obliquely rounded or cordate at base; entire or irregularly and sparingly toothed; thin; light green and smooth or slightly rough above; smooth below, with veinlets not conspicuous; petioles ¼–½ inch long.

FRUIT. ¼ inch long; subglobose; dark orange-red; on pedicels shorter or slightly longer than leaf petioles.

BARK. Rather thin (⅓–⅔ inch thick); pale gray; covered with prominent wartlike excrescences.

SILVICAL CHARACTERS. Intermediate in tolerance; rapid growing; lateral roots; site varies from moist stream banks to the variety *texana* (Scheele) Sarg. on dry rocky bluffs in West.

* * *

Netleaf Hackberry

Celtis reticulata Torr. (*Celtis douglasii* Planch.) (*Celtis laevigata* var. *brevipes* Sarg.)

HABIT. A shrub or small tree rarely 30 feet high and 1 foot in diameter; crown open with stout, ascending branches.

LEAVES. Broadly ovate; 1¼–3 inches long; acute or acuminate tips; obliquely rounded at base; margins entire or with a few coarse teeth; thick; dark green and rough or smooth above; paler below with conspicuous reticulate veinlets: petioles ⅛–½ inch long.

FRUIT. ¼ inch long; subglobose; orange-red to yellow; on pedicels longer but not twice as long as leaf petiles.

BARK. Thick; red-brown to ash-gray; rough with prominent, short, projecting ridges.

SILVICAL CHARACTERS. Moderately intolerant; on dry, rocky hillsides; a confused species including many forms previously considered distinct.

a. Winter twig, x 1.

b. Twig, enlarged.

c. Leaf, x ½.

d. Staminate flowers, x 1.

e. Flower, enlarged.

f. Pistillate flowers, x 1

g. Flower, enlarged.

h. Fruit, x 1.

[226]

MORACEAE

RED MULBERRY
Morus rubra L.

HABIT. A small tree 20–40 feet high and 8–15 inches in diameter (max. 70 by 3½ feet); dense, round-topped crown.

LEAVES. Alternate; simple; suborbicular; 3–5 inches long; unlobed or deeply 1–3 lobed; margins coarsely serrate; thin; deciduous; dark blue-green and smooth or rough above; paler and more or less hairy below.

FLOWERS. Monoecious or dioecious; minute; appearing with the leaves; in dense spikes; calyx 4-lobed, green; corolla absent.

FRUIT. Drupaceous, enclosed in thickened, berry-like calyx and united into a multiple fruit (syncarp) which resembles a blackberry; 1–1¼ inches long; purple; oblong; edible.

TWIGS. Slender; brown; smooth. Winter buds: terminal absent, lateral ovoid, acute, lustrous, ¼ inch long, light brown.

BARK. Thin; dark brown tinged with red; scaly and furrowed.

WOOD. Rather heavy and hard; ring-porous; dark; unimportant.

SILVICAL CHARACTERS. Tolerant; on rich, moist sites; taproot.

* * *

The 2 native and 3 naturalized mulberries can be separated by the following characters:

1. Fruits ovoid to cylindric; buds with 3–6 outer scales.......*Morus*
    2. Leaves usually rough above, hairy below, usually undivided on old shoots, 2½–6 inches long.
        3. Leaves truncate or slightly heart-shaped at base; fruit dark purple at maturity; native.....*M. rubra* L., **Red Mulberry**
        3. Leaves deeply heart-shaped at base; fruit dark red; Asiatic ....*M. nigra* L., **Black Mulberry**
    2. Leaves smooth above, nearly glabrous below, variously lobed.
        3. Leaves 2½–7 inches long, lustrous; fruit white, pink, or violet; Chinese.............*M. alba* L., **White Mulberry**
        3. Leaves 1–2 inches long; fruit nearly black; Arizona to west Texas.............*M. microphylla* Buckl., **Texas Mulberry**
1. Fruits globose, orange-red; buds with 2–3 outer scales; leaves 1–3 lobed, 3–8 inches long, velvety hairy below; Asiatic......... ....*Broussonetia papyrifera* (L.) Nent., **Paper-mulberry**

a. Winter twig, x 1.
b. Twig, enlarged.
c. Leaf, x ½.
d. Staminate flowers, x ½.
e. Flower, enlarged.
f. Pistillate flowers, x ½.
g. Flower, enlarged.
h. Fruit, x ¼.

MORACEAE

Osage-orange

Maclura pomifera (Raf.) Schneid. (*Toxylon pomiferum* Raf.)

HABIT. A small tree 20–30 feet high and 1–2 feet in diameter (max. 65 by 6 feet); rounded open crown with few large, curving branches; extensively planted for hedges and ornamentals.

LEAVES. Alternate; simple; ovate to oblong-lanceolate; 3–5 inches long; long-pointed apex; entire; thick and firm; deciduous; dark green and shining above, paler and smooth below.

FLOWERS. Dioecious; minute; appearing after the leaves; the male in dense racemes and the female in dense, globose heads; calyx 4-lobed, hairy; corolla absent.

FRUIT. Drupaceous; numerous small drupes crowded and grown together into a multiple fruit resembling an orange; 4–5 inches in diameter; pale green; containing a bitter, milk, juice; becoming woody.

TWIGS. Stout; orange-brown; armed with straight, stout, axillary spines about ½ inch long. Winter buds: terminal absent; lateral small, globular, brown, depressed and partially embedded in the bark.

BARK. Thin; dark orange-brown; furrowed; with flat ridges.

WOOD. Hard and heavy; tough; durable; ring-porous; bright orange; used for bows; a yellow dye is extracted from the roots.

SILVICAL CHARACTERS. Intolerant; a monotypic genus with a small natural distribution, but now widely planted throughout much of the United States.

* * *

Fig

Ficus L.

Two species of fig are native to southern Florida, *Ficus aurea* Nutt., the Florida strangler fig, and *Ficus laevigata* Vahl, the shortleaf fig. *Ficus carica* L. of western Asia is often cultivated for fruit and sometimes found as an escape in the southern states.

MAGNOLIACEAE

THE MAGNOLIAS

Characteristics of the Genus *Magnolia* L.

HABIT. Handsome trees with straight stems and round-topped, pyramidal crowns; frequently planted as ornamentals.

LEAVES. Simple; alternate; deciduous or persistent; margins entire; unlobed; sometimes auriculate at base; mostly large and thin and very conspicuous.

FLOWERS. Perfect; appearing after the leaves; large and usually showy; terminal and solitary; sepals 3; petals 6–15, in series of 3, white or yellow to greenish; stamens and pistils spirally arranged, numerous.

FRUIT. A large, conelike aggregate of spirally arranged follicles; each follicle 1–2 seeded, the seed drupelike with a scarlet, fleshy outer coat, and suspended from the cone by a long slender thread at maturity.

TWIGS. Stout; round; aromatic and somewhat bitter tasting; pith homogeneous or nearly so, round; conspicuously marked by large leaf scars and narrow stipular rings. Winter buds: terminal present, large, with a single outer scale, the bud scales being large, membranaceous stipules which are adnate to the base of the petiole and deciduous with the unfolding of each successive leaf.

BARK. Ash-gray or brown; smooth or scaly.

WOOD. Rather light and soft; diffuse-porous; light yellow-brown heartwood; unimportant except for cucumbertree, the wood of which is often sold for yellow-poplar, and southern magnolia.

SILVICAL CHARACTERS. Intolerant; fairly rapid growth; short-lived; deep, wide root systems; typical of moist forest sites; in mixture with other hardwoods.

GENERAL. About 35 species of magnolia are native to Asia and North America, with 8 species native to the United States. Numerous native and Asiatic species are commonly planted through the southern part of the United States as ornamentals for their showy flowers, which in some species are over a foot in diameter.

KEY TO THE SPECIES OF MAGNOLIA

1. Leaves evergreen, persistent 2 years, thick and leathery, 5–8 inches long, densely red-hairy below; fruit, buds, and twigs densely red or white-hairy; flowers white, fragrant, 7–8 inches across; North Carolina to Florida, west to Texas and Arkansas.............. ....*M. grandiflora* L., **Southern Magnolia**, p. 233.
1. Leaves deciduous (in Sweetbay semi-evergreen in the south); parts not densely red-hairy.
   2. Leaves 4–10 inches long.
      3. Leaves obovate-spatulate, auriculate at base; buds, twigs, and lower leaf surface glabrous; flowers creamy white; Georgia and Florida west to Louisiana................... ....*M. pyramidata* Bartr., **Pyramid Magnolia**
      3. Leaves elliptic to oblong-obovate; buds and lower leaf surfaces usually white-hairy.
         4. Leaves oblong-ovate to elliptic; flowers greenish or yellow; styles deciduous from follicles of fruit................. ....*M. acuminata* L., **Cucumbertree**, p. 233.
         4. Leaves oblong-lanceolate to elliptic, 4–6 inches long; flowers white; styles persistent on follicles of fruit; Massachusetts to Pennsylvania and Tennessee, south to Florida, west to Texas.......*M. virginiana* L., **Sweetbay**
   2. Leaves 10–30 inches long; styles persistent on follicles of fruit.
      5. Leaves, buds, and fruit glabrous.
         6. Leaves obovate-lanceolate, wedge-shaped at base, 18–20 inches long; flowers white; Pennsylvania to Ohio, Missouri, Oklahoma and south......................... ....*M. tripetala* L., **Umbrella Magnolia**
         6. Leaves obovate-spatulate, auriculate at base, 10–12 inches long; flowers pale yellow; Virginia and Kentucky to Alabama and Georgia....*M. fraseri* Walt., **Fraser Magnolia**
      5. Leaves, buds, and fruit hairy.
         7. Leaves silvery hairy on lower surface, obovate, heart-shaped at base, 20–30 inches long; fruit ovoid to globose; North Carolina to Kentucky and Arkansas, south to Florida and Louisiana............................ ....*M. macrophylla* Michx., **Bigleaf Magnolia**
         7. Leaves hairy on midrib of lower surface, obovate-spatulate, 16–22 inches long; fruit ovoid cylindric; western Florida and Texas...*M. ashei* Weatherby, **Ash Magnolia**

a. Twig, x ⅔.
b. Leaf, x ⅓.
c. Fruit, x ⅓.

SOUTHERN MAGNOLIA

a. Flower, x ⅙.
b. Leaf, x ½.
c. Fruit, x ⅓.

[232]

MAGNOLIACEAE

CUCUMBERTREE. CUCUMBER MAGNOLIA
Magnolia acuminata L.

HABIT. A medium-sized tree 70–90 feet high and 3–4 feet in diameter (max. 100 by 6 feet); clear, straight bole; pyramidal crown with small branches.

LEAVES. Deciduous; broadly elliptical to ovate; 6–10 inches long; acute to acuminate at apex; rounded to broadly wedge-shaped at base; margin entire or slightly repand; thin; bright yellow-green and glabrous above; paler and glabrous to hairy below.

FLOWERS. Yellow-green; 2–3 inches long; not showy.

FRUIT. Conelike aggregate of follicles, cylindric to ovoid, 2–3 inches long, glabrous. Seed; ½ inch long, red, suspended on slender, white thread.

TWIGS. Moderately stout; lustrous. Winter buds: terminal ½–¾ inch long, with white silvery hairs, lateral smaller.

BARK. Thin; dark brown; shallowly furrowed with narrow scaly ridges.

GENERAL. The rare and local variety *cordata* (Michx.) Sarg., with yellow flowers and hairy twigs ranges from central North Carolina to central Georgia.

* * *

SOUTHERN MAGNOLIA. EVERGREEN MAGNOLIA
Magnolia grandiflora L.

HABIT. A medium-sized tree 60–80 feet high and 2–3 feet in diameter (max. 135 by 4½ feet); clear, straight bole; pyramidal crown with small spreading branches.

LEAVES. Persistent 2 years; narrowly oval to ovate; 5–8 inches long; acute to acuminate at apex; wedge-shaped at base; margin entire; thick and leathery; bright green and lustrous above; at maturity red-woolly below.

FLOWERS. White; showy and fragrant; 6–8 inches in diameter; with 6–12 large petals.

FRUIT. Conelike aggregate of follicles, ovoid, 3–4 inches long; red-woolly. Seed: ½ inch long, red, suspended on slender white thread.

TWIGS. Stout; red-woolly. Winter buds: terminal 1–1½ inches long, white- or red-woolly, lateral smaller.

BARK. Thin; gray to light brown; on old stems scaly with small scales rarely over 1 inch in length.

[233]

a. Leaf, x ½.

b. Flower, x ½.

c. Opened fruit, x ½.

d. Twig, x 1.

e. Seed, x 1.

MAGNOLIACEAE

Yellow-poplar. Tuliptree
Liriodendron tulipifera L.

HABIT. A large, handsome tree 80–100 feet high and 4–6 feet in diameter (max. 198 by 12 feet); clear straight bole; open, oblong or conical crown with small branches.

LEAVES. Simple; alternate; deciduous; suborbicular; 4–6 inches long; characteristically 4-lobed resembling a tulip in outline; lobes entire margined; truncate at base and truncate or notched at apex; glabrous; lustrous dark green above, paler below; petioles slender, 5–6 inches long; stipules large, conspicuous.

FLOWERS. Perfect; appearing after the leaves; yellow-green; cup-shaped; 1½–2 inches long; 3 sepals; 6 petals in 2 rows; stamens and pistils numerous and spirally arranged around a central axis.

FRUIT. A large (2½–3 inches long) erect, conelike aggregate of spirally arranged samaras; each samara 1½ inches long, 4-angled, terminally winged, deciduous from the slender, more or less persistent, central axis.

TWIGS. Rather stout; lustrous red-brown; bitter; pith round, diaphragmed. Winter buds: terminal present, about ½ inch long, flattened, dark red, with valvate stipular scales only 2 outer scales being visible, the entire bud resembling a duck's bill.

BARK. Smooth and dark green on young stems; becoming thick, ash-gray, furrowed, and with rough, rounded ridges; inner bark bitter.

WOOD. Highly important and a valuable hardwood species; rather light and soft; light yellow to dark brown heartwood; easily worked; used for plywood, furniture, interior finish, and construction work.

SILVICAL CHARACTERS. Very intolerant; fast growing; reaching maturity at 200–250 years; deep, wide-spreading roots; in mixture with other hardwoods; typical of moist forest sites.

GENERAL. Only 2 species of this genus are now in existence, one a native of central China, *Liriodendron chinense* Sarg. The native species attains the greatest height of any of our broadleaf species and perhaps the greatest diameter.

a. Fruit, x 1.
b. Leaves, x 1.
c. Smaller leaves, x 1.

LAURACEAE

CALIFORNIA-LAUREL. OREGON-MYRTLE
Umbellularia californica (Hook. and Arn.) Nutt.

HABIT. A small to medium-sized tree 20–80 feet high and 1–3 feet in diameter (max. 175 by 12 feet); broad, rounded, dense crown; trunk often divided; shrubby on dry sites.

LEAVES. Alternate; simple; lanceolate to elliptical; 2–5 inches long; thick and leathery; entire; glabrous; persistent 2–6 years; spicy-scented; dark green and lustrous above, paler and dull below.

FLOWERS. Perfect; small; in umbels; appearing before the new leaves; calyx yellow-green, 6-parted; corolla absent.

FRUIT. An olive-like, acrid, yellow-green drupe about 1 inch in diameter; maturing in 1 year; surrounded at base by enlarged lobes of calyx; seed ovoid, light brown.

TWIGS. Slender; yellow-green; glabrous; aromatic. Winter buds: terminal present, minute, naked.

BARK. Rather thin; dark brown; with tight scales; smooth and gray-green on branches.

WOOD. Rather hard and heavy; diffuse-porous; fine textured; lustrous light brown; expensive and highly valued for furniture, finish and novelties; sold under the name of myrtle wood.

SILVICAL CHARACTERS. Moderately tolerant; deep, wide-spreading, fleshy roots; on varied sites, but best growth on moist bottomlands; a monotypic genus.

* * *

ANNONACEAE

PAWPAW
Asimina triloba (L.) Dunal

This distinctive shrub or small tree is found scattered throughout the eastern United States. It is characterized by a banana-like fruit, which is a cylindric, yellow-green, edible berry 3–5 inches long and containing numerous seeds about 1 inch long; simple, alternate, deciduous, entire, membranaceous leaves 10–12 inches long and 4–6 inches wide; large, perfect flowers with 3 sepals and 6 petals; slender, glabrous twigs with small, red-woolly, naked buds; and thin, dark brown bark, containing whitish blotches and wartlike protuberances.

[237]

SASSAFRAS

a. Pistillate flowers, x ½.
b. Fruit, x ½.
c. Staminate flowers, x ½.
d. Leaves, x ½.

REDBAY

a. Fruiting twig, x ½.

LAURACEAE

SASSAFRAS

Sassafras albidum (Nutt.) Nees [*Sassafras variifolium* (Salisb.) Ktze.]

HABIT. A shrub to medium-sized tree 20–50 feet high and 1–2 feet in diameter (max. 90 by 5 feet); flat, open crown.

LEAVES. Alternate; simple; deciduous; oval to obovate; three forms appearing on same tree, entire, 1-lobed, or 3-lobed; 3–6 inches long; entire; thin; dull dark green above.

FLOWERS. Dioecious; small; in racemes; yellow-green; with the leaves.

FRUIT. A subglobose, lustrous, blue drupe, ⅓ inch long; borne on bright red, club-shaped pedicel 1½–2 inches long; maturing in one year.

TWIGS. Rather stout; glabrous; yellow-green; aromatic. Winter buds: terminal present, ⅓ inch long, green scaly.

BARK. Thick, red-brown, and furrowed on old trunks.

SILVICAL CHARACTERS. Very intolerant; fast-growing; short-lived; indicator of poor sites; oil of sassafras distilled from roots and bark.

* * *

REDBAY

Persea borbonia (L.) Spreng.

HABIT. A small to medium-sized tree, rarely 60 feet high; rounded, dense crown with stout, erect branches,

LEAVES. Alternate; simple; persistent; elliptic to lanceolate; 2–4 inches long; entire; thick; aromatic; nearly glabrous; bright green and lustrous above; paler and glaucous below.

FLOWERS. Perfect; small; yellow; in panicles; corolla absent.

FRUIT. An oblong, dark blue, lustrous drupe, ½ inch long; borne on glabrous red peduncles ½–1 inch long; calyx persistent.

TWIGS. Slender; glabrous; dark green. Winter buds: terminal present, naked, ¼ inch long, red-woolly.

BARK. Thin; dark red; furrowed and scaly.

SILVICAL CHARACTERS. Intermediate in tolerance; wet swampy sites.

GENERAL. The swampbay, *P. palustris* (Raf.) Sarg., of the coastal plain from North Carolina to Florida and Texas differs from redbay in having lower leaf surfaces and twigs brown-woolly, peduncles 1½–2 inches long, and fruit about ¾ inch long. Coker and Totten hold that these distinctions are vague and unsatisfactory. The avocado, *P. americana* Mill, is naturalized in southern Florida.

SWEETGUM

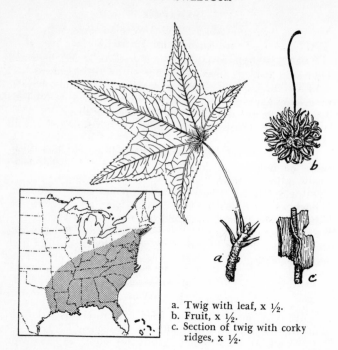

a. Twig with leaf, x ½.
b. Fruit, x ½.
c. Section of twig with corky ridges, x ½.

WITCH-HAZEL

a. Twig with leaf, x ½.

HAMAMELIDACEAE

Sweetgum. Redgum
Liquidambar styraciflua L.

HABIT. A medium-sized to large tree 80–120 feet high and 2–4 feet in diameter (max. 200 by 7 feet); small, oblong crown with small branches; long, clear, frequently buttressed bole.

LEAVES. Alternate; simple; deciduous; star-shaped; deeply and palmately 5–7 lobed; 4–7 inches long; lobes toothed and acuminate; lustrous and bright green above; paler below and glabrous except for tufts of hairs in the axils of the veins.

FLOWERS. Monoecious; both male and female in heads; the male in terminal racemes 2–3 inches long without calyx or corolla and with an indefinite number of stamens; the female in solitary long-stalked heads with a minute calyx and a 2-celled ovary; appearing with the leaves.

FRUIT. A multiple, globose fruit 1–1½ inches in diameter, of woody, 2-celled, beaked capsules; maturing in one year but persistent through the winter; 2 seeds in each capsule, each about ⅜ inch long with a short terminal wing.

TWIGS. Slender to stout; round or slightly angled; frequently developing corky wings during the second year; green to red-brown; pith star-shaped and homogeneous. Winter buds: terminal present, ¼–½ inch long, ovate, orange-brown, scaly.

BARK. Thick; gray-brown; deeply furrowed, with narrow, rounded and somewhat scaly ridges.

WOOD. Very important, exceeded only among hardwoods by oaks in volume of timber cut; diffuse-porous; fairly hard and heavy; heartwood dark red-brown and often figured; used for veneer, lumber, furniture, and containers.

SILVICAL CHARACTERS. Very intolerant; on rich moist bottomlands or swampy sites; wide, shallow, lateral roots; reproduction aggressive; storax gum, used in drugs and soaps, is obtained from the bark.

* * *

Witch-hazel
Hamamelis virginiana L.

Witch-hazel is a distinctive shrub or small tree found through the eastern United States. It is characterized by conspicuous, perfect, yellow, autumnal flowers; woody, 2-valved capsules from which the black seeds are forcibly ejected; simple, alternate, deciduous, oval leaves, 4–6 inches long, which are crenately toothed or lobed and smooth; and naked buds, ¼–½ inch long.

a. Winter twig, x 1.
b. Twig, side view, x 1.
c. Vertical section of twig, summ[...]
   bud and leaf petiole.
d. Leaf, x 3/8.
e. Flowering branchlet, x 1/2.
f. Staminate flower, enlarged.
g. Pistillate flower, enlarged.
h. Fruit, x 3/8.
i. Achene, enlarged.

[242]

PLATANACEAE

American Sycamore. Planetree
Platanus occidentalis L.

HABIT. A large tree 70–100 feet high and 3–8 feet in diameter (max. 175 by 14 feet); with yellow-poplar the largest of eastern hardwoods; long, clear bole; open crown.

LEAVES. Alternate; simple; deciduous; broadly ovate; 3–5 lobed; 4–7 inches long; lobe margins coarsely toothed; thin and firm; bright green and smooth above, paler and hairy along the veins below; petiles 2–3 inches long.

FLOWERS. Monoecious; both male and female in heads with minute individual flowers, each containing 3–8 sepals and petals; appearing with the leaves.

FRUIT. A multiple, globose fruit 1–1¼ inches in diameter; of elongated, obovoid achenes with spur at apex and ring of erect hairs around base; maturing in one year; borne singly on items 3–6 inches long.

TWIGS. Rather stout; round; orange-brown; lustrous; pith round, homogeneous. Winter buds: terminal absent, lateral ¼–⅜ inch long, conical, brown, with single visible scale, formed within petiole base.

BARK. Red-brown and scaly near base; thin and characteristically mottled on upper trunk by exfoliating outer layers which expose lighter colored inner layers.

WOOD. Intermediate in importance; diffuse-porous with broad rays; fairly hard and heavy; heartwood light red-brown; used for boxes, cooperage, vehicles, furniture, ties, and fuel.

SILVICAL CHARACTERS. Very intolerant; rapid growth; on moist sites; shallow, lateral roots; withstands smoke.

* * *

The following key distinguishes between our 3 native and 2 widely planted introduced species:

1. Heads of fruit solitary or in pairs; leaves not deeply lobed.
  2. Leaf lobes broader than long; fruit heads usually single.......
  ....*P. occidentalis* L., **American Sycamore**
  2. Leaf lobes about as long as broad; 2 (rarely 3) fruit heads per stem................x *P. acerifolia* Willd., **London Planetree**
1. Heads of fruit usually 3 or more; leaves deeply lobed.
  2. Leaves mostly 5–7 lobed, glabrous to hairy below; Eurasian...
  ....*P. orientalis* L., **Oriental Planetree**
  2. Leaves woolly below; native and western.
    3. Arizona and New Mexico; leaves 5–7 lobed.............
    ....*P. wrightii* S. Watts., **Arizona Sycamore**
    3. California; leaves 3–5 lobed............................
    ....*P. racemosa* Nutt., **California Sycamore**

ROSACEAE

The Apples

Characteristics of the Genus *Malus* Mill.

HABIT. Shrubs to medium-sized trees, the native species having little or no importance; broad, rounded, open crowns.

LEAVES. Alternate; simple; deciduous, or rarely half-evergreen; toothed and in native species more or less lobed; stipules free from the petioles, early deciduous; petiolate.

FLOWERS. Regular; perfect; in short terminal racemes; on spurlike, sometimes spinescent branches; appearing with or after the leaves; calyx 5-lobed, sometimes persistent and erect on fruit; petals white to red, showy; stamens 15–50; ovary inferior, usually with 5 carpels.

FRUIT. A fleshy pome with papery carpels joined at their apex; indehiscent; important as food in some species. Seed: 1–2 in each cell, ovoid, acute, chestnut-brown.

TWIGS. Slender to stout; round; fruit spurs roughened by leaf scars. Winter buds: terminal present, small, scaly, obtuse.

BARK. Thin; scaly; gray to red-brown; often fissured.

WOOD. Heavy; hard; fine-textured; diffuse-porous; heartwood red-brown; used to some extent for tool handles.

GENERAL. This taxonomically difficult genus contains about 25 species scattered through the Northern Hemisphere, The 6 species native to North America are unimportant, however, several Eurasian species are widely cultivated for their fruits or flowers. Many authors combine *Malus* with *Pyrus*, the name for apple becoming *Pyrus malus* L.

* * *

Common Pear

Pyrus communis L.

This Eurasian species is widely cultivated for its fruit and is a common escape in North America. In addition to its distinctive "Pear-shaped" pomaceous fruit, it differs from the closely related apple in having more lustrous, thinner, and less hairy leaves.

KEY TO THE SPECIES OF APPLE

1. Leaves never lobed, rolled up in bud; naturalized.
    2. Calyx persistent on fruit; leaves hairy below; fruit 1 inch or more in diameter...............*Malus pumila* Mill., **Apple**, p. 247.
    2. Calyx deciduous from fruit; leaves glabrous; fruit ⅛–½ inc in diameter..........*M. baccata* (L.) Borkh, **Siberian Crab Apple**
1. Leaves more or less lobed, at least on vigorous shoots, folded in bud; native.
    3. Eastern; calyx persistent on green (rarely yellow) waxy fruit.
        4. Leaves and calyx woolly; Great Plains, Wisconsin, and Minnesota to Louisiana and Texas..................................
            ....*M. ioensis* (Wood) Britt., **Prairie Crab Apple**
        4. Mature leaves and calyx not woolly.
            5. Leaves on vigorous shoots distinctly and deeply lobed.
                6. Leaves rounded or wedge-shaped at base; North and Central...
                    ....*M. coronaria* (L.) Mill., **Sweet Crab Apple**, p. 247.
                6. Leaves heart-shaped at base; North Carolina to Alabama
                    ....*M. glabrata* Rehd., **Biltmore Crab Apple**
            5. Leaves on vigorous shoots slightly lobed.
                7. Fruit about 2 inches broad, much broader than high, with deep cavity at top and base; Ohio to West Virginia, south to North Carolina and Georgia..................
                    ....*M. platycarpa* Rehd., **Bigfruit Crab Apple**
                7. Fruit about 1 inch broad and long, with shallow cavities. Virginia to Illinois, south to Florida and Louisiana......
                    ...*M. angustifolia* (Ait.) Michx., **Southern Crab Apple**
    3. West Coast; calyx deciduous on yellow to red non-waxy fruit; Alaska to California.......................................
        ....*M. diversifolia* (Bong.) Roem, **Oregon Crab Apple**

* * *

Torrey Vauquelinia

Vauquelinia californica (Torr.) Sarg.

This is a shrub or small tree rarely 20 feet high, native to southern Arizona, southwestern New Mexico, and northern Mexico. It is characterized by simple, persistent, lanceolate leaves 1½–3 inches long, with remote, small, glandular teeth; small, regular, perfect, white flowers borne in leafy, woolly panicles; and a woody, ovoid, capsular, 5-celled fruit about ¼ inch long, which is woolly, subtended by the remnants of the flower, and long persistent on the branches.

a. Leaf, x ⅔.

b. Flowers, x ½.

c. Flower without corolla, x 1.

d. Fruit, x ½.

e. Twig, x 1.

f. Section of twig, x 4.

ROSACEAE

Sweet Crab Apple

Malus coronaria (L.) Mill. (*Pyrus coronaria* L.)

HABIT. A bushy shrub or small tree 15–30 feet high and ½–1 foot in diameter; crown broad, rounded, and bushy.

LEAVES. Ovate to ovate-oblong; 3–4 inches long; 3-lobed on vigorous shoots; sharply and deeply toothed; thin and smooth; dark green above, paler below; petioles long and slender.

FLOWERS. Handsome; fragrant; 1¼–2 inches across; white to rose-colored; in 5–6 flowered umbel-like racemes; appearing after the leaves.

FRUIT. Pome depressed-globose; 1–1½ inches in diameter; pale to yellow-green; waxy; fragrant; flesh very tart; ripening in late autumn and often hanging to the tree until spring.

TWIGS. Rather stout; developing short, stout, often spine-like spurs; red-brown. Winter buds: terminal ⅛–¼ inch long, scaly, bright red.

BARK. Thin; red-brown; divided by shallow fissures into broad, scaly ridges.

SILVICAL CHARACTERS. Intolerant; rich, moist sites along streams or in thickets along roads and fences; fibrous roots; planted as an ornamental for its showy flowers.

* * *

Apple

Malus pumila Mill. (*Pyrus malus* L.)

This species, native to Eurasia, is the parent of most of our cultivated apples and has escaped in many parts of North America. It is stated that over 3,000 varieties of this species have been developed by pomologists. The apple is a small to medium-sized tree which can be identified from its unlobed, crenate-serrate to entire, thick leaves which are hairy below and rolled up in the bud.

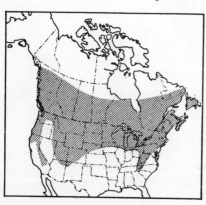

a. Winter twig, x 1.

b. Portion of twig, enlarged.

c. Leaf, x ½.

d. Vertical section of flower, enla

e. Portion of a fruiting cyme, x 1.

ROSACEAE

American Mountain-ash

Sorbus americana Marsh. [*Pyrus americana* (Marsh.) DC.]
(*Sorbus sitchensis* Roem.)

HABIT. A shrub or small tree, seldom 30 feet high and 12 inches in diameter; crown round-topped, handsome; with spreading, slender branches.

LEAVES. Alternate; pinnately compound; 6–8 inches long; with 7–17 mostly sessile leaflets; oblong-oval to lanceolate; 2–4 inches long and ½–1 inch wide; serrate; glabrous; dark green above, pale below; deciduous.

FLOWERS. Regular; perfect; small; in broad, flat cymes 3–5 inches across; on short, stout pedicels; appearing after leaves; 5 petals, cream-white, ¼ inch in diameter.

FRUIT. Berry-like pome; subglobose; ¼–½ inch in diameter; bright orange-red; thin, acrid flesh; papery carpels. Seed: 1 or 2 in each cell, ⅛ inch long, ovoid, brown.

TWIGS. Stout; round; red-brown and pubescent, becoming dark brown and glabrous; marked by large leaf scars and oblong lenticels. Winter buds: terminal ¼–¾ inch long, acute, dark red, pilose, with gummy exudation.

BARK. Thin (⅛ inch); light gray; smooth or slightly roughened by scales; inner bark fragrant.

WOOD. Light; soft; weak; close-grained; diffuse-porous; heartwood pale brown; sapwood thick and lighter colored.

SILVICAL CHARACTERS. Intolerant; slow-growing; short-lived, abundant seeder; fibrous roots; prefers moist sites, but grows well on rocky hillsides; often cultivated.

GENERAL. The taxonomy within this genus is confused. The western form of this species, S. *americana* var. *sitchensis* (Roem.) Sudw., is usually a shrub and its distribution is included in the map. The following key separates the native and naturalized species reaching tree size:

1. Winter buds densely covered with long white hairs; leaflets 1–2 inches long, oblong; widely planted and naturalized through the northern United States and Canada.........................
.....................*S. aucuparia* L., **European Mountain-ash**
1. Winter buds glabrous or slightly hairy; leaflets 1½–4 inches long.
   2. Winter buds glabrous or slightly white-hairy; leaflets usually lanceolate and acuminate...............................
   ....*S. americana* Marsh., **American Mountain-ash**
   2. Winter buds slightly red-hairy; leaflets oblong, short-pointed; Northeast and Central states...............................
   ....*S. decora* Schneid., **Showy Mountain-ash**

a. Winter twig, x 1.

b. Portion of twig, enlarged.

c. Leaf, x 1.

d. Flowering branchlet, x ½.

e. Vertical section of flower, x 2.

f. Fruiting branchlet, x ½.

ROSACEAE

Downy Serviceberry. Shad Bush

Amelanchier arborea (Michx.) Fern. (*Amelanchier canadensis* auth.)

HABIT. A shrub or small tree 25–40 feet high and 8–14 inches in diameter (max. 70 by 2 feet); crown open.

LEAVES. Alternate; simple; oblong-ovate to oval or ovate; 2–4 inches long; acute at apex; finely serrate; dark green and glabrous above, pale below; deciduous; petioles slender.

FLOWERS. Regular; perfect; in erect, crowded racemes; appearing with leaves; calyx tube persistent on fruit; corolla white, ½–¾ inch long, of 5, strap-shaped petals.

FRUIT. Berry-like pome; globose; ¼–½ inch in diameter; dark red to purple; more or less covered with glaucous bloom; flesh sweet; open at summit. Seed: 5–10, dark chestnut-brown.

TWIGS. Slender; round; becoming glabrous and red-brown to dark gray-brown. Winter buds: terminal ¼–½ inch long, conical, acute or acuminate, chestnut-brown.

BARK. Thin (⅛ inch); light brown, tinged with red; smooth or slightly furrowed with scaly ridges.

WOOD. Heavy; hard; close-grained; diffuse-porous; heartwood light brown; sapwood thick, light; unimportant.

SILVICAL CHARACTERS. Tolerant when young; abundant seeder; deep fibrous roots; capable of sprouting repeatedly; moist valleys and borders of streams to dry mountain slopes.

GENERAL. The taxonomy within this genus is confused, relatively minor characters being used to separate species. Three species, keyed out below, commonly form small trees and the following shrubby species have been reported as reaching tree size: *A. alnifolia* Nutt., *A. interior* Niel., *A. sanguinea* (Pursh) DC., and *A. utahensis* Koehne.

1. Leaves coarsely toothed, usually only above the middle, with about 7–13 teeth per inch, rounded at apex; top of ovary woolly; buds ovoid..............*A. florida* Lindl., **Pacific Serviceberry**

1. Leaves finely toothed nearly to base with about 15–30 teeth per inch, pointed at apex; top of ovary glabrous; buds lanceolate.

    2. Leaves woolly when young; flowers in woolly racemes; fruit dry, on pedicels ½–1 inch long............................
    ....*A. arborea* (Michx.) Fern., **Downy Serviceberry**

    2. Leaves nearly glabrous from first; racemes glabrous; fruit sweet and juicy, on pedicels 1–2 inches long; Newfoundland to Minnesota, south to Kansas and Alabama.........................
    ....*A. laevis* Wieg., **Allegheny Serviceberry**

a. Twig with leaves and flowers, x 1.

b. Twig with fruit, x 1.

c. Diagram of flower, x 2.

ROSACEAE

The Hawthorns

Characteristics of the Genus *Crataegus* L.

HABIT. Deciduous shrubs or small trees; usually spiny; crown generally rounded and wide-spreading.

LEAVES. Alternate; simple; deciduous; usually serrate and often more or less lobed; membranaceous to coriaceous; stipules persistent until autumn or deciduous in spring, small to leaflike, often bright-colored; petiolate.

FLOWERS. Regular; perfect, in few- or many-flowered terminal corymbs; pedicellate; calyx 5-lobed, tubular, persistent on fruit or deciduous; corolla 5-petaled, white, inserted on edge of disk lining calyx-tube; stamens 5–25; ovary inferior, of 1–5 carpels connate at base, with 2 ovules in each cell; styles as many as carpels.

FRUIT. Small, variously colored pome with 1–5 bony, 1-seeded nutlets; flesh usually dry and mealy; generally open or concave at apex.

TWIGS. Round; rigid; more or less zigzag; generally armed with stiff, sharp thorns; marked by oblong lenticels and small leaf scars. Winter buds: terminal usually present; small, globose, scaly, lustrous, brown.

BARK. Dark red to gray; scaly or shallowly furrowed.

WOOD. Heavy; hard; tough; close-grained; diffuse-porous; heartwood red-brown; sapwood thick, light-colored; unimportant; used for tool handles, canes, and turned articles.

SILVICAL CHARACTERS. Intolerant; reproduction aggressive; growth slow.

GENERAL. An extremely large and complex genus containing over a thousand species, the identification of which presents great diffiulties even to the specialist; hybridizing is common, the number of stamens, which is variable but usually within constant limits, and the color of the anthers appear to be the most satisfactory characters for the identification of species. Some 149 species have been listed as trees in the United States and Alaska; of these *C. douglasii* Lindl., the black hawthorn, which is common through the west, has been pictured on the opposite page as being typical of the genus.

a. Twig with leaves and flowers, x 1.

b. Twig with fruit, x 1.

ROSACEAE

CURLLEAF MOUNTAIN-MAHOGANY

Cercocarpus ledifolius Nutt.

HABIT. A shrub or small tree rarely 40 feet high and 30 inches in diameter; trunk short and crooked; crown round and compact with stout, more or less crooked, spreading branches.

LEAVES. Alternate; simple; lanceolate to lance-elliptic; ½–1 inch long; acute; entire; coriaceous; revolute margins; dark green and lustrous above, pale and tomentulose below; resinous; persistent for 2 years; short-petiolate; stipules minute, deciduous.

FLOWERS. Regular; perfect; solitary; inconspicuous; sessile in axils of leaves; calyx tube long, hoary-tomentose, whitish; corolla absent; stamens 15–30, in 2–3 rows, free, anthers hairy; ovary inferior, composed of 1 carpel and ovule.

FRUIT. Linear-oblong, coriaceous achene ¼ inch long, enclosed in persistent calyx tube ½ inch long; chestnut-brown; covered with long hairs; tipped with persistent, hairy, elongated style 2–3 inches long. Seed: solitary, linear, acute.

TWIGS. Stout; round; rigid; red-brown and pubescent at first, becoming dark brown or silver-gray and glabrous; spur-like lateral branches. Winter buds: minute, scaly, pubescent.

BARK. Thick on old trunks (1 inch); red-brown; hard; firm; furrowed and scaly.

WOOD. Exceedingly heavy and hard; brittle; close-grained; diffuse-porous; warping badly; heartwood clear red or dark brown; sapwood rather thin, yellow; unimportant.

SILVICAL CHARACTERS. Intolerant; rather long-lived; slow-growing; on dry, gravelly, wind-swept slopes.

GENERAL. Three other shrubby species occasionally reach tree size; the tree species are keyed out below:

1. Leaves entire, lanceolate, leathery, persistent; flowers solitary or in 2's or 3's....*C. ledifolius* Nutt., **Curlleaf Mountain-mahogany**
1. Leaves usually somewhat toothed, elliptic to broadly obovate, deciduous.
    2. Leaves entire or slightly toothed near apex; flowers solitary or in 2's or 3's; Texas to Arizona and south...................
    ....*C. breviflorus* A. Gray., **Hairy Mountain-mahogany**
    2. Leaves with numerous teeth above the middle; flowers in many flowered racemes; Oregon and California to Arizona and Mexico....*C. betuloides* Nutt., **Birchleaf Mountain-mahogany**

ROSACEAE

The Cherries, Plums, and Peaches

Characteristics of the Genus *Prunus* L.

HABIT. Shrubs or usually small trees, only a few species reaching sizes of commercial importance.

LEAVES. Alternate; simple; deciduous or persistent; usually serrate, rarely entire; stipules free from petiole, early deciduous; petiolate.

FLOWERS. Regular; perfect or rarely dioecious; solitary or in terminal or axillary racemes, corymbs, or umbels; appearing from separate buds with, before, or after leaves; calyx 5-lobed, tubular; corolla 5-petaled, usually white, deciduous, stamens usually 15–20; ovary inserted in bottom of calyx tube, inferior or superior, 1-celled, 2-ovuled.

FRUIT. Thin dry, or thick fleshy, 1-seeded drupe; stone bony, smooth, or rugose; indehiscent; important as food in several species. Seed: filling cavity of nut, suspended, thin-coated, pale brown.

TWIGS. Slender or stout; round; astringent; red to brown; marked by lenticles and usually by small, elevated, horizontal leaf scars. Winter buds: terminal present or absent, lateral nearly equal in size, scales imbricated and the inner accrescent and often colored.

BARK. Astringent; gray to dark brown; plated or scaly.

WOOD. From light to heavy and hard; fine-textured; diffuse-porous; durable; heartwood light or dark brown, often reddish; sapwood lighter colored; a few species are important timber trees.

GENERAL. About 30 species of *Prunus* are native to North America, 18 of these being arborescent at times. Seven introduced species, four of which are highly important fruit trees, have become naturalized in various parts of the United States and Canada. These species, which are included in the key are: *P. avium* (L.) L., Mazzard cherry; *P. cerasus* L., sour cherry; *P. domestica* L., garden plum; *P. insititia* L., Damson plum; *P. mahaleb* L., Mahaleb cherry; *P. persica* (L.) Batsch., peach; and *P. spinosa* L., sloe or blackthorn. The almond, *P. amygdalus* Batsch., and the apricot, *P. armeniaca* L., while not naturalized, are commonly planted in warmer regions. As with other cultivated fruits, these have been improved until there are numerous forms or varieties. The commonly planted ornamental flowering almond, *P. triloba* Lindl., is a shrub or small tree.

KEY TO THE SPECIES OF CHERRIES, PLUMS, AND PEACHES

1. Fruit usually over ½ inch in diameter and usually slightly 2-lobed by ventral groove.
    2. Terminal bud present; fruit and ovary hairy; naturalized........
    ....*P. persica*, **Peach**, p. 259.
    2. Terminal bud absent; fruit and ovary glabrous..........**Plums**
        3. Leaves rolled up in bud; flowers 1 or 2; naturalized.
            4. Twigs glabrous; fruit 1 inch across.....................
            ....*P. domestica*, **Garden Plum**, p. 265.
            4. Twigs hairy or woolly; fruit about ½ inch across.
                5. Flowers single; buds round.........*P. spinosa* L., **Sloe**
                5. Flowers in 2's; buds ovate.........................
                ....*P. insititia*, **Damson Plum**, p. 265.
        3. Leaves folded in bud (except Klamath Plum); flowers 3 to many; native.
            6. West Coast; leaves round-ovate, rolled in bud............
            ....*P. subcordata* Benth., **Klamath Plum**
            6. East of Pacific Coast; leaves ovate to lanceolate.
                7. Leaves with sharp teeth, dull dark green above.
                    8. Leaves lanceolate to elliptic; fruit purple, glaucous.
                        9. Fruit stone turgid; calyx hairy; Connecticut to North Carolina................................
                        ....*P. alleghaniensis* Port, **Allegheny Plum**
                        9. Fruit stone flattened; calyx glabrous; North Carolina to Texas and Arkansas.....................
                        ....*P. umbellata* Ell., **Flatwoods Plum**
                    8. Leaves oblong to obovate; fruit red to yellow; stone flattened.
                        10. Leaves hairy below; twigs hairy; central and south
                        ....*P. mexicana* Wats., **Mexican Plum**
                        10. Leaves nearly glabrous below; twigs glabrous; Canada to Florida, west to the Rocky Mountains
                        ....*P. americana*, **American Plum**, p. 265.
                7. Leaves with dull, rounded teeth.
                    11. Leaves dull green, elliptic to obovate, coarsely or doubly toothed; stone flattened...................
                    ....*P. nigra* **Canada Plum**, p. 265.
                    11. Leaves lustrous, thin, ovate to lanceolate, finely toothed; stones turgid; southern Indiana to Kansas and south.
                        12. Leaves 2½–6 inches long; fruit ¾–1 inch; calyx glandular.
                            13. Leaves oblong to obovate.................
                            ....*P. hortulana* Bail, **Hortulan Plum**
                            13. Leaves elliptic to lanceolate...............
                            P. munsoniana W. & H., **Wildgoose Plum**
                        12. Leaves 1–2 inches long; fruit ½ inch; calyx lobes without glands................................
                        ....*P. angustifolia* Marsh, **Chickasaw Plum**
1. Fruit seldom ½ inch across, not lobed; leaves folded in bud; terminal bud present...**Cherries**
    14. Flowers solitary or few, in umbels or corymbs.
        15. Calyx persistent on fruit; naturalized.
            16. Leaves thin, 2½–5 inches long, hairy below at least along veins; fruit sweet...*P. avium*, **Mazzard Cherry**, p. 259.
            16. Leaves semi-leathery, 2–3 inches long, glabrous; fruit sour
            ....*P. cerasus* L., **Sour Cherry**, p. 259.
        15. Calyx deciduous from fruit.
            17. Leaves orbicular to broad ovate; naturalized..........
            ....*P. mahaleb* L., **Mahaleb**

17. Leaves narrower; native.
    18. Leaves oblong-obovate; Montana and British Columbis to Arizona and New Mexico..................
        ....*P. emarginata* Bitter Cherry, p. 263.
    18. Leaves oblong-lanceolate; Newfoundland to British Columbia, south to Georgia, Iowa, and Colorado...
        ....*P. pensylvanica* Pin Cherry, p. 263.
14. Flowers 12 or more in elongated racemes.
  19. Leaves deciduous; flowers in terminal, usually leafy racemes.
    20. Calyx deciduous from fruit; leaves oblong-oval to obovate, with spreading teeth; entire area................
        ....*P. virginiana* Common Chokecherry, p. 261.
    20. Calyx persistent on fruit; leaves with incurved teeth....
        ....*P. serotina*, Black Cherry, p. 261.
  19. Leaves persistent; flowers in axillary, leafless racemes.
    21. Southeast; leaves entire or rarely with few small spiny teeth.
      22. Leaves elliptic to ovate; Southern Florida..........
        ....*P. myrtifolia* Urb., Myrtle Laurelcherry
      22. Leaves oblong-lanceolate: North Carolinia to Texas..
        ....*P. caroliniana* Ait., Carolina Laurelcherry
    21. California.
      23. Leaves spiny toothed............................
        ....*P. ilicifolia* Dietr, Hollyleaf Cherry
      23. Leaves entire or minutely toothed...............
        ....*P. lyonii* Sarg, Catalina Cherry

* * *

CHRISTMASBERRY

Photinia arbutifolia Lindl. (*Heteromeles arbutifolia* Roem.)

An evergreen shrub or small tree native to lower mountain slopes in California and Lower California which is widely planted as an ornamental because of its lustrous evergreen leaves and clusters of red fruits which resemble those of mountain-ash. This tree is characterized by alternate, simple, thick, glossy, serrate, persistent leaves; small, white, perfect flowers in terminal corymbs; and fruit a red, ovoid, clustered pome about ⅓ inch long.

* * *

CLIFFROSE. QUININEBUSH

Cowania mexicana D. Don

This shrub or small tree rarely 25 feet high is found on dry slopes from Nevada to Colorado and south into Mexico. It is characterized by odd, simple, alternate leaves, which are 3–5 lobed, ⅓–½ inch long, thick, dark green above and woolly below, and tardily deciduous to persistent; perfect, regular, solitary, showy flowers, which are pale yellow to white and about one inch across; from which develop 5–12 achenes, each about ¼ inch long and tipped with a 2 inch white, hairy style.

ROSACEAE
PEACH
Prunus persica (L.) Batsch (*Amygdalus persica* L.)

This small Asiatic tree with its many improved varieties produces the peaches of commerce. It has escaped from cultivation, mostly along roads or fences. The peach differs from other subgenera of *Prunus* in having large, grooved, hairy fruits; 1–2 sessile flowers with hairy ovaries; and scaly buds with the terminal present and separate lateral flower buds.

* * *

ALMOND
Prunus amygdalus Batsch

A small Asiatic tree cultivated for the edible kernels of the stone in the drupaceous fruit. This species is restricted to warm climates. This tree closely resembles the peach, differing from it in that the fruit becomes dry and splits open at maturity. The commonly planted flowering almond, *P. triloba* Lindl., is a handsome, pink-flowered shrub or small tree native to China. The desert almond, *P. fasiculata* Gray, is a shrub or rarely a small tree native to the Southwest.

* * *

SOUR CHERRY
Prunus cerasus L.

This native of southeastern Europe and Asia is widely naturalized as an escape through much of North America. It is important as the source of numerous varieties of canning cherries.

* * *

SWEET CHERRY. MAZZARD
Prunus avium L.

Native to Europe and Asia, but widely naturalized through North America, this species is widely cultivated for its garden cherries.

* * *

APRICOT
Prunus armeniaca L.

This small to medium-sized tree, native to western Asia, is widely planted for its distinctive fruits. It closely resembles the peach in its hairy, grooved fruit, but differs from it in having no terminal bud and solitary axillary buds, and in having broad-ovate leaves which are rolled up in the bud.

BLACK CHERRY

a. Winter twig, x 1.
b. Leaf, x ⅔.
c. Margin of leaf, enlarged.
d. Flowering branchlet, x ½.
e. Vertical section of flower, enlarged.
f. Fruiting branchlet, x ½.

COMMON CHOKECHERRY

a. Winter twig, x 1.
b. Leaf, x ¾.
c. Flowering branchlet, x ½.
d. Fruiting branchlet, x ½.

ROSACEAE

Black Cherry
Prunus serotina Ehrh.

HABIT. A medium-sized tree 40–60 feet high and 1–3 feet in diameter (max. 100 by 5 feet); clear bole and narrow, oblong crown.

LEAVES. Oval to oblong-lanceolate; acuminate or acute at apex; finely serrate with incurved callous teeth; dark green and lustrous above, paler and with red-brown hairs along base of midrib below; 2–6 inches long; petioles short, usually with 2 glands near blade.

FLOWERS. In many-flowered, loose racemes 4–5 inches long; appearing with the leaves; calyx cup-shaped; petals 5, white, about ⅛ inch long.

FRUIT. Globose; in racemes; ⅓–½ inch in diameter; nearly black when ripe; flesh juicy, edible, slightly bitter.

TWIGS. Slender; round; glabrous; red-brown; bitter and aromatic; short spur shoots common on old growth. Winter buds: terminal ¼ inch long, ovoid, scaly, light brown.

BARK. Thin; smooth and red-brown on young stems; nearly black and exfoliating into distinctive, persistent scales with upturned edges on old trunks.

WOOD. Moderately important; rather heavy and hard; diffuse-porous; heartwood red-brown; a prized and valuable furniture wood.

SILVICAL CHARACTERS. Intermediate in tolerance; typical of rich, moist sites; usually in mixed stands; long taproot.

* * *

Common Chokecherry
Prunus virginiana L.

This unimportant shrub or small tree is one of the most widely distributed in North America. It closely resembles black cherry, but can be distinguished from it by usually red fruit; leaves with sharply serrate, spreading teeth; and smooth or slightly fissured bark. The western forms are designated as either western chokecherry, *P. virginiana* var. *demissa* (Nutt.) Torr., or black chokecherry, *P. virginiana* var. *melanocarpa* (A. Nels.) Sarg.

PIN CHERRY

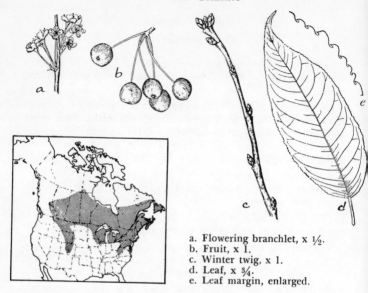

a. Flowering branchlet, x ½.
b. Fruit, x 1.
c. Winter twig, x 1.
d. Leaf, x ¾.
e. Leaf margin, enlarged.

BITTER CHERRY

a. Twig with leaves and fruit, x ¾.

ROSACEAE

Pin Cherry. Wild Red Cherry
Prunus pensylvanica L.

HABIT. A shrub or small tree rarely 30–40 feet high and 18–20 inches in diameter; short trunk; crown narrow, rounded or flat-topped, with slender, horizontal branches.

LEAVES. Obovate to oblong-lanceolate; acuminate or acute at apex; sharply and coarsely serrate, with incurved teeth; glabrous; bright green and lustrous above, paler below; 3–4 inches long and 1–2 inches broad; turning bright yellow in autumn; petiole slender, glabrous or pilose.

FLOWERS. In 2–5-flowered, sessile umbels; on slender pedicels nearly 1 inch long; appearing when leaves half grown; calyx tube glabrous, marked by conspicuous, orange band in mouth of throat; corolla cream-white; ½ inch in diameter.

FRUIT. Globose; in 2–5-fruited umbels; ¼–⅓ inch in diameter; on slender pedicels; light red; thick-skinned; flesh thin, quite sour; occasionally made into jelly; stone oblong, thin-walled, pointed, 3/16 inch long, ridged.

TWIGS. Slender; round; puberulous and light red at first, becoming glabrous and bright to dull red; marked by orange-colored, raised lenticels; bark easily separable from green inner bark; lateral branchlets short, spurlike. Winter buds: terminal ⅛ inch long, acute, ovoid, bright red-brown.

BARK. Thin (⅓–½ inch); red-brown, marked by orange-colored bands of lenticels; smooth or scaly.

WOOD. Light; soft; close-grained; heartwood light brown; sapwood thin, yellow; unimportant.

SILVICAL CHARACTERS. Intolerant; fast-growing; short-lived; the abundant reproduction often completely taking over burned areas.

* * *

Bitter Cherry
Prunus emarginata (Dougl.) D. Dietr.

This cherry closely resembles pin cherry in its flowers and fruit; it can be distinguished by its oblong-obovate, obtuse leaves and its more western distribution where it extends from British Columbia to Montana and south to California, Arizona, and New Mexico.

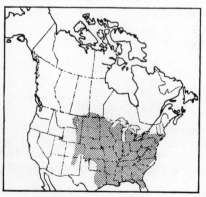

a. Winter twig, x 1.

b. Portion of twig, enlarged

c. Leaf, x ½.

d. Flowering branchlet, x ½

e. Vertical section of flower
    x 1.

f. Fruiting branchlet, x ½.

ROSACEAE

AMERICAN PLUM
Prunus americana Marsh.

HABIT. A shrub or small tree 25–30 feet high and rarely 12 inches in diameter; trunk short, usually dividing near the ground; crown broad, with many spreading branches; usually spreading by shoots from the roots into dense thickets.

LEAVES. Oval to slightly oblong-oval, or sometimes obovate; acuminate at apex; sharply and often doubly serrate; thick and firm; dark green above, pale and glabrous below; 3–4 inches long and 1½–1¾ inches wide; petiole slender, ½–¾ inch long.

FLOWERS. In 2–5-flowered umbels; on slender, glabrous pedicels ½–⅔ inch long; appearing before or with leaves; ill-scented; calyx tube narrow, bright red without, green and pubescent within; corolla white, 1 inch in diameter.

FRUIT. Subglobose; about 1 inch in diameter; red and often spotted at maturity; thick-skinned; nearly free from bloom; flesh bright yellow, juicy, acid; used for jellies; stone oval, rounded at apex, ¾–1 inch long.

TWIGS. Slender; glabrous; bright green at first, becoming orange-brown and marked by minute, circular, raised lenticels; sometimes spiny-tipped. Winter buds: terminal absent, lateral ⅛–¼ inch long, acute, chestnut-brown.

BARK. Up to ½ inch thick; dark brown, tinged with red; outer layer forming persistent plates.

WOOD. Heavy; hard; close-grained; strong; heartwood dark brown, tinged with red; sapwood thin, lighter colored.

SILVICAL CHARACTERS. Intolerant; on moist bottomlands to banks of intermittent streams on dry uplands and mountain slopes.

* * *

CANADA PLUM
Prunus nigra Ait.

The Canada plum is very similar to the American plum and is often classed as a variety of it. It differs in having leaves with small rounded teeth and bi-glandular petioles. Canada plum ranges from New Brunswick to southern Manitoba and south to New York, Indiana, and North Dakota. The garden plum, *P. domestica* L., while native to Europe and Asia has escaped through much of North America, as has the Bullace or Damson plum, *P. institia* L.

[265]

LEGUMINOSAE

Characteristics of the Pea Family

This important family contains about 500 genera and over 15,000 species among which are many of our important food plants. The family is characterized by its distinctive fruit known as a legume; as well as by alternate, usually compound leaves; and regular or distinctive papilionaceous flowers.

The genera growing in North America and reaching tree size are keyed out on the opposite page and species which are important, common, or distinctive are described on succeeding pages. The several unimportant forms which occasionally reach tree size in the southern fringe of the United States are briefly described below:

Smokethorn, *Dalea spinosa* A. Gray, is a desert shrub with minute or no leaves, green, spiny twigs, and a small 1-seeded legume.

Southwestern coralbean, *Erythrina flabelliformis* Kearney, in southern Arizona and New Mexico is characterized by 3 foliolate leaves and showy red flowers. The eastern coralbean, *E. herbacea* L., from North Carolina to Texas is usually a perennial herb but becomes a tree in Florida. The South American *E. crista-galli* L. is cultivated and escaped in the Gulf states.

Kidneywood, *Eysenhardtia polystachya* (Ortega) Sarg., is a shrubby southwestern form characterized by small leaflets and a legume only ½ inch long. *E. angustifolia* Pen. is a small tree in Texas.

Littleleaf leadtree, *Leucaena retusa* Benth., of southern Texas and New Mexico differs from Lysiloma in having a linear legume 6–10 inches long on a peduncle 3–5 inches long. Three similar species, *L. glauca* Benth., *L. greggii* S. Wats., and *L. pulverulenta* Benth., form small trees in southern Texas and Mexico.

Lysiloma, *Lysiloma microphylla* Beth., is a shrub or small tree in Arizona characterized by bi-pinnately compound, persistent leaves and a linear-oblong, compressed legume 5–8 inches long. *L. bahamensis* Beth. is found in southern Florida.

Tesota, *Olneya tesota* A. Gray, a beautiful spiny small tree of the Arizona-California desert, with purple flowers and a compressed, glandular-hairy legume 2–2½ inches long.

Paradise poinciana, *Poinciana gilliesii* Hook., is an ill-scented shrub or small tree native to South America but naturalized in southern Texas, New Mexico, and Arizona. It is characterized by large, showy, flowers with long-exserted red stamens and pistil. *P. mexicana* (Gray) Rose, is found is southern Texas and Mexico.

[266]

KEY TO THE GENERA OF LEGUMINOSAE
REACHING TREE SIZE

1. Leaves bi-pinnately compound (3–4-pinnate in some genera and sometimes only pinnate in Gleditsia); flowers regular or nearly so.
  2. Flowers in globose heads or cylindrical spikes; leaflets mostly less than ½ inch long; southwestern shrubs seldom becoming trees.
    3. Twigs armed with spines; filaments free; legume terete or compressed, indehiscent.
      4. Flowers in heads or spikes, yellow or white, stamens more than 10; petioles not spiny or glandular at apex............
        ....*Acacia* Mill., **Acacia**, p. 269.
      4. Flowers in cylindric spikes, greenish-white, stamens 10; petioles minutely glandular at apex and tipped with small spinescent rachis..........*Prosopis* L., **Mesquite**, p. 271.
    3. Twigs unarmed; legume compressed, dehiscent; flowers in heads, whitish, or pink.
      5. Stamens numerous, long-exserted; flowers pink; planted in southeast..............*Albizia* Dur., **Mimosa**, p. 271.
      5. Stamens 10–20; flowers white; western.
        6. Stamens 12–20, exserted, their filaments united into a tube; legume broad..*Lysiloma* Benth., **Lysiloma**, p. 266.
        6. Stamens 10, inserted, their filaments free; legume linear.
          ....*Leucaena* Benth., **Leadtree**, p. 266.
  2. Flowers in racemes; stamens 10 or less, their filaments free.
    7. Flowers large and showy, yellow, perfect; leaflets less than ½ inch long; southwestern shrubs or rarely small trees.
      8. Stamens red and long-exserted; legume broad and flat; naturalized..............*Poinciana* L., **Poinciana**, p. 266.
      8. Stamens inserted; native.
        9. Legume linear, terete; rachis of leaf spinescent..........
        ....*Parkinsonia* L., **Parkinsonia**, p. 279.
        9. Legume oblong, compressed; rachis of leaf not spinescent
        ....*Cercidium* Tulasne, **Paloverde**, p. 279.
    7. Flowers not showy, greenish-white, polygamous or dioecious; leaflets over ½ inch long; eastern trees, but widely planted.
      10. Leaves 1–3 feet long with leaflets 2–2½ inches long; legume thick and woody with seeds ¾ inch long.............
      ......*Gymnocladus* Lam., **Coffeetree**, p. 275.
      10. Leaves ½–1 foot long with leaflets ½–1½ inches long; legume leathery with seeds ⅛ inch long...........
      ......*Gleditsia* L., **Honeylocust**, p. 277.
1. Leaves simple or pinnately compound; flowers papilionaceous.
  11. Leaves simple.
    12. Leaves heart-shaped; flowers in fascicles, red, with free stamens; spineless..............*Cercis* L., **Redbud**, p. 273.
    12. Leaves oblong or absent; flowers in racemes, blue, stamens with 9 united anthers; twigs reduced to spines; Arizona and California....................*Dalea* Juss., **Dalea**, p. 266.
  11. Leaves pinnately compound.
    13. Leaflets 1–4 inches long.
      14. Leaves 3-foliate; flowers red..............
      ......*Erythrina* L., **Coralbean**, p. 266.
      14. Leaves many-foliate; flowers white, yellow, or blue.
        15. Leaflets 3–4 inches long; flowers white, in panicles; legume compressed.............
        ......*Cladrastis* Raf., **Yellowwood**, p. 275.
        15. Leaflets 1–2½ inches long.
          16. Twigs with stipular spines; legumes compressed, not constricted.....*Robinia* L., **Locust**, p. 283.
          16. Twigs unarmed; legumes terete, constricted....
          ....*Sophora* L., **Sophora**, p. 281.
    13. Leaflets less than 1 inch long.
      17. Leaves with glandular dots..............
      ....*Eysenhardtia* H. B. K., **Kidneywood**, p. 266.
      17. Leaves without glandular dots.
        18. Flowers fascicled, yellow..............
        ......*Caragana* Lam., **Pea Tree**, p. 281.
        18. Flowers racemose, purple..............
        ......*Olneya* Gray, **Tesota**, p. 266.

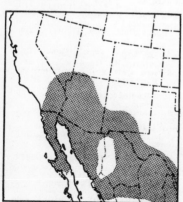

Twig with leaves and fruit, x 1.

LEGUMINOSAE

Catclaw Acacia. Paradise Flower
Acacia greggii Gray

HABIT. A shrub or small tree rarely 30 feet high and 10–12 inches in diameter; trunk short; crown irregular.

LEAVES. Alternate; evenly doubly pinnate; 1–3 pairs of pinnae, each with 4–5 pairs of obovate, obtuse, thick, pubescent leaflets ¹⁄₁₆–¼ inch long; persistent; petiole short, glandular near middle; stipules linear, caducous.

FLOWERS. Nearly regular; perfect or polygamous; fragrant; in dense, pubescent spikes; calyx 5-lobed, puberulous; corolla 5-petaled, bright yellow, ⅛ inch long; stamens numerous, exserted, ¼ inch long; ovary stalked and hairy.

FRUIT. Linear-oblong, flat, much-curved and contorted, indehiscent, light brown legume 2–6 inches long and ½–¾ inch wide; contracted between the seeds; valves thin and membranaceous. Seed: compressed, dark brown, lustrous, ¼ inch long.

TWIGS. Slender; angled; puberulous or glabrous; pale brown; armed with stout, broad, recurved, infrastipular spines ¼ inch long, giving tree its common name.

BARK. Thin (⅛ inch); furrowed and scaly; light gray-brown; astringent.

WOOD. Very heavy; hard; strong; close-grained; durable; ring-porous; heartwood red-brown; sapwood thin, light yellow.

SILVICAL CHARACTERS. Lower Sonoran zone; intolerant; vigorous reproducer; thrives in driest and poorest soils; on dry mesas, plains, and in low canyons.

Eight other species of Acacia may reach tree size in the Southwest:

* * *

1. *A. amentacea* DC., with long spines, yellow flowers in spikes, and a flattened arcuate legume; southwestern Texas.
2. *A. angustissima* Kuntze, with no spines, white flowers in capitate heads, and flat legume; New Mexico and Texas.
3. *A. constricta* var. *paucispina* Woot., with long spines, yellow flowers in capitate heads, and a terete legume; Texas to Arizona.
4. *A. emoryana* Benth., with short spines, flowers in short spikes, and flat, hairy legume with thickened sutures.
5. *A. farnesiana* (L.) Willd., with spines, yellow flowers in capitate heads, and a terete legume; Texas.
6. *A. millefolia* S. Wats., with slender or no spines, cream-colored flowers in racemes, and a very flat pod; rare in southern Arizona and Mexico.
7. *A. tortuosa* Willd., like No. 5 but with longer pod (3–5″); Texas.
8. *A. wrightii* Benth., yellow flowers in spikes; short spines; Texas.

Twig with leaves and fruit, x ½.

LEGUMINOSAE

Mesquite

Prosopis juliflora (Sw.) DC. [*Prosopis chilensis* (Mol.) Stuntz.]

HABIT. A shrub or small tree rarely 20 feet high and 6–8 inches in diameter; trunk short; crown loose and straggling.

LEAVES. Alternate; evenly, doubly (rarely 3–4) pinnate; pinnae with 12–30 linear to linear-oblong, small, deciduous, glabrous leaflets ½–2 inches long; petioles glandular and spine-tipped; stipules membranaceous, deciduous.

FLOWERS. Nearly regular; perfect; fragrant; minute; in spikes 1½–4 inches long; green-white; stamens 10.

FRUIT. Linear, flat to subterete, indehiscent, yellowish, straight or falcate legume 4–9 inches long and ¼–½ inch wide; edible. Seed: oblong, compressed, light brown, ¼ inch long.

TWIGS. Slender; round; smooth; yellow-green becoming darker; usually with spines ½–2 inches long. Winter buds: terminal absent; lateral small, obtuse, dark brown.

BARK. Thick; dark red-brown; furrowed and scaly.

WOOD. Very heavy; hard; close-grained; not strong; very durable; ring-porous; heartwood dark brown or red; sapwood clear yellow, thin; used for posts, fuel, etc.

SILVICAL CHARACTERS. Intolerant; long-lived; adapted to desert sites by huge taproot descending 40–50 feet; abundant seeder; aggressive; confined to areas below 6,000 feet.

GENERAL. Screwbean mesquite, *Prasopis pubescens* Benth., ranging from Texas to California and north into Nevada and Utah, is readily distinguished by its thick, linear, indehiscent, pale yellow legume 1–2 inches long, which is twisted by 12–20 turns into a narrow, straight spiral.

* * *

Mimosa. Silktree

Albizia julibrissin Durazz.

A handsome ornamental which is widely planted and has escaped from Maryland to Indiana and south. The powder puff appearance of the flowers is distinctive.

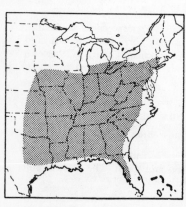

a. Winter twig, x 1.

b. Portion of twig, front view, enlarged.

c. Portion of twig, side view, enlarged.

d. Leaf, x ⅔.

e. Flowering branchlet, x 1.

f. Vertical section of flower, enlarged.

g. Fruit, x ½.

[272]

LEGUMINOSAE

Eastern Redbud

Cercis canadensis L.

HABIT. Usually a shrub, but not infrequently a small tree up to 40 feet high and 2½ feet in diameter; frequently planted as an ornamental.

LEAVES. Alternate; simple; broad ovate to reniform; 3–5 inches in diameter; apex acute; base cordate; margins entire; glabrous; deciduous; petioles long, slender; stipules small, membranaceous, caducous.

FLOWERS. Irregular (subpapilionaceous); perfect; in simple fascicles; appearing before the leaves; calyx short, top-shaped, purple, 5-toothed, persistent; corolla 5-petaled, rose-colored; stamens 10, free, inserted in 2 rows on margin of thin disk, persistent; ovary short-stalked; ovules numerous in 2 ranks.

FRUIT. Stalked, flat, oblong, russet-brown legume 2–3 inches long; tipped with remnant of style. Seed: ¼ inch long, ovoid or oblong, compressed, red-brown.

TWIGS. Slender; round; unarmed; marked by numerous pale lenticels and elevated leaf scars. Winter buds: terminal absent; axillary small, scaly, obtuse, chestnut-brown.

BARK. Thin; gray; smooth or becoming scaly on old trunks.

WOOD. Heavy; hard; not strong; ring-porous; heartwood dark red-brown; sapwood white, thin; unimportant.

SILVICAL CHARACTERS. Tolerant; reproduction vigorous; typical of bottomlands and stream borders; a variety recognized in the Southwest is *texensis* (S. Wats.) Hopkins, the Texas redbud.

* * *

California Redbud

Cercis occidentalis Torr.

This similar species is usually shrubby but has been reported as a tree in California and in the Grand Canyon. Its range is from southern Utah and Nevada to California and Arizona and it differs from Eastern redbud in having leaves 2–3 inches long which are obtuse or emarginate at the apex.

KENTUCKY COFFEETREE

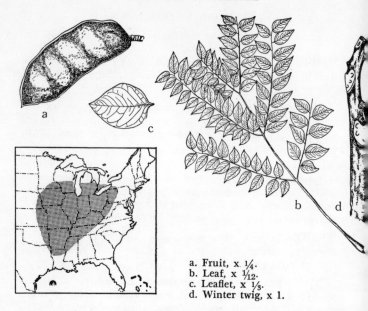

a. Fruit, x ¼.
b. Leaf, x 1/12.
c. Leaflet, x ⅓.
d. Winter twig, x 1.

YELLOWWOOD

a. Fruit, x ⅓.
b. Flowering twig, x ¼.

LEGUMINOSAE

Kentucky Coffeetree

Gymnocladus dioicus (L.) K. Koch

HABIT. A medium-sized to large tree 50–75 feet high and 2–3 feet in diameter (max. 110 by 4 feet); open, pyramidal crown.

LEAVES. Alternate; doubly pinnate with 40 or more leaflets; 1–3 feet long; leaflets 2–2½ inches long, ovate, acute, entire, short-stalked, glabrous, dark green above and paler below; appearing late in the spring; deciduous.

FLOWERS. Nearly regular; dioecious; in racemes; calyx tubular, hairy; petals 5, greenish-white; stamens 10; ovary hairy; appearing after the leaves.

FRUIT. A turgid, woody, short-stalked, red-brown legume 4–10 inches long and 1½–2 inches wide; containing sugary pulp between the 6–9 seeds. Seed: ovoid, ¾ inch long, with thick bony coat, used as substitute for coffee in early days.

TWIGS. Very stout; unarmed; coated at first with short, dense, red hairs; roughened by large, pale, conspicuous leaf scars. Winter buds: terminal absent, lateral small, depressed, brown, silky hairy, with 2 in the axil of each leaf.

BARK. Smooth and brown to gray on limbs; becoming ¾–1 inch thick, gray, fissured, and with distinctive reflexed scales.

WOOD. Unimportant; heavy and hard; ring-porous; reddish and closely resembling honey locust; sapwood very thin, white.

SILVICAL CHARACTERS. Intolerant; fast growing; rare throughout its range; a handsome tree often planted as an ornamental.

* * *

Yellowwood

Cladrastis lutea (Michx.) K. Koch

This medium-sized tree is rare and unimportant except for occasional use as an ornamental. It is characterized by alternate, deciduous, pinnately compound leaves with 5–11 leaflets, each 3–4 inches long, obovate, entire, acute, and yellow-green; by perfect, showy, white, papilionaceous flowers; by a glabrous, flat, short-stalked, linear legume 3–4 inches long containing 4–6 flat, brown seeds; by slender, glabrous twigs containing naked lateral buds enclosed in the hollow base of the petiole; and by smooth, thin, gray bark.

a. Winter twig, x 1.

b. Section through lateral buds.

c. Leaf, x ⅙.

d. Leaflet, x 1.

e. Flowering branchlet, x ½.

f. Staminate flower, enlarged.

g. Pistillate flower, enlarged.

h. Fruit, x ¼.

i. Spine from trunk, x ½.

LEGUMINOSAE

HONEYLOCUST
Gleditsia triacanthos L.

HABIT. A medium-sized tree 50–75 feet high and 2–3 feet in diameter (max. 140 by 5 feet); open, spreading crown; trunk and branches usually armed with clusters of straight or branched spines several inches long.

LEAVES. Alternate; pinnately or bi-pinnately compound with both types often on the same tree; 6–12 inches long; leaflets ½–1½ inches long, lanceolate-oblong, remotely crenulate, thin, glabrous, lustrous dark green above and yellowgreen below; deciduous.

FLOWERS. Regular; polygamous; small; in axillary racemes; calyx 3–5 lobed; petals 3–5, greenish-white; stamens 3–10; ovary 1-celled, woolly; appearing after the leaves.

FRUIT. A strap-shaped, red-brown, usually twisted legume 12–18 inches long and 1 inch wide; containing 12–14 dark brown, oval seeds, each about ⅓ inch long.

TWIGS. Slender to rather stout; usually with straight or 3-branched spines 2–3 inches long; green to red-brown. Winter buds: terminal absent, lateral minute, brownish, 3 or more superposed.

BARK. Smooth and gray on limbs; becoming ½–¾ inch thick, gray to nearly black, and broken by longitudinal fissures into plates or scaly ridges.

WOOD. Of slight importance; heavy and hard; durable; red-brown; ring-porous; used for veneer and fuel.

SILVICAL CHARACTERS. Intolerant; fast growing; hardy; prefers rich, moist sites, but hardy on arid, sandy locations; the thornless variety *inermis* (Pursh) Schneid., is commonly planted in cities.

* * *

WATERLOCUST
Gleditsia aquatica Marsh.

This similar species is native to the coastal region from North Carolina to Texas and up the Mississippi Valley to southern Indiana. It is readily distinguished by its oval, oblique, 1–3 seeded legume, which is 1–2 inches long. The Texas honeylocust, x *Gleditsia texana* Sarg., is a hybrid between waterlocust and honeylocust and is characterized by a legume 4–5 inches long. It has been reported from Indiana to Texas.

a. Twig with leaves and flowers, x 1

b. Twig with fruit, x 1.

LEGUMINOSAE

BLUE PALOVERDE. GREENBARKED-ACACIA

Cercidium floridum Benth. [*Cercidium torreyanum*
(Wat.) Sarg.]

HABIT. A thorny shrub or small tree 15–30 feet high; wide, irregular, open crown with stout, tortuous branches.

LEAVES. Alternate; doubly and evenly pinnate with 2–3 pairs of oblong, obtuse, glaucous leaflets $\frac{1}{12}$–$\frac{1}{6}$ inch long; few and totaling less area than green twigs; falling soon, but frequently bearing a second crop during the rainy season.

FLOWERS. Nearly regular; perfect; in conspicuous 4–5-flowered, axillary racemes; on slender pedicels $\frac{3}{4}$–1 inch long; calyx 5-lobed, reflexed; corolla of 5, clawed, bright yellow petals, $\frac{3}{4}$ inch in diameter; stamens 10, free, exserted.

FRUIT. Oblong, compressed or somewhat turgid legume 3–4 inches long and $\frac{1}{4}$–$\frac{1}{3}$ inch wide; straight or somewhat contracted between the 2–8 seeds. Seed: ovoid, compressed.

TWIGS. Stout; glabrous and glaucous; light yellow or pale olive-green; armed with thin spines $\frac{1}{4}$ inch long.

BARK. Thin ($\frac{1}{8}$ inch); smooth and pale olive-green on young trunks, becoming furrowed, scaly, and red-brown.

WOOD. Unimportant; soft; weak; close-grained; ring-porous; heartwood light brown; sapwood yellow; used as fuel.

SILVICAL CHARACTERS. Lower Sonoran zone; intolerant; abundant seeder; typical of arid, desert sinks, canyons, and depressions; in sandy or gravelly soil.

GENERAL. Two other species may reach tree size in the Southwest:
1. Yellow Paloverde, *C. microphyllum* (Torr.) R. & J., in California and Arizona has leaves with 4–6 pairs of leaflets; a 1–2 seeded legume; and twigs terminating in spines.
2. Border Paloverde, *C. macrum* Johnst., in southern Texas has slightly glandular leaflets, $\frac{1}{16}$ inch long, and a 2–3 seeded legume.

The distribution map includes *floridum* and *microphyllum* in Arizona and California and *macrum* in Texas.

* * *

JERUSALEM-THORN

Parkinsonia aculeata L.

Jerusalem-thorn is a similar small tree ranging from southern Arizona and Texas to South America. It differs from Paloverde in having a linear, terete legume and leaves with 25–30 pairs of small leaflets and a spinescent rachis.

a. Twig with leaves and flowers, x

b. Fruit, x ½.

LEGUMINOSAE

Mescalbean. Frijolito

Sophora secundiflora (Ortega) Lag. (*Broussonetia secundiflora* Ortega)

HABIT. A shrub or rarely a small tree 20–35 feet high and 6–8 inches in diameter; crown narrow with numerous upright branches; commonly thicket-forming.

LEAVES. Alternate; unequally pinnate with 7–9 oblong-elliptic, coriaceous, glabrous, entire, thick-margined leaflets 1–2½ inches long and ½–1½ inches wide; rounded at apex; lustrous and yellow-green above, paler below; persistent.

FLOWERS. Irregular (papilionaceous); perfect; fragrant; appearing with leaves; in conspicuous 1-sided, canescent, terminal racemes; on stout pedicels; calyx campanulate, 2 upper teeth larger; corolla 1 inch long, of 5, clawed, violet-blue or rarely white, petals, the standard broad, erect; stamens 10, mostly free or slightly diadelphous at base; ovary coated with long, silky, white hairs; ovules numerous.

FRUIT. Oblong, terete, indehiscent legume 1–7 inches long and ½ inch broad; thick, woody valves; much contracted between seeds; covered with dense, hoary tomentum; tipped with remnant of style. Seed: short-oblong, rounded, ½ inch long, bright scarlet, contain sophorin and are very poisonous.

TWIGS. Slender; round; unarmed; tomentose at first, becoming glabrous and pale orange-brown. Winter buds: terminal absent; lateral minute, scaly.

BARK. Thin, red-brown.

WOOD. Very heavy; hard; close-grained; ring-porous; heartwood orange; sapwood thick, yellow; unimportant.

SILVICAL CHARACTERS. Lower Sonoran zone; intolerant; fibrous roots; moist sites; borders of streams, and seacoasts.

GENERAL. The Texas sophora, *S. affinis* Torr. & Gray, of Texas, Arkansas, Oklahoma, and Louisiana, differs in having thin deciduous leaves, a fleshy legume, and white flowers in axillary racemes.

* * *

Siberian Pea Tree

Caragana arborescens Lam.

This introduced form has been extensively planted for shelterbelts and as an ornamental. It is characterized by even pinnate leaves with 8–12 leaflets; and papilionaceous, yellow flowers, ½–¾ inch long, in fascicles of 1–4.

a. Winter twig, x 1.

b. Vertical section through later buds, enlarged.

c. Leaf, x ½.

d. Raceme of flowers, x ½.

e. Flower, with part of corolla removed, enlarged.

f. Fruit, x ½.

[282]

LEGUMINOSAE

BLACK LOCUST

Robinia pseudoacacia L.

HABIT. A medium-sized tree 40–60 feet high and 1–2 feet in diameter (max. 100 by 5 feet); open, irregular crown.

LEAVES. Alternate; pinnately compound; 8–14 inches long; with 7–21 ovate-oblong, entire, glabrous leaflets, 1½–2 inches long, dark blue-green above and paler below; deciduous.

FLOWERS. Papilionaceous; perfect; showy; fragrant; in racemes; calyx bell-shaped; corolla 5-petaled, white; stamens 10; ovary 1-celled; appearing after the leaves.

FRUIT. A smooth, dark brown, flat, linear-oblong legume, 2–4 inches long; containing 4–8 flat brown seeds about ³⁄₁₆ inch long.

TWIGS. Rather stout; red-brown; armed with stipular spines about ½ inch long. Winter buds: terminal absent, lateral minute, red-hairy, submerged within leaf scar, 3–4 superposed.

BARK. Red-brown to nearly black; deeply fissured into rounded, scaly ridges.

WOOD. Moderately important; very heavy and hard; very durable; dark brown or golden; used for posts, ties, and insulator pins.

SILVICAL CHARACTERS. Intolerant; fast growing; seriously threatened by locust borer (*Cyllene robiniae*); prefers moist, rich soils, but hardy on poor, dry sites; a clan of this species which propagates only by vegetative means is known as Shipmast locust (var. *rectissima* Raber).

GENERAL. There are about 20 species of *Robinia*, all native to North America, with 4 reported to reach tree size.

These tree species are keyed out below:

1. Legume, twigs, and peduncle glabrous or nearly so.............
   ....*R. pseudoacacia* L., **Black Locust**
1. Legume and peduncle hispid, glandular, or viscid.
   2. Twigs glabrous; usually a shrub; eastern...................
      ....*R. kelseyi* Hutchins, **Kelsey Locust**
   2. Twigs glandular pubescent or viscid.
      3. Glands not viscid. Southwestern.........................
         ....*R. neomexicana* A. Gray, **New Mexican Locust**
      3. Glands exuding a clammy, sticky substance; eastern United States..................*R. viscosa* Vent, **Clammy Locust**

Twig with leaves and fruit, x 1/

RUTACEAE

Hoptree. Wafer-ash

Ptelea trifoliata L.

HABIT. An unarmed shrub or small tree 20–25 feet high and 6–8 inches in diameter; crown round-topped.

LEAVES. Alternate or rarely opposite; compound with 3 (rarely 5) subsessile, ovate to oblong leaflets; acuminate at apex; entire or crenulate-serrate margins; becoming glabrous and rather leathery; dark green above, pale and dotted with transparent glands below; deciduous; long-petioled.

FLOWERS. Regular; polygamous; in terminal cymes or compound umbels; on pubescent pedicels; calyx 4–5-parted, pubescent; corolla green-white; 4–5 petaled; stamens 3–4.

FRUIT. Dehiscent samara; 2–3-celled; broad, thin, almost orbicular wing, nearly 1 inch across; in drooping clusters on slender pedicels; persisting on branches through winter. Seed: ⅓ inch long, oblong, acute, dark red-brown.

TWIGS. Slender; round; pubescent at first, becoming glabrous, dark brown, lustrous and marked by wartlike excrescences and conspicuous leaf scars. Winter buds: terminal absent; lateral small, depressed, pale, tomentose.

BARK. Smooth; thin; bitter; ill-scented; dark brown on old trunks; that of the roots sometimes used as a tonic.

WOOD. Rather heavy; hard; close-grained; ring-porous; heartwood yellow-brown; sapwood thin; unimportant.

SILVICAL CHARACTERS. Rather tolerant and often an "understory" tree; dry, rocky soils.

GENERAL. The western form ranging from Texas to Colorado, Utah, and California is known as narrowleaf hoptree, *P. augustifolia* Benth.

* * *

Hercules-club. Prickly-ash

Zanthoxylum clava-herculis L.

A distinctive small tree with peculiar conical, corky growths 1 inch or more in diameter on the smooth gray bark; leaves alternate, late-deciduous, pinnately compound with 7–19 leathery, ovate, toothed leaflets; dioecious, clustered flowers; an ovoid, brown, wrinkled capsule ¼ inch long, with the single black seed hanging from it at maturity; and spiny twigs. The common prickly-ash, *Z. americanum* Mill., ranges widely through eastern North America and while commonly a shrub, has been reported as a small tree.

a. Winter twig, x 1.
b. Leaf, x ⅛.
c. Leaflet, x ½.
d. Staminate inflorescence, x ¼.
e. Staminate flower, enlarged.
f. Pistillate flower, enlarged.
g. Fruit, x 1.

ELEPHANTTREE

(a) Twig with fruit and leaves, x 1.

SIMAROUBACEAE

AILANTHUS. TREE-OF-HEAVEN

Ailanthus altissima (Mill.) Swingle (*Ailanthus glandulosa* Desf.)

HABIT. A handsome naturalized tree 40–60 feet high and 2–4 feet in diameter; loose, open crown with very large leaves.

LEAVES. Alternate; deciduous; 1½–4 feet long; pinnately compound with 13–41 leaflets; leaflets ovate-lanceolate, 3–6 inches long, entire except for 1–2 glandular teeth at the base.

FLOWERS. Regular; polygamo-dioecious; small; yellow-green; in panicles; calyx 5-lobed; petals 5; staminate ill-smelling; appearing after the leaves.

FRUIT. Oblong, twisted samara 1–1½ inches long with seed in center; yellow-green; in crowded clusters.

TWIGS. Very thick; velvety-downy; red-brown. Winter buds: terminal absent, lateral small, subglobose, brown.

BARK. Thin, gray, and smooth; becoming shallowly furrowed with age.

WOOD. Unimportant; soft; weak; pale yellow; ring-porous.

SILVICAL CHARACTERS. Intolerant; very fast-growing; short-lived; hardy on sterile sites and in smoky cities; root-suckers aggressively; a common city ornamental.

* * *

MELIACEAE

CHINABERRY

Melia azedarach L.

This small Asiatic tree is commonly cultivated and naturalized from North Carolina to Oklahoma and south. It is characterized by alternate, bi-pinnately compound, tardily deciduous leaves 10–30 inches long with ovate, toothed or lobed, glabrous leaflets 1–2 inches long; purple, showy flowers in loose panicles; and distinctive subglobose, yellow, fleshy drupes ½–¾ inch long. A low-spreading, flat-topped variety known as the umbrella Chinaberry (var. *umbraculifera* Sarg.) is popular. The West Indies mahogany, *Swietenia mahagoni* Jacq., is native to southern Florida.

* * *

BURSERACEAE

ELEPHANTTREE

Bursera microphylla A. Gray

This rarely becomes a small tree in the desert in southern California and Arizona. It is characterized by alternate, deciduous, bi-pinnately compound leaves with 20–40 leaflets ¼ inch long; small, polygamous, white flowers; and a red, capsule-like drupe ¼ inch long. The fragrant bursera, *B. fagaroides* Eng. is a similar form in southern Arizona. Gumbo-limbo, *B. simaruba* Sarg., is native to southern Florida.

a. Fruit cluster, x ½.
b. Single fruit, x 2.
c. Leaves and flowers, x ½.
d. Laminate flower, x 2.
e. Pistillate flower, x 2.

ANACARDIACEAE

Staghorn Sumac

Rhus typhina Torner

HABIT. A shrub or small tree to 40 feet high and 1 foot in diameter; commonly in broad thickets.

LEAVES. Alternate; deciduous; pinnately compound with 11–31 oblong, glabrous, serrate, dark green leaflets each 2–5 inches long.

FLOWERS. Regular; dioecious or polygamous; small; green-white; in dense, hairy panicles 6–12 inches long; after the leaves.

FRUIT. Compact, conelike clusters of red, hairy drupes, each ¼ inch.

TWIGS. Thick; velvety-hairy; milky juice; thick pith. Winter buds: terminal absent, lateral ¼ inch long, conical, brown, silky hairy.

BARK. Thin; dark brown; smooth, becoming scaly with age.

WOOD. Unimportant; soft and weak; ring-porous; orange-colored.

SILVICAL CHARACTERS. Intolerant; fast-growing; short-lived.

About 17 species are native to North America with 9 rarely reaching tree size and keyed out below. Two species, poisonous to the touch, are placed either in the genus *Rhus* or *Toxicodendron*; these are poison-sumac, *T. vernix* (L.) Ktze. and poison ivy or oak, *T. radicans* (L.) Ktze.
1. Leaves simple or rarely 3-foliolate, leathery, evergreen.
  2. Leaves broadly ovate, entire; flowers in dense spikes; fruit red; California and Arizona.........*R. ovata* S. Wats., **Sugar Sumac**
  2. Leaves oval to ovate, rounded at apex.
    3. Fruit white in branched panicles; southern California.........
    ....*R. laurina* Nutt., **Laurel Sumac**
    3. Fruit red.
      4. Leaves toothed or entire; southern coastal California.......
      ......*R. integrifolia* (Nutt.) B. & H., **Mahogany Sumac**
      4. Leaves entire; Yuma County, Arizona...................
      ....*R. kearneyi* Bark., **Kearney Sumac**
1. Leaves pinnately compound, deciduous.
  5. Flowers in dense, terminal panicles; fruit red, hairy.
    6. Twigs and petioles velvety-hairy...................
    ....*R. typhina* Torn., **Staghorn Sumac**
    6. Twigs and petioles glabrous or hairy.
      7. Rachis terete; twigs glabrous and glaucous; leaves serrate; most of North America......*R. glabra* L., **Smooth Sumac**
      7. Rachis winged; twigs pubescent; leaves nearly entire.
        8. Leaflets ovate-lanceolate; New Hampshire to Michigan and Kansas, south to Georgia and Texas..............
        ....*R. copallina* L., **Shining Sumac**
        8. Leaflets narrow-lanceolate, often falcate; south Oklahoma to Texas and New Mexico...................
        ....*R. lanceolata* Britt., **Prairie Shining Sumac**
  5. Flowers not numerous in terminal or axillary panicles.
    9. Fruit red; rachis winged; leaves less than 1 inch long; west Texas to Arizona........*R. microphylla* Engelm., **Littleleaf Sumac**
    9. Fruit white; rachis terete; leaves ½–2½ inches long; Quebec to Minnesota, south to Gulf...................
    ....*R. (or T.) vernix* (L.) Ktze., **Poison Sumac**

a. Fruiting branch, x ½.
b. Flowering branch, x ½.

MOUNTAIN WINTERBERRY

a. Flowering branch, x ½.
b. Fruiting branch, x ½.

AQUIFOLIACEAE

AMERICAN HOLLY

Ilex opaca Ait.

HABIT. The largest native holly forming a tree 40–60 feet high and 1–2 feet in diameter (max. 100 by 3½ feet); narrow, dense crown.

LEAVES. Alternate; simple; persistent 3 years; elliptical; 2–4 inches long; spiny toothed or sometimes entire; with a spiny tip; leathery; yellow-green above, paler or yellow below.

FLOWERS. Regular; dioecious; small; solitary or in short cymes; green-white; appearing with the leaves.

FRUIT. A berry-like drupe persisting into the winter; bright red; ¼ inch long; with a bony nutlet in each of 3–8 cells of ovary.

TWIGS. Slender; glabrous; green with single bundle trace. Winter buds: terminal present, scaly, ⅛–¼ inch long, ciliate.

BARK. Thin; smooth; gray-white; with warty growths.

WOOD. Unimportant; hard and heavy; white; fine-textured; diffuse-porous; used for turning, novelties, and finish.

SILVICAL CHARACTERS. Tolerant; slow-growing; reproduction sparse; commonly cultivated; rare near cities because of Christmas demand.

* * *

About 14 species of *Ilex* are native to the eastern or southeastern parts of the United States, six of these commonly forming trees, and keyed out below. Most of the others, while typically shrubs up to 6 feet high, have been reported as rarely reaching tree size. The English holly, *I. aquifolium* L., is grown in plantations for decorations.

1. Leaves persistent, thick and leathery; pedicels with bractlets.
  2. Leaves with spiny teeth or a spiny tip.
    3. Flowers and fruits usually clustered on last year's twigs; cultivated in warm areas . . . . *I. aquifolium* L., **English Holly**
    3. Flowers and fruits usually single on current growth.
      4. Leaves less than twice as long as broad . . . . *I. opaca* Ait., **American Holly**
      4. Leaves more than twice as long as broad; coastal plain, Virginia to Louisiana . . . . *I. cassine* L., **Dahoon**
  2. Leaves without spiny teeth or tip, entire to serrate.
    5. Fruit red; coastal plain, Virginia to Texas.
      6. Leaves oblanceolate to oblong-obovate, entire . . . . *I. cassine* L., **Dahoon**
      6. Leaves oval with few crenate teeth *I. vomitoria* Ait., **Yaupon**
    5. Fruit brown-purple; southern Florida . . . . *I. krugiana* Loes., **Tawnyberry Holly**
1. Leaves deciduous, not leathery; pedicels without bractlets.
  7. Leaves sharply toothed; apex pointed; Massachusetts and New York, south to Florida and Louisiana . . . . *I. montana* T. & G., **Mountain Winterberry**
  7. Leaves with few rounded teeth; apex obtuse; Maryland to Kansas and south . . . . *I. decidua* Walt., **Possumhaw**

[291]

a. Twig with flowers, x 1.
b. Twig with fruit, x 1.

WAHOO

SWAMP CYRILLA

(a) Fruiting twig, x ½.

(a) Fruit, x 6; (b) Twig, x ½.

[292]

CELASTRACEAE

Canotia. Mohavethorn

Canotia holacantha Torr.

HABIT. An odd, leafless shrub or small shrublike tree 20–30 feet high; trunk short and stocky; branches rushlike.

FLOWERS. Regular; perfect; small; in 3–7-flowered fascicles; calyx 5-lobed, persistent, minute; corolla 5-petaled, white.

FRUIT. Dry, woody, ovoid, acuminate capsule 1 inch long; crowned with subulate, persistent style; 5-valved, splitting open at top. Seed: solitary or paired; about ¾ inch long.

TWIGS. Slender, rushlike, round, alternate, glabrous, rigid, and spine-tipped; pale green and carrying on photosynthetic functions; characteristic, black, triangular, cushion-like processes located at base of each twig and flower cluster.

BARK. Light brown and deeply furrowed.

WOOD. Heavy; hard; close-grained; light brown; diffuse-porous; unimportant.

SILVICAL CHARACTERS. Intolerant; monotypic genus; on dry, mountain slopes and mesas between 2,000–4,000 feet.

* * *

Wahoo. Burning Bush

Euonymus atropurpureus Jacq.

This widespread shrubby species reaches tree size in Arkansas and eastern Texas. It can be distinguished by its winged twigs; simple, opposite, petioled leaves; 4-parted flowers; and fleshy, capsular fruit enclosed in a thin scarlet aril. The western wahoo, *E. occidentalis* Nutt. is found in the Pacific Coast states.

* * *

CYRILLACEAE

Swamp Cyrilla

Cyrilla racemiflora L.

This small tree of wet sites in the Coastal Plain from Virginia to Texas is characterized by simple, alternate, oblong, entire, thick leaves 2–3 inches long; small, regular, perfect, white flowers in slender axillary racemes; and a 2-celled, ovoid, unwinged capsule ⅛ inch long.

The buckwheat-tree, *Cliftonia monophylla* (Lam.) Britt., is a similar species of the same habitat. It differs in having glandular-punctate leaves; flowers in terminal racemes; and a 3–4 celled capsule ¼ inch long with 2–4 wings.

[293]

ACERACEAE

THE MAPLES

Characteristics of the Genus *Acer* L.

HABIT. Deciduous trees or shrubs, with handsome foliage, usually assuming brillian colors in autumn.

LEAVES. Opposite; simple or compound; deciduous; petioled; without stipules; simple leaves palmately 3–7-lobed; compound leaves pinnate, with 3–7 leaflets.

FLOWERS. Regular; polygamous, dioecious, or rarely perfect; small; borne either in lateral fascicles from separate flower buds and appearing before the leaves, or in lateral and terminal racemes, panicles, or corymbs and appearing with or after the leaves; calyx colored, generally 5-parted; corolla usually 5-petaled or absent; stamens 4–12, usually 7–8; ovary 2-celled, 2-lobed, compressed, with 2 styles; ovules 2 in each cell, ascending.

FRUIT. Double samara united at base (key); each nutlike carpel laterally compressed and produced into large, obovate wing. Seed: usually solitary by abortion, ovoid, compressed.

TWIGS. Slender to moderately stout; round; pith homogeneous, round; marked at base by bud scales with ringlike scars; leaf scars more or less U-shaped, with 3 (rarely 5–7) bundle scars. Winter buds: with valvate or imbricated scales. inner scales accrescent, terminal buds larger than lateral.

BARK. Astringent and variable.

WOOD. Variable from soft to heavy and hard; diffuse-porous; pores all small and not crowded; rays distinct on cross section without lens; widely used for interior finish, etc., sap of some species manufactured into sugar.

SILVICAL CHARACTERS. Mostly tolerant; fibrous root systems; widely used for ornamental and shade trees.

GENERAL. This genus contains over 60 species of trees widely scattered through the Northern Hemisphere with one species extending into Sumatra and Java. In the United States there are 13 native species. Several introduced species are planted extensively, among these Norway and Sycamore maples are very common and better known than many native species (both are included in the key).

[294]

KEY TO THE SPECIES OF MAPLES

1. Leaves pinnately compound with 3–7 leaflets; twigs stout, smooth, with encircling leaf scars............*A. negundo* Boxelder, p. 307.
1. Leaves simple, palmately lobed (rarely compound in Rocky Mountain Maple).
   2. Leaves with closely, often doubly, toothed margins and sharp-angled sinuses between lobes................SOFT MAPLES.
      3. Winter buds bright green; leaves 4–7 inches across, 5-lobed, bluntly toothed; fruit wings 1½–2 inches long, diverging at right angle or less; Eurasian ornamental................
      ....*A. pseudoplatanus* L., Sycamore Maple
      3. Winter buds red to brownish; native.
         4. Flowers appearing before the leaves from lateral, leafless buds; fruits maturing in late spring; buds with 4–8 visible scales; upper trunk bark smooth, light gray; eastern.
            5. Leaves very deeply 5-lobed, sides of middle lobe diverging, silvery-white beneath; fruit woolly when young, wings 1½–2 inches long, widely diverging; petals absent......
            ....*A. saccharinum* Silver Maple, p. 299.
            5. Leaves 3–5 lobed, sides of middle lobe usually converging toward apex, pale green beneath; fruit smooth, wings ½–1 inch long, slightly diverging; petals present........
            ....*A. rubrum* Red Maple, p. 299.
         4. Flowers with petals, appearing with or after the leaves from leaf buds; fruit maturing in late summer; 2 (rarely 4) visible bud scales.
            6. Leaves essentially glabrous; flowers in corymbs; western.
               7. Leaves 7–9 lobed; fruit wings widely divergent; Pacific Coast............*A. circinatum* Vine Maple, p. 301.
               7. Leaves 3-lobed (rarely 3-parted); fruit wings not divergent; through west........................
               ......*A. glabrum* Rocky Mountain Maple, p. 301.
            6. Leaves hairy beneath; flowers in racemes; eastern.
               8. Leaves coarsely toothed, 3–5 lobed; fruit wings ½ inch long, diverging at about right angles; bark red-brown..
               ....*A. spicatum* Mountain Maple, p. 303.
               8. Leaves finely doubly toothed, 3-lobed at apex; fruit wings ¾ inch long, widely diverging; bark green with white stripes *A. pensylvanicum* Striped Maple, p. 303.
   2. Leaf lobes entire or with few remote teeth, or slightly lobed; sinuses rounded between lobes; buds with several scales; flowers appearing with leaves......................HARD MAPLES.
      9. Petioles red with milky juice; fruit wings 1½–2 inches long, widely diverging; leaves 5–7 lobed, 5–7 inches across; naturalized Eurasian species......*A. platanoides* L., Norway Maple
      9. Petioles with watery juice; fruit wings usually diverging at right angles or less; leaves 3–5 lobed; native.
         10. Buds red, scales hairy on margins; western.
            11. Leaves 8–12 inches across.......................
            ....*A. macrophyllum* Bigleaf Maple, p. 305.
            11. Leaves 2–5 inches across....................
            ....*A. grandidentatum* Bigtooth Maple, p. 305.
         10. Buds brown; eastern.
            12. Leaves 1½–3 inches across; bark smooth, pale; Virginia to Missouri and south.
               13. Leaves pale and hairy beneath; fruit wings diverging at right angles.....................
               ....*A. barbatum* Michx., Florida Maple
               13. Leaves green and hairy beneath; fruit wings diverging at more than right angles..................
               ....*A. leucoderme* Small, Chalk Maple
            12. Leaves 3–6 inches across; bark rough and dark; eastern North America.
               14. Twigs red-brown; leaves 5-lobed, glabrous beneath
               ....*A. saccharum* Sugar Maple, p. 297.
               14. Twigs orange; leaves mostly 3-lobed, usually hairy beneath........*A. nigrum* Black Maple, p. 297.

SUGAR MAPLE

a. Winter twig, x 1½.
b. Leaf, x ½.
c. Staminate flowering branchlet, x ½.
d. Pistillate flowering branchlet, x ½.
e. Fruit, x 1.

BLACK MAPLE

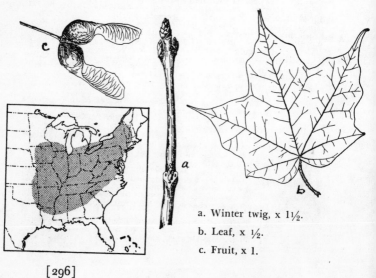

a. Winter twig, x 1½.

b. Leaf, x ½.

c. Fruit, x 1.

[296]

ACERACEAE

Sugar Maple

Acer saccharum Marsh. (*Acer saccharophorum* K. Koch)

HABIT. A handsome tree 60–80 feet high and 2–3 feet in diameter (max. 135 by 5½ feet); dense, broad, rounded crown.

LEAVES. Simple; orbicular; palmately 5-lobed (rarely 3-lobed); 3–5 inches long; lobe margins entire or sparingly wavy-toothed; thin and firm; glabrous; bright green above, paler below; turning bright red or yellow in autumn.

FLOWERS. Polygamous; in crowded corymbs; apetalous; yellow-green; appearing with the leaves.

FRUIT. Key U-shaped, with nearly parallel wings about 1 inch long; red-brown; glabrous; maturing in autumn.

TWIGS. Slender; smooth; red-brown; shiny. Winter buds: terminal ¼–⅜ inch long, acute, red-brown; nearly glabrous, with 4–8 pairs of visible scales.

BARK. Smooth and gray on young stems; becoming dark gray, thick, and deeply furrowed; often with long, scaly plates.

WOOD. Very important; hard, heavy and strong; flooring, furniture, etc.

SILVICAL CHARACTERS. Tolerant; rather slow-growing; long-lived; wide-spreading, lateral roots; important as an ornamental and as a source of maple syrup and sugar. The form growing on the Edwards Plateau of Texas has been designated the variety *sinuosum* Rous.

* * *

Black Maple

Acer nigrum Michx.

This species very closely resembles the sugar maple and by many authors is considered to be a variety of it. It is distinguished from the sugar maple by the following characters: leaves mostly 3-lobed and lower leaf surface and petioles downy, leaf blades thicker and drooping at sides; twigs orange-brown; buds hoary-pubescent; bark often nearly black and more deeply and sharply furrowed.

[297]

SILVER MAPLE

a. Leaf, x ½.
b. Winter twig, x 1.
c. Fruit, x ½.
d. Staminate flowers, x 1.
e. Pistillate flowers, x 1.

RED MAPLE

a. Leaf, x ½.
b. Winter twig, x 1.
c. Fruit, x ½.

ACERACEAE

Silver Maple

Acer saccharinum L.

HABIT. A handsome tree 60–80 feet high and 2–3 feet in diameter (max. 120 by 7½ feet); trunk often separating near ground into several upright branches; crown broad and rounded.

LEAVES. Simple; orbicular; deeply 5-lobed, with the side of the terminal lobe diverging toward the apex; 4–7 inches long; lobe margins sharply toothed; light green above, glabrous; silvery white below; turning pale yellow in autumn.

FLOWERS. Polygamous; in crowded fascicles; apetalous; red to yellow-green; appearing before the leaves.

FRUIT. Key with widely divergent wings 1½–2 inches long; greenish; glabrous; one samara often aborted; maturing in late spring and germinating immediately.

TWIGS. Slender; dark red; lustrous; with fetid odor when bruised. Winter buds: terminal ⅛–¼ inch long, blunt, dark red, with 2–4 pairs of visible scales with ciliate margins.

BARK. Smooth and light gray on young stems; on old trunks becoming separated into scaly plates by narrow fissures.

WOOD. Moderately important; less heavy and hard than sugar maple and used as a substitute for it.

SILVICAL CHARACTERS. Tolerant; fast-growing; rather short-lived; moist sites; wide-spreading lateral roots; a common ornamental.

* * *

Red Maple

Acer rubrum L.

This species closely resembles silver maple and differs from it in the following characters:

LEAVES. Palmately 3-lobed (rarely 5-lobed) with short, broad lobes; the sides of the terminal lobe converging toward the apex; 2–6 inches long; lobe margins toothed; glabrous; light green above, paler and glaucous below; turning scarlet in autumn.

FLOWERS. Petals present; reddish.

FRUIT. Key with slightly divergent wings ½–1 inch long.

TWIGS. Without fetid odor when bruised.

ROCKY MOUNTAIN MAPLE

a. Twig with leaf and fruit, x ½.
b. and c. Different forms of leaves, x ½.
d. Fruit, x 1.

VINE MAPLE

a) Leaf, x ½;   (b) Fruit, x ⅔.

ACERACEAE

Rocky Mountain Maple. Dwarf Maple
Acer glabrum Torr.

HABIT. A shrub or small tree rarely 20–30 feet high and 6–12 inches in diameter; narrow crown with small branches.

LEAVES. Mostly 3–5-lobed and simple, but sometimes divided into 3 leaflets; 3–5 inches long; sharply and doubly serrate; glabrous; thin; dark green above, paler below.

FLOWERS. Mostly dioecious; in loose, racemose corymbs: petals yellow-green; appearing after the leaves.

FRUIT. Key with slightly spreading or nearly erect wings. ¾–⅞ inch long; glabrous; often rose-colored in summer.

TWIGS. Slender; glabrous; becoming bright red-brown. Winter buds: acute, ⅛–¼ inch long, bright red.

BARK. Thin, smooth, dark red-brown.

WOOD. Unimportant; heavy; hard; close-grained.

SILVICAL CHARACTERS. Rather tolerant; in moist locations; the northwestern form (var. *douglasii* Dibb.) has shallower leaf sinuses.

* * *

Vine Maple
Acer circinatum Pursh

HABIT. A shrub or small tree rarely 35 feet high; often vine-like or prostrate and forming dense thickets; irregular crown.

LEAVES. Simple; orbicular; 7–11 lobed; 2–6 inches long; lobes sharply doubly toothed; glabrous; light green above, paler below; turning red or orange in the autumn.

FLOWERS. Polygamo-monoecious; in loose corymbs; petals greenish-white, shorter than red calyx: appearing with the leaves.

FRUIT. Key with widely divergent wings 1½ inches long; glabrous; red; maturing in late autumn.

TWIGS. Slender; glabrous; green to red-brown. Winter buds: terminal ⅛ inch long, obtuse, bright red.

BARK. Thin; smooth or with shallow fissures; bright red-brown.

WOOD. Unimportant; heavy and hard; used for handles and fuel.

SILVICAL CHARACTERS. Very tolerant; moist stream banks.

STRIPED MAPLE

a. Winter twig, x ⅔.
b. Twig, enlarged.
c. Leaf, x ½.
d. Fruit, x ⅔.
e. Staminate flower,
   enlarged.
f. Pistillate flower, enlarged.

MOUNTAIN MAPLE

a. Winter twig, x ⅔.

b. Twig, enlarged.

c. Leaf, x ½.

d. Fruit, x ⅔.

ACERACEAE

STRIPED MAPLE. MOOSEWOOD

Acer pensylvanicum L.

HABIT. A shrub or small tree rarely 25 feet high and 8 inches in diameter; striped, upright branches with compact crown.

LEAVES. Simple; orbicular; shallowly 3-lobed above the middle; 5–6 inches long; sharply doubly toothed; glabrous; yellow-green above, paler below; turning pale yellow in autumn.

FLOWERS. Usually monoecious; in pendulous racemes; petals bright yellow; appearing after the leaves.

FRUIT. Key with widely divergent wings ¾ inch long; glabrous; red-brown; maturing in autumn.

TWIGS. Slender; smooth; red to green-brown; mottled. Winter buds: terminal ½ inch long; bright red; short-stalked.

BARK. Thin; red-brown to bright green; marked by vertical, broad, white stripes.

WOOD. Unimportant; rather light and soft; pinkish brown.

SILVICAL CHARACTERS. Tolerant; cool, moist, shaded sites.

* * *

MOUNTAIN MAPLE

Acer spicatum Lam.

HABIT. A shrub or small tree rarely 35 feet high and 8 inches in diameter; upright branches, forming a compact, rounded crown.

LEAVES. Simple; orbicular; shallowly 3-lobed (rarely 5-lobed) above the middle; 3–5 inches long; coarsely toothed; dark green and glabrous above, white downy below; turning red to orange in autumn.

FLOWERS. Polygamous; in erect, terminal racemes; petals yellow-green; appearing after the leaves.

FRUIT. Key with widely divergent wings ½–1 inch long; glabrous; bright red; maturing in autumn.

TWIGS. Slender; slightly hairy; red to brown. Winter buds: terminal ⅛ inch long, bright red, more or less hairy.

BARK. Very thin; red-brown; smooth or slightly furrowed.

WOOD. Unimportant, rather light and soft; light brown.

SILVICAL CHARACTERS. Tolerant; cool, moist, shaded sites but less demanding of shade than striped maple; a common ornamental.

BIGLEAF MAPLE

(a) Leaf, x ⅕; (b) Fruit, x 1.

BIGTOOTH MAPLE

(a) Leaf, x 1; (b) Fruit, x 1.

ACERACEAE

BIGLEAF MAPLE

Acer macrophyllum Pursh

HABIT. A medium-sized tree often 80–100 feet high and 3–4 feet in diameter (max. 9 feet); narrow, compact crown.

LEAVES. Simple; orbicular; palmately 5-lobed; 8–12 inches long; lobe margins entire or sparingly wavy-toothed; glabrous; bright green above, paler below; turning bright orange in autumn.

FLOWERS. Polygamous; in pendulous racemes; petals present, bright yellow, ¼ inch long; appearing with the leaves.

FRUIT. Key with slightly diverging wings 1¼–2 inches long; wings densely hairy over seed cavity, nearly glabrous elsewhere; maturing in autumn.

TWIGS. Stout; smooth; red to green-brown. Winter buds: terminal ¼ inch long, blunt, with 3-4 pairs of red-green, hairy-margined scales.

BARK. Smooth and gray-brown on young stems; becoming red-brown, deeply fissured and broken into square scales on the surface.

WOOD. One of few important hardwoods on West Coast; medium hard and strong; veneer, furniture, flooring, etc.

SILVICAL CHARACTERS. Tolerant; moist sites; fast-growing; wide, shallow roots; vigorous reproduction; a common ornamental.

* * *

BIGTOOTH MAPLE

Acer grandidentatum Nutt.

HABIT. A small tree 30–40 feet high and 8–10 inches in diameter.

LEAVES. Simple; orbicular; 3–5 lobed; 2–5 inches in diameter; lobe margins entire or lobulate; dark green and lustrous above, paler and hairy below; turning red or yellow before falling.

FLOWERS. Polygamous; calyx yellow; petals absent.

FRUIT. Key with slightly spreading wings ½–1 inch long; glabrous or sparingly hairy; green at maturity in autumn.

TWIGS. Slender; glabrous; bright red. Terminal bud red, ¹⁄₁₆ inch long.

BARK. Thin; dark brown; with platelike scales.

SILVICAL CHARACTERS. Rather tolerant; moist sites; shallow roots.

[305]

a. Winter twig, x 1.

b. Leaf, x ½.

c. Staminate flowering
   branchlet, x ½.

d. Staminate flower,
   enlarged.

e. Pistillate flowering
   branchlet, x ½.

f. Pistillate flower, enlarged.

g. Fruit, x 1.

ACERACEAE

BOXELDER

Acer negundo L.

HABIT. A small tree, rarely 75 feet high and 4 feet in diameter; trunk usually irregular and dividing near ground into several, stout, wide-spreading branches.

LEAVES. Compound, 3 (rarely 5–7) leaflets; petiole long, slender, puberulous; leaflets ovate to lanceolate, 3–4 inches long, and 1½–4 inches wide, glabrous, acuminate, coarsely serrate and sometimes 3-lobed at base.

FLOWERS. Dioecious; minute; the male fascicled; the female in drooping racemes; appearing with leaves or a little before them; calyx 5-lobed, hairy, yellow-green; corolla absent; stamens 4–6 with slender, exserted, hairy filaments; ovary hairy, partly enclosed by calyx.

FRUIT. Pendent; 1–2 inches long; glabrous; ripening in autumn; in drooping racemes 6–8 inches long. Seed: narrowed at the ends, smooth, bright red-brown, ½ inch long.

TWIGS. Moderately stout; greenish; pubescent, or rarely nearly glabrous; marked by conspicuous bud scale scars and crescent-shaped leaf scars which surround the twig. Winter buds: acute, ⅛–¼ inch long, tomentose.

BARK. Thin (¼–½ inch); pale gray or light brown; deeply divided by furrows into broad, rounded ridges.

WOOD. Light, soft, close-grained, weak; heartwood cream-white to yellow-brown, often streaked; sapwood thick; used occasionally for cheap furniture, woodenware, etc.

SILVICAL CHARACTERS. Upper Sonoran and Transition zones; moderately tolerant; shallow-rooted, except on deep soils; hardy to extremes of climate; rapid grower but short-lived and usually of poor form; reproduction by sprout and seed plentiful.

GENERAL. Five varieties are recognized: *arizonicum* Sarg. in Arizona and New Mexico, with serrate leaves and glabrous leaves, twigs, and petioles; *californicum* Sarg. in California, with coarsely serrate or nearly entire leaflets with matted hairs on the lower surface; *interius* Sarg. through the west, with hairy twigs and petioles; *texanum* Pax through the southeast, with woolly twigs and lower leaf surface; and *violaceum* J. and B. through the northern half of the United States, with bluish glabrous twigs and entire or dentate leaves hairy on the lower surface. The distribution of all varieties is included on the map.

HIPPOCASTANACEAE

The Buckeyes and Horsechestnuts
Characteristics of the Genus *Aesculus* L.

HABIT. Handsome shrubs to medium-sized trees with dense, rounded crowns; commonly planted as ornamentals for their flowers or foliage.

LEAVES. Opposite; palmately compound with 5–9 serrate leaflets arising at the end of a long stem; deciduous; stipules absent.

FLOWERS. Regular; polygamo-monoecious; bell-shaped; in many-flowered, showy, upright panicles; yellow, red, or white; flowers near base of panicles perfect and fertile; calyx 5-lobed (rarely 2-lobed); petals 4–5; stamens 5–8, inserted on the disc; ovules 3-valved, 2 in each cell; appearing after the leaves.

FRUIT. A large, leathery, smooth to spiny capsule, containing one or more large, lustrous, brown, leathery-coated seeds marked by a large light colored hilum which gives the name of buckeye to this genus.

TWIGS. Stout; round; marked by conspicuous triangular leaf scars; pith large, circular, light-colored. Winter buds: terminal present, large, scaly, resin-covered in some species.

BARK. Intermediate in thickness; fissured and scaly; bitter.

WOOD. Moderately important; fine textured; diffuse-porous; creamy white; used for containers, novelties, furniture, etc.

SILVICAL CHARACTERS. Moderately tolerant; varied sites; fast-growing; short-lived; in mixed hardwood stands.

GENERAL. This genus contains about 20 species scattered over the Northern Hemisphere, with 7 species native to the United States; the European horsechestnut, *A. hippocastanum* L., is widely planted and has escaped from cultivation in the northern states; the red buckeye, x *A. carnea* Hayne, is a hybrid of *A. hippocastanum* and *A. pavia* often planted for its red flowers.

* * *

TAMARICACEAE

Tamarix. Tamarisk
Tamarix-gallica L.

A large shrub or small tree introduced from Europe but more or less naturalized in the south and central parts of the west. Characterized by alternate, scalelike, feathery, sparse leaves (resembling those of conifers); showy, pink flowers; and 3–5 valved, capsular fruit containing many minute seeds.

1. Winter buds thickly coated with resin; flowers white to pink (often red in *A. carnea*).
    2. Leaflets usually 7 (rarely 5), sessile or nearly so; fruit 2–2 ½ inches long, with short spines; widely planted and naturalized..................................*Aesculus hippocastanum* L., **Horsechestnut**
    2. Leaflets usually 5, leaflets on stalks ½–1 inch long; fruit 2–3 inches long, smooth; California...*A. californica* (Spach) Nutt., **California Buckeye**
1. Winter buds not resinous, or slightly so; flowers yellow to scarlet; leaflets stalked; eastern.
    3. Fruit spiny, 1–2 inches long; flowers yellow-green.
        4. Leaflets 5 (rarely 7); small to medium-sized tree; Pennsylvania and Michigan to Nebraska and south..............................*A. glabra* Willd., **Ohio Buckeye** p. 311.
        4. Leaflets 7–9; shrub or rarely small tree; southern Oklahoma and east Texas............*A. arguta* Buckl., **Texas Buckeye**
    3. Fruit nearly smooth, not spiny.
        5. Leaflets 5–7; flowers yellow with glandular-hairy calyx; fruit 2–3 inches long; large tree; Pennsylvania to Illinois and south..............*A. octandra* Marsh., **Yellow Buckeye**, p. 311.
        5. Leaflets 5; flowers red to red-yellow, calyx not glandular-hairy; fruit 1–2 inches long; shrubs or small trees.
            6. Petals hairless but glandular on margin; Virginia to Kentucky and south..............*A. pavia* L., **Red Buckeye**
            6. Petals hairy but not glandular on margin; North Carolina to Florida and Alabama..*A. sylvatica* Bartr., **Painted Buckeye**

* * *

ANACARDIACEAE

AMERICAN SMOKETREE

Cotinus obovatus Raf.

This handsome shrub or small tree ranges from Tennessee to Missouri and Oklahoma and south. It is characterized by simple, alternate, deciduous leaves 4–6 inches long, which are oval to obovate, entire, and dark green; by dioecious, clustered flowers, many being abortive and hairy giving the tree its name; and by a dry, oblong, brown, hairy drupe about ¼ inch long borne on stems 1–3 inches long.

* * *

TEXAS PISTACHE

Pistacia texana Swingle

This shrub or small tree extends into southern Texas from Mexico. It is characterized by alternate, persistent, pinnately compound leaves with 9–19 spatulate leaflets; small dioecious flowers without petals or calyx; and an oval, red-brown drupe ¼ inch long.

YELLOW BUCKEYE

a. Fruiting twig, x ⅓.
b. Flowering branch, x ⅓.
c. Twig, x ⅓.
d. Seed, x ⅓.

OHIO BUCKEYE

a. Twig, x ⅓.
b. Fruit, x ⅓.
c. Seed, x ⅓.
d. Flowering branch, x ⅓.

[310]

HIPPOCASTANACEAE

Yellow Buckeye

Aesculus octandra Marsh.

HABIT. A medium-sized tree 60–90 feet high and 2–3 feet in diameter (max. 110 by 5 feet); broad, rounded crown.

LEAVES. Five-foliate (rarely 7); 4–10 inches long; with elliptical, glabrous, or tomentose serrate leaflets; dark yellow-green above, paler below.

FLOWERS. Whitish-yellow; glandular-hairy calyx and pedicel; stamens inserted.

FRUIT. Capsule pale brown; 2–3 inches long; usually smooth; containing usually 2 red-brown seeds about 1–1½ inches long and poisonous.

TWIGS. Stout; hairy at first, becoming smooth and red-brown to gray. Winter buds: terminal ⅔–1 inch long, glabrous, pale brown, non-resinous.

BARK. Gray to dark brown; ¾ inch thick; with thin scales.

SILVICAL CHARACTERS. Tolerant; moist sites; the largest American species.

* * *

Ohio Buckeye. Fetid Buckeye

Aesculus glabra Willd.

HABIT. A small to medium-sized tree 30–50 feet high and 1–2 feet in diameter (max. 90 by 3 feet); broad, rounded crown.

LEAVES. Five-foliate (rarely 7); 3–6 inches long; with ovate or oval, glabrous, finely serrate leaflets; yellow-green above and paler below.

FLOWERS. Yellow-green; hairy; small; stamens exserted.

FRUIT. Capsule red-brown; 1–2 inches long; usually spiny; containing a single brown seed about 1 inch long.

TWIGS. Stout; hairy at first becoming smooth and red-brown to ash-gray; with disagreeable odor when bruised. Winter buds: terminal ⅔ inch long, red-brown, resinous, with prominently keeled scales.

BARK. Ash-gray; thick; deeply fissured and plated; ill-scented.

SILVICAL CHARACTERS. Tolerant; moist sites; becoming rare.

WESTERN SOAPBERRY

(a) Leaf, x ½;   (b) Floral stalk, x ½;   (c) Fruit, x ⅔.

MEXICAN-BUCKEYE

(a) Leaf, x ⅓;   (b) Fruit, x ½;   (c) Flowers, x ⅓.

SAPINDACEAE

Western Soapberry

Sapindus drummondii Hook. & Arn.

HABIT. A shrub or small tree rarely 40–50 feet high and 1½–2 feet in diameter; branches round, usually erect.

LEAVES. Alternate; pinnately compound with 4–9 pairs of lanceolate leaflets, each 2–3 inches long; margins entire; glabrous above and pubescent beneath; pale yellow-green; deciduous.

FLOWERS. Regular; polygamo-dioecious; minute; in many-flowered clusters 6–9 inches long; calyx of 4–5 acute sepals; corolla of 4–5 white petals; stamens 8–10, filaments hairy; ovary superior, 2–4-celled; ovules solitary and ascending in each cell.

FRUIT. Drupaceous, ripening into a leathery, 1–3-celled and seeded berry; ½ inch in diameter; glabrous; yellow, turning black in drying; persistent on branches until spring; formerly used as soap. Seed: solitary in each carpel; obovoid; dark brown; with a smooth, bony coat.

TWIGS. Moderately stout; round; at first pubescent and pale yellow-green, becoming puberulous, gray. Winter buds: terminal absent; lateral small, globose, often superposed in pairs.

BARK. Thin (⅓–½ inch); red-brown; furrowed into long, superfically scaly plates; bitter and astringent.

WOOD. Unimportant; heavy; hard; strong; close-grained; ring-porous; heartwood light brown, tinged with yellow.

SILVICAL CHARACTERS. Intolerant; roots fleshy; growth large quantities of saponin, a severe poison. Florida soapberry, *S. marginatus* Willd., is a small tree from South Carolina to Florida.

* * *

Mexican-buckeye

Ungnadia speciosa Endl.

This shrub or small tree of southern Texas and New Mexico is characterized by alternate, deciduous, pinnately compound leaves with 5–7 ovate-lanceolate leaflets, each 3–5 inches long, thick and dark green; by small, irregular, polygamous flowers; and by a leathery, 3-valved capsular fruit 2 inches wide and red-brown, which contain black, shiny, leathery seeds about ½ inch long and reputed to be poisonous.

a. Leaf, x ½.

b. Flowers, x ½.

c. Twig with leaves and fruit, x ½.

RHAMNACEAE

CASCARA BUCKTHORN

Rhamnus purshiana DC.

HABIT. A shrub or tree 20–40 feet high and 6–20 inches in diameter; wide, open crown with numerous, stout branches.

LEAVES. Alternate, or rarely obliquely opposite; simple; broad-elliptic; 2–7 inches long; undulate margins finely serrate or nearly entire; thin; villous below and on veins above; deciduous; turning pale yellow before falling; petioles stout, hairy, ½–1 inch long; stipules minute, deciduous.

FLOWERS. Regular; perfect; small; in axillary peduncled cymes; long-pedicelled; calyx 5-lobed; corolla greenish, ninute, 5-lobed; stamens 5; ovary 2–4-celled; ovules solitary, erect.

FRUIT. Drupaceous; subglobose; ⅓–½ inch in diameter; black; bearing remnants of style; flesh thin and juicy; with 2–3 obovoid, 1-seeded nutlets with a thin, gray or yellow-green shell.

TWIGS. Slender; round; pubescent, usually becoming glabrous; yellow-green or red-brown. Winter buds: terminal absent; lateral small, naked, hoary-tomentose.

BARK. Thin (¼ inch); gray to dark brown, often tinged with red; scaly; important because of laxative properties.

WOOD. Unimportant; rather light; soft; not strong; ring-porous; heartwood brown, tinged with red.

SILVICAL CHARACTERS. Moderately tolerant; prolific seeder and coppices freely; no taproot; few enemies.

GENERAL. A related shrubby form, *R. purshiana* var. *betulaefolia* (Green) Cory, is shown in the Southwest on the map. Three native and two naturalized species reach tree size and are keyed out below.

* * *

1. Winter buds scaly; leaves oval to broad-ovate.
  2. Leaves deciduous, thin, opposite or nearly so, finely crenate-serrate; fruit black; naturalized . . . . *R. cathartica* L., **European Buckthorn**
  2. Leaves persistent, thick, mostly alternate, spiny-toothed; fruit red; California and Arizona. . . . . *R. crocea* var. *ilicifolia* Greene, **Hollyleaf Buckthorn**, p. 317.
1. Winter buds naked; leaves entire or finely toothed.
  3. Leaves deciduous, thin.
    4. Flowers in umbel-like cymes; leaves 2–7 inches long, with 8–15 pairs of veins; native.
      5. Leaves with 10–15 pairs of veins; peduncles longer than petioles; West Coast *R. purshiana* DC., **Cascara Buckthorn**
      5. Leaves with 8–10 pairs of veins; peduncles shorter than petioles; Southeast . . . . *R. caroliniana* Walt., **Carolina Buckthorn**
    4. Flowers fascicled or solitary; leaves 1½–2½ inches long, with 8–9 pairs of veins; naturalized. . . . . *R. frangula* L., **Glossy Buckthorn**
  3. Leaves persistent thick; southeastern California to Nevada and New Mexico . . . . *R. californica* var. *ursina* (Greene) McMinn, **California Buckthorn**

HOLLYLEAF BUCKTHORN

(a) Fruiting branch, x ¾.

BLUEBLOSSOM CEANOTHUS

a. Flowering twig, x ¾.
b. Fruiting branch, x ½.
c. Fruit, x 2.

RHAMNACEAE

Hollyleaf Buckthorn

Rhamnus crocea var. *ilicifolia* (Kell.) Greene

HABIT. A shrub or small evergreen tree rarely 25 feet high and 6–8 inches in diameter; crown round; branches stout.

LEAVES. Alternate or sub-opposite; simple; oval or orbicular; 1–1½ inches long; margin spinulose-dentate; leathery; glabrous; yellow-green above, often golden below; persistent.

FLOWERS. Regular; polygamo-dioecious; in small axillary clusters; calyx about ⅛ inch long, 4-lobed; petals absent.

FRUIT. Drupaceous; obovoid; ¼ inch in diameter; red; flesh thin and dry; with 2–3 brown nutlets ⅛ inch long, hard.

TWIGS. Slender; round; rigid and often spinescent; red-brown; glabrous. Winter buds: terminal absent; lateral 1⁄16 inch long, scaly, obtuse, scales hairy-fringed.

BARK. Thin (1⁄16–⅛ inch); dark gray; slightly roughened by minute tubercles; acrid and bitter.

WOOD. Moderately heavy and hard; brittle; fine-grained; ring-porous; heartwood light yellow-brown; unimportant.

SILVICAL CHARACTERS. Intolerant; prolific seeder; on hot, dry hillsides; in pure groups or scattered.

* * *

Bluewood. Logwood

Condalia obovata Hook

This velvety-pubescent shrub or small tree is one of the common chaparral species of western Texas and southeastern New Mexico, commonly forming dense thickets. It is characterized by small (½–¾ inch long), entire, tardily deciduous, alternate or fascicled leaves; small axillary flowers; and a deep red, subglobose drupe ⅕ inch in diameter, to which the calyx is attached.

* * *

Blueblossom Ceanothus

Ceanothus thyrsiflorus Eschs.

This shrub or small tree is common in coastal forests from southern Oregon to central California. It is characterized by simple, alternate, minutely toothed, persistent leaves 1–1½ inches long; small, perfect, blue or white flowers; a subglobose, 3-lobed, dry drupe ¼ inch long which separates into 3 nutlets; and scaly lateral buds. *C. arboreus* Greene and *C. spinosus* Nutt. are small trees in southern California.

a. Winter twig, x 1.

b. Leaf, x ⅓.

c. Bract with flowers, x ½.

d. Flower, enlarged.

e. Stamen, enlarged.

f. Bract bearing fruit, x ½.

TILIACEAE

American Basswood. Linden

Tilia americana L. (*Tilia glabra* Vent.)

HABIT. A medium-sized tree 60–80 feet high and 2–3 feet in diameter (max. 125 by 4½ feet); dense, rounded crown.

LEAVES. Alternate; simple; deciduous; 5–6 inches long; broadly ovate; coarsely serrate; unequally heart-shaped base; glabrous; dull dark green above, paler beneath; petioles slender, 1–2 inches long.

FLOWERS. Regular; perfect; in loose cymes, the long stalk attached to a leafy bract for half its length; yellow-white; fragrant; 5 sepals; 5 petals; many stamens; 5-celled ovary; appearing after the leaves.

FRUIT. A gray, globose, woolly, nutlike drupe ⅓–½ inch long; in cymes and attached to leafy persistent bracts.

TWIGS. Generally rather slender; green to red-gray, becoming dark gray. Winter buds: terminal absent, lateral subglobose, acute, red, lopsided, ¼ inch long, with 2 scales usually visible.

BARK. Smooth and gray-green on young trunks, becoming thick, dark gray, furrowed, with narrow, scaly ridges.

WOOD. Important; light; soft; fine-textured; diffuse-porous; used for novelties, patterns, excelsior, containers, etc.

SILVICAL CHARACTERS. Tolerant; moist sites; abundant seed produced; sprouts vigorously; rapid growth; mixed hardwoods; deep lateral roots; prized as source of honey.

GENERAL. Some authors have recognized as many as 16 native species of *Tilia*, the differences being minor and variable. Four species are tentatively accepted in the 1953 checklist, with *T. caroliniana* Mill. and *T. floridana* Small being unimportant trees in the southeast. White basswood, *T. heterophylla* Vent., is an important tree differing from American basswood by having leaves which are woolly on the lower surface and by having 10–25 flowers in a cluster; this species grows from New York to southern Illinois and south.

Several European species are planted for ornamental purposes, the most common being the European linden, *T. vulgaris* Hayne, and the small-leaved linden, *T. cordata* Mill.

FREMONTIA

a. Flowering branchlet,
   x 1.
b. Fruit, x 1.

ALLTHORN

a. Flowers, x 1.

b. Branch with fruit, x 1.

STERCULIACEAE

FREMONTIA FLANNELBUSH

Fremontia californica Torr. (*Fremontodendron californicum* Cov.)
(*Fremontia mexicana* (Dav.) Macb.)

HABIT. A shrub or small tree 20–30 feet high and 12–14 inches in diameter; crown open with stout branches.

LEAVES. Alternate, simple; broadly ovate; 1½ inches in diameter; usually 3-lobed; thick; stellate rusty-pubescent below; persistent 2 years; petioles stout, ½–⅔ inch long.

FLOWERS. Regular; perfect; solitary; calyx, deeply 5-lobed, yellow, 1 inch long; corolla absent; stamens 5; ovary 5-celled.

FRUIT. Ovoid, acuminate, 4-valved capsule; 1 inch long; densely woolly dehiscent; inner surface villose-pubescent. Seed: oval, small (about ⅜₆ inch long), very dark brown.

TWIGS. Stout; round; stellate rusty-pubescent at first, becoming glabrous and light red-brown. Winter buds: naked.

BARK. Thin; furrowed; dark red-brown.

WOOD. Unimportant; heavy; hard; ring-porous; red-brown.

SILVICAL CHARACTERS. Intolerant; on very poor, dry foothills; forming dense thickets; a monotypic genus.

* * *

KOEBERLINACEAE

ALLTHORN. CORONO DE CRISTO

Koeberlinia spinosa Zucc.

HABIT. A shrub or small bushy tree rarely 20–25 feet high; often appearing to bear neither leaf, flower, nor fruit.

LEAVES. Alternate; simple; early deciduous, the tree usually leafless; scalelike and minute (not over ⅛ inch long).

FLOWERS. Regular; perfect; small; in short umbel-like racemes; petals 4, green-white, much longer than sepals.

FRUIT. Small (⅜₆–¼ inch), subglobose, 2-celled, black berry; flesh thin and succulent; cells 1–2-seeded. Seed: coiled and shell-shaped; seed coat brittle and wrinkled.

TWIGS. Stout; glabrous; terminating in sharp, rigid spine; pale green in color. Winter buds: minute and inconspicuous.

BARK. Thin, red-brown, scaly.

WOOD. Unimportant; very hard; heavy (sp. gr. 1.12); fine-textured; diffuse-porous; heartwood dark brown.

SILVICAL CHARACTERS. Intolerant; on dry, gravelly plains and foothills; a monotypic botanical curiosity.

GORDONIA

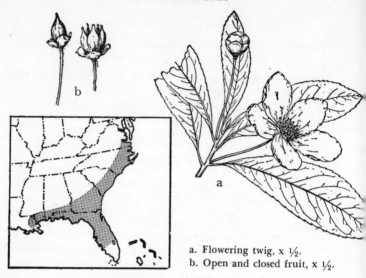

a. Flowering twig, x ½.
b. Open and closed fruit, x ½.

DEVILS-WALKINGSTICK

a. Leaf, x ½.
b. Twig, x ½.
c. Fruit panicle, x ½.

THEACEAE

LOBLOLLY-BAY. GORDONIA
Gordonia lasianthus (L.) Ellis

HABIT. A beautiful medium-sized tree 60–75 feet high and 1–2 feet in diameter; narrow, compact crown.

LEAVES. Alternate; simple; persistent; 3–6 inches long; lanceolate to elliptic; leathery; shallowly toothed; dark green; turning scarlet before falling.

FLOWERS. Regular; perfect; showy; white; fragrant; 2½ inches across petals and sepals silky; stamens numerous; ovary 3–5 celled.

FRUIT. A woody, oblong, 5-celled capsule ⅔ inch long; with silky surface. Seed: 1⁄16 inch long, flat, nearly square, winged.

TWIGS. Slender; dark brown; rough. Winter buds: terminal present, ¼ inch long, acute, silky hairy.

BARK. Thick; red-brown; deeply fissured and ridged.

WOOD. Unimportant; soft; light red.

SILVICAL CHARACTERS. Rather intolerant; wet sites; short-lived; hard to grow ornamentally.

* * *

ARALIACEAE

DEVILS-WALKINGSTICK
Aralia spinosa L.

HABIT. A prickly shrub or small tree rarely 35 feet high with few branches and a flat crown; presenting an interesting and grotesque appearance.

LEAVES. Alternate; doubly pinnately compound; deciduous; 2–4 feet long; pinnate usually bearing 5–6 pairs of ovate, acuminate, serrate, thin, dark green leaflets 2–3 inches long and prickly.

FLOWERS. Regular; perfect or staminate; small; in many-flowered panicles 3–4 feet long; green-white; appearing after the leaves.

FRUIT. Small, juicy, black berry ¼ inch long; tipped with persistent style. Seed: 2–5, oblong, compressed, red-brown.

TWIGS. Stout (½–1 inch thick); orange; lustrous; armed with stout prickles. Winter buds: terminal present, conical, ½ inch long, red.

BARK. Thin; shallow fissures; brown; inner bark yellow.

WOOD. Unimportant; soft; brown streaked with yellow.

SILVICAL CHARACTERS. Intolerant; short-lived; fast-growing; planted as an ornamental.

[323]

CACTACEAE

Characteristics of the Cactus Family

HABIT. Shrubs or seldom trees, rarely 50–60 feet high and 2 feet in diameter; stems commonly columnar, fluted, succulent, and branched; numerous spines springing from cushions of small bristles (areolae).

LEAVES. Alternate; simple; mostly reduced to spines or scales or absent; photosynthetic processes taking place in the green parts of the fleshy stems.

FLOWERS. Regular; perfect; usually single; large and showy; calyx of numerous sepals forming a tube, those of inner series petal-like; corolla showy, of numerous petals; stamens many, inserted on calyx tube; ovary inferior, 1-celled, with several parietal placentae and numerous horizontal ovules, styles united into one, stigmas as many as placentae.

FRUIT. 1-celled, fleshy (rarely dry) berry, often edible. Seed: numerous and small.

WOOD. An internal, woody frame or skeleton, made up of a cylinder or a meshed network of strands.

BUDS. Modified into pulvini or cushions which are usually depressions often consisting of a complex series of spines, wool, glands, and growing points.

SILVICAL CHARACTERS. Very intolerant; although seed generally produced abundantly, natural reproduction by seed is rather scanty because of unfavorable environment; vegetative reproduction common; typical of very dry desert areas where they are often the only woody plants.

GENERAL. This family contains about 120 genera and 1,200 species; there are 2 genera and 5 species reaching tree size in the United States in southern California, Arizona, and New Mexico. Two species, *Cereus schottii* Engelm. and *Cereus thurberi* Engelm., of southern Arizona and Mexico have columnar branches 20 to 25 feet high but cannot be considered trees as they do not have a definite trunk.

KEY TO THE ARBORESCENT SPECIES
OF CACTACEAE

1. Branches and stems columnar, ribbed, not tuberculate, continuous; areoles (growing centers) without glochids (minute bristles); leaves spinelike; tube of flower elongated; seeds dark-colored; spines not barbed; a tree often 50–60 feet high; the state flower of Arizona . . . . *Cereus giganteus*, Engelm. [*Carnegiea gigantea* (Engelm.) B. & R.]; **Saguaro.**
1. Branches and stems slender, columnar, tuberculate, conspicuously jointed; areoles with both glochids and spines; leaves small and fleshy on young parts; tube of flower short; seed light-colored; spines retrorsely barbed; small plants not over 15 feet high *Opuntia.*
    2. Tubercles of branches broad, full and rounded below areolae; flowers pink or purple; fruit sparingly spiny or without spines.
        3. Flowers pink; fruit green, proliferous (one growing from another), usually spineless; joints pale olive-green, readily detached, freely falling, their tubercles broad and ovoid; spines yellow . . . . *Opuntia fulgida* Engelm.; **Cholla.**
        3. Flowers yellow; fruit yellow, rarely proliferous, spiny; joints green or purple, not readily detached, persistent, their tubercles elongated; spines white to red-brown . . . . *Opuntia spinosior* (Engelm.) Toumey; **Tasajo.**
    2. Tubercles of branches narrow, high and flattened laterally. Flowers purple, or green tinted with red or yellow.
        4. Fruit smooth or but slightly tuberculate, spiny, green; branch tubercles ⅔″ long; spines 5–11, ⅛″ long or less, dark red-brown; flowers green, tinted with red or yellow . . . . *Opuntia versicolor* Engelm.; **Staghorn Cholla.**
        4. Fruit manifestly tuberculate, naked, yellow; branch tubercles ¾″ long; spines 8–30, ¾–1¼″ long, brown; flowers purple . . . . *Opuntia imbricata* (Haw.) DC. (*Opuntia arborescens* Engelm.); **Cane Cactus.**

BLACK TUPELO

a. Winter twig, x 1.
b. Leaf, x ⅔.
c. Staminate flowering branchlet, x ½.
d. Pistillate flowering branchlet, x ½.
e. Fruit, x ½.

WATER TUPELO

a. Fruiting twig, x ⅔.
b. Flowers, x ⅔.
c. Fruit pit, x ⅔.

NYSSACEAE

BLACK TUPELO. BLACKGUM
Nyssa sylvatica Marsh.

HABIT. A medium-sized tree 40–80 feet high and 1–3 feet in diameter (max. 125 by 6 feet); rounded crown with horizontal branches.

LEAVES. Alternate; simple; deciduous; 2–5 inches long; obovate; entire or wavy-margined; thick and lustrous; dark green above, paler and often hairy below; scarlet in autumn.

FLOWERS. Regular; polygamo-dioecious; small; staminate in heads; green-white; appearing with the leaves.

FRUIT. A fleshy, ovoid, blue-black drupe ⅓–⅔ inch long with indistinctly ribbed pit (distinctly ribbed in swamp tupelo, the variety *biflora* (Walt.) Sarg., of the Coastal Plain).

TWIGS. Slender; green to red-brown; smooth, pith diaphragmed. Winter buds: terminal present, scaly, ¼ inch long, ovoid, yellow-brown.

BARK. Thick; red-brown; deeply fissured and broken into conspicuous square blocks.

WOOD. Important; rather heavy and hard; fine-textured; diffuse-porous; light-colored; used for furniture, containers, etc.

SILVICAL CHARACTERS. Intolerant; moist sites; rapid growth; shallow, lateral roots; scattered and never abundant. The genus *Nussa* is placed in the family *Cornaceae* by some authors including the check list (1953), it is considered by most, however, to constitute a separate family, the *Nyssaceae*.

* * *

WATER TUPELO
Nyssa aquatica L.

This species, which is an important timber species, occurs in pure stands or mixed with cypress in the southern swamps that are often under water. It differs from black tupelo in the following ways; leaves 5–7 inches long, oblong-obovate, entire or sometimes irregularly toothed; fruit red-purple, 1 inch long, with conspicuously ribbed pit; bark thin, gray-brown, with scaly ridges; buds globose, not over ⅛ inch long; and the butt of the tree is often conspicuously swollen.

* * *

OGEECHEE TUPELO
Nyssa ogeche Bartr.

This small, rare tree of the Coastal Plain from South Carolina to Florida resembles water tupelo and is distinguished from it by its red fruit containing a pit with broad, thin, papery wings. Bear tupelo, *Nyssa ursina* Small, is a shrub or small tree of northwestern Florida.

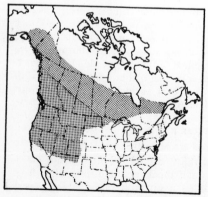

a. Twig with leaves and flower, x ½.

b. Section through flower, x 2.

c. Fruit, x 2.

d. Stone, x 2.

ELAEAGNACEAE

Silver Buffaloberry. Silverberry

Shepherdia argentea (Pursh) Nutt. (*Elaeagnus utilis* A. Nels.)

HABIT. A bushy, silvery shrub or small tree rarely 15–16 feet high, stoloniferous and thicket-forming.

LEAVES. Opposite; simple; elliptic to oblong; 1–3 inches long and ⅓–1 inch wide; rounded or acute at apex; margin entire; densely silvery-scurfy on both faces; thick; deciduous; petioles stout, ¼ inch long.

FLOWERS. Regular; polygamous; 1–3 in axil of each leaf; appearing after leaves; calyx tube silvery without, ¼ inch long, 4-lobed; corolla lacking, stamens 4, short, attached near calyx throat; ovary enveloped in receptacle.

FRUIT. Drupe; globose to oval; ⅓–½ inch long; silvery; flesh mealy; the stone with about 8 longitudinal ridges.

TWIGS. Rather slender; round; rusty-brown and covered with scurfy scales; leaf scars minute. Winter buds: ⅛–¼ inch long, oblong, scales scurfy.

BARK. Thin; dull gray; smooth or slightly furrowed.

WOOD. Light; soft; weak; coarse-grained; heartwood dark brown; farily durable; unimportant.

SILVICAL CHARACTERS. Upper Sonoran to Alpine zones; along streams or on moist to dry hillsides.

* * *

Russian-olive

Elaeagnus angustifolia L.

An introduced shrub or small tree which has become established in parts of the region. Hardy, very drouth and alkaline resistant and much planted as a dry area ornamental and for windbreaks. Characterized by lanceolate, silvery-scurfy leaves; silvery and often spiny branches; and yellow, silvery-scurfy, drupaceous fruit, ½ inch in diameter.

a. Winter twig, with leaf buds, x 1.
b. Portion of twig, enlarged.
c. Winter twig, with flower bud, x 1.
d. Leaf, x ½.
e. Flowering branchlet, x ½.
f. Flower, enlarged.
g. Fruit, x 1.

FLOWERING DOGWOOD

PACIFIC DOGWOOD

CORNACEAE

FLOWERING DOGWOOD

Cornus florida L.

HABIT. A shrub or small tree rarely 40 feet high and 1 foot in diameter; bushy, flat crown; a valuable ornamental.

LEAVES. Opposite; simple; deciduous; 3–6 inches long; oval; entire; thick; arcuately veined; hairy; bright green above, paler beneath; turning scarlet in autumn.

FLOWERS. Perfect; small; in heads; the heads surrounded by 4 showy, petal-like, notched, white or pink bracts (red in variety *rubra* West.); appearing with leaves.

FRUIT. An ovoid, scarlet drupe ½ inch long; in clusters of 3–4; flesh bitter; containing a 2-celled pit.

TWIGS. Slender; glaucous; green or purplish. Winter buds: terminal present, ⅛ inch long, narrow-conical, acute, covered with 2 valvate scales; terminal flower buds subglobose, gray.

BARK. Thin; dark red-brown; broken into small, square blocks.

WOOD. Moderately important; very heavy and hard; fine-textured; diffuse-porous; in demand for shuttles.

SILVICAL CHARACTERS. Very tolerant; moist sites as "understory" species; slow-growing; lateral roots.

* * *

PACIFIC DOGWOOD

Cornus nuttallii Aud.

This small, handsome tree of the Pacific Coast is very similar to flowering dogwood in its appearance and differs from it in the following ways: petal-like flower bracts not notched; often producing a second crop of flowers in later summer; bark remaining smooth on trunk.

* * *

Three other of the 16 species of dogwood native to North America while typically shrubs may form small trees. These are the alternate-leaf dogwood, *C. alternifolia* L., and the rough-leaf dogwood, *C. drummondii* Meyer, of the eastern United States and the western dogwood, *C. occidentalis* Cov. in the Northwest.

a. Fruiting branch, x 1.
b. Leafy branch, x ⅔.

ERICACEAE

PACIFIC MADRONE

Arbutus menziesii Pursh

HABIT. A medium-sized tree 20–100 feet high and 1–4 feet in diameter (max. 125 by 9 feet); rounded crown.

LEAVES. Alternate; simple; presistent; 3–6 inches long; oval to oblong; entire or toothed on vigorous growth; leather; glabrous; dark green and lustrous above, glaucous beneath.

FLOWERS. Regular; perfect; in terminal panicles; white; urn-shaped; ¼ inch long; appearing with or after the leaves.

FRUIT. A globose, orange, semifleshy, glandular-coated, drupaceous berry ⅓–½ inch long. Seed: several in each cell, small, brown, angled.

TWIGS. Slender; green to red-brown; glabrous. Winter buds: terminal ⅓ inch long, ovoid, scaly, bright brown.

BARK. Thin; distinctive; red-brown; separating into papery scales exposing the light red inner bark.

WOOD. Unimportant; heavy; hard; diffuse-porous; red-brown.

SILVICAL CHARACTERS. Moderately tolerant; varied sites; pure or mixed stands; occasionally planted as an ornamental.

GENERAL. Two other species are native to the Southwest: Texas madrone, *A. texana* Buckl., similar to Pacific madrone except for smaller leaves (1–3 inches long) and pubescent ovary, is a small tree on dry sites in southern Texas and New Mexico; Arizona madrone, *A. arizonica* (Gray) Sarg., with gray bark and a glabrous ovary, is native to Arizona and Mexico.

* * *

Elliottia, *Elliottia racemosa* Muhl., is a rare, interesting tree now known only in Georgia. It is characterized by simple, alternate, oblong, entire, deciduous leaves, 3–4 inches long; perfect flowers with 4 straplike petals; and small capsular fruit.

* * *

Tree Lyonia, *Lyonia ferruginea* Nutt., is a small tree of coastal areas from South Carolina to Florida. It is characterized by simple, alternate, persistent, entire, obovate leaves 1–3 inches long and scaly below; by fascicled flowers ⅛ inch in diameter with a white, globular corolla; and by an ovoid, many-seeded, capsular fruit ¼ inch long.

ROSEBAY RHODODENDRON

a. Flowering branch, x ⅓.

b. Fruits, x ⅓.

c. Section of fruit, x 1.

MOUNTAIN-LAUREL

a. Flowering branch,
   x ⅓.

b. Fruit, x 1.

ERICACEAE

ROSEBAY RHODODENDRON. GREAT RHODODENDRON
Rhododendron maximum L.

HABIT. A beautiful shrub or small tree rarely 35 feet high and 1 foot in diameter; short, crooked trunk; bushy, rounded crown; an important ornamental.

LEAVES. Alternate; simple; persistent 2–3 years; 4–12 inches long and 1½–2½ inches wide; oblong; leathery; revolute, entire margins; dark green and lustrous above, paler beneath.

FLOWERS. Regular; perfect; showy; in 16–24 terminal flowered clusters; white, pink, or purple; campanulate; 1 inch across; appearing after the leaves.

FRUIT. A woody, oblong-ovoid, red-brown, sticky, glandular-hispid, 5-celled capsule ½ inch long. Seed: small, many.

TWIGS. Stout; glabrous; dark green to red-brown. Winter buds: terminal present, conical, green, scaly; flower buds 1–1½ inches long.

BARK. Thin; red-brown; broken into thin scales.

WOOD. Unimportant; heavy; hard; diffuse-porous; fine-textured; used for pipe bowls.

SILVICAL CHARACTERS. Tolerant; moist, cool, shady sites; often in thickets; does not like limy soils.

GENERAL. Two other species reach tree size: Catawba rhododendron, *R. catawbiense* Michx., with broader leaves 3–5 inches long and ranging from Virginia to Alabama; and Pacific rhododendron, *R. macrophyllum* D. Don, ranging from British Columbia to California. The Azaleas are shrubby species of this genus with deciduous leaves.

* * *

MOUNTAIN-LAUREL
Kalmia latifolia L.

This beautiful shrub or small tree resembles rhododendron and is a common ornamental. It can be distinguished by its flat, alternate, simple, persistent, elliptic-lanceolate leaves 3–4 inches long; by its showy, white to rose-colored flowers with a saucer-shaped corolla with a short tube and 10 pouches below the 5-parted limb; and by the globose, woody, glandular-hispid, 5-celled capsule 3/16 inch in diameter which splits at maturity into 5, persistent carpels releasing the many, minute, oblong, winged seeds.

SOURWOOD

a. Flowering branch, x ½.
b. Fruiting branch, x ½.
c. Fruit sectioned, x 1.

SOURWOOD

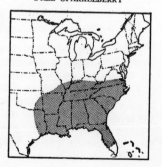

TREE SPARKLEBERRY

ERICACEAE

SOURWOOD

Oxydendrum arboreum (L.) DC.

HABIT. A small to medium-sized tree 20–50 feet high and ⅔–1 foot in diameter (max. 80 by 2 feet); narrow, rounded crown.

LEAVES. Alternate; simple; deciduous; 5–7 inches long; oblong to lanceolate; thin; finely toothed; nearly glabrous; dark green and lustrous above, paler beneath; sour tasting; turning scarlet in autumn.

FLOWERS. Regular; perfect; small; in delicate panicles of racemes 6–8 inches long; corolla white, bell-shaped, 5-lobed, ⅓ inch long; appearing after the leaves.

FRUIT. A 5-valved, 5-lobed, dry, persistent capsule ⅓–½ inch long; terminated by a persistent style. Seed: ⅛ inch long, pointed, pale brown.

TWIGS. Slender; glabrous; yellow-green to red-brown. Winter buds: terminal absent; lateral small, scaly, red-brown, partially embedded in bark.

BARK. Thick; gray, tinged with red; furrowed; with broad, scaly ridges.

WOOD. Unimportant; heavy; hard; diffuse-porous; red-brown.

SILVICAL CHARACTERS. Rather tolerant; dry, well-drained sites; does not like limy soils; an attractive ornamental; a monotypic genus.

* * *

TREE SPARKLEBERRY. FARKLEBERRY

Vaccinium arboreum Marsh.

This shrub or small tree of the blueberry-cranberry genus is found on moist well-drained sites. It is characterized by alternate, simple, persistent (deciduous during winter in north) leaves which are obovate to oblong, entire or minutely toothed, leathery, dark green and lustrous above and paler beneath, and 1–2½ inches long; small, white, bell-shaped flowers either solitary or in racemes; and a black, globose, dry, scarcely edible berry about ¼ inch long which persists on the branch into the winter.

[337]

a. Flowering branchlet, x 1.

b. Fruit, x 1.

SAPOTACEAE

GUM BUMELIA. GUM ELASTIC

Bumelia lanuginosa (Michx.) Pers.

HABIT. A shrub or small tree 40–50 feet high and 1–2 feet in diameter; narrow crown with short, spinescent, spiny branches.

LEAVES. Alternate; simple; 1–3 inches long; oblanceolate to obovate; margins entire; thin; dark green above; soft, rusty-brown hairs below; tardily deciduous in winter; stipules absent.

FLOWERS. Regular; perfect; minute; in axillary clusters; corolla white, campanulate, 5-lobed.

FRUIT. Drupe; oblong; ½ inch long; black; solitary or in 2–3 fruited clusters; thick flesh. Seed: ¼ inch long, shiny.

TWIGS. Slender; rounded; spinescent or with stout spines; red-brown to ash-gray. Winter buds: scaly, small, obtuse.

BARK. Thin; dark gray-brown; divided into scaly ridges.

WOOD. Unimportant; heavy; not strong; close-grained; ring-porous; light brown; producing clear, viscid gum.

SILVICAL CHARACTERS. Intolerant; dry hills or along streams; generally shrubby.

GENERAL. Four native species sometimes become trees and are keyed out below:

1. Leaves persistent, thick and leathery, dull blue-green; Florida and Texas . . . . *B. celastrina* H. B. K., **Saffron-Plum.**
1. Leaves deciduous.
   2. Leaves glabrous or nearly so, Virginia to Illinois and south . . . . *B. lycioides* (L.) Pers., **Buckthorn Bumelia.**
   2. Leaves hairy on lower surface.
      3. Leaves with silky, golden hairs; South Carolina to Florida. . . . . *B. tenax* (L.) Willd., **Tough Bumelia.**
      3. Leaves reddish, dull, woolly hairs . . . . *B. lanuginosa* Pers.

COMMON PERSIMMON

a. Twig, x 1.
b. Fruiting branch, x ½.

CAROLINA SILVERBELL

a. Flowers, x ½.
b. Fruit, x ⅓.
c. Leaf, x ⅓.
d. Twig, x ½.

EBENACEAE

Common Persimmon
Diospyros virginiana L.

HABIT. A small to medium-sized tree 25–50 feet high and 1 foot in diameter (max. 130 by 3 feet); broad, rounded crown.

LEAVES. Alternate; simple; deciduous; 3–6 inches long; oblong-ovate to oval; leathery; glabrous; entire; dark green and lustrous above, paler and sometimes hairy below.

FLOWERS. Regular; dioecious; ½–¾ inch long; corolla urn-shaped or tubular; yellow-green; appearing with leaves.

FRUIT. A globose, orange to purple, berry 1–1½ inches long; subtended by 4 woody, persistent calyx-lobes; astringent till frost, then edible. Seed: 1–8, compressed, oblong, rounded.

TWIGS. Slender; gray-brown; hairy or glabrous. Winter buds: terminal absent; lateral ovate, acute, ⅛ inch long, red, 2-scaled.

BARK. Thick; hard; dark gray; in distinctive square, scaly blocks.

WOOD. Moderately important; heavy; hard; strong; ring-porous; used for shuttles, golf clubs, billiard cues, brushes, etc.

SILVICAL CHARACTERS. Rather intolerant; varied sites.

GENERAL. This tropical genus contains over 200 species including the ebony of commerce. *Diospyros texana* Scheele is a small Texas tree.

* * *

STYRACACEAE

Carolina Silverbell
Halesia carolina L.

HABIT. A small handsome tree; rounded crown.

LEAVES. Alternate; simple; deciduous; 3–4 inches long; oblong-ovate; finely toothed; yellow-green and glabrous above, pale and hairy below.

FLOWERS. Regular; perfect; showy; corolla white, bell-shaped, ½ inch long.

FRUIT. A dry, oblong, 4-winged drupe 1½ inches long.

GENERAL. Twigs slender; terminal buds absent; bark thin, scaly; moist sites; stump sprouts vigorously. Three other species form trees; the related mountain species *H. monticola* Sarg. with flowers and fruit 2 inches long is included on the map; *H. parviflora* Michx. with small flowers and club-shaped fruits extends from Georgia and Mississippi into Florida; and *H. diptera* Ellis with a 2-winged fruit extends from South Carolina to Oklahoma and south.

[341]

OLEACEAE

The Ashes

Characteristics of the Genus *Fraxinus* L.

HABIT. Deciduous trees, or rarely shrubs; ornamental with handsome foliage; several species are important timber trees.

LEAVES. Opposite; odd-pinnately compound (rarely reduced to a single leaflet); without stipules; petiolate; deciduous; leaflets serrate or entire, sessile or petiolulate.

FLOWERS. Regular; perfect; dioecious, or polygamous; small, but quite conspicuous in slender-branched panicles; appearing before or with the leaves; calyx 4-lobed or wanting; corolla usually 4-lobed or wanting; stamens usually 2 (rarely 3 or 4); single 2-celled ovary (rarely 3-celled); ovules suspended in pairs from inner angle of the cell.

FRUIT. Samara; 1-, rarely 2- or 3-seeded; with an elongated terminal wing. Seed: oblong, compressed, filling cavity in the fruit, chestnut-brown, albuminous.

TWIGS. Slender to stout; glabrous or pubescent; pith thick, rounded, homogeneous; leaf scars suborbicular to semi-circular, sometimes notched on the upper edge; bundle scars numerous. Winter buds: terminal larger than lateral, both with 1–3 pairs of scales, the inner accrescent.

BARK. Thick and furrowed or rarely thin and scaly.

WOOD. Ring-porous; late wood with rather few pores not in distinct radial lines and with tangential bands of parencyhma; tough; straight-grained; not structural timber, but important for specialty purposes; sapwood not durable.

SILVICAL CHARACTERS. Rather intolerant trees; rapid growing; fibrous root system; reproducing well naturally and artificially; comparatively free from destructive attacks by insects and fungi.

GENERAL. This genus contains about 65 species of trees scattered through the Northern Hemisphere and extending into the tropical forests of Java and Cuba. In North America there are 18 recognized native species.

1. Flowers with corolla, perfect, showy, in terminal panicles; leaves 5–7 inches long with 3–7, lanceolate, stalked leaflets; Southwest . . . .
. . . . *F. cuspidata*, Fragrant Ash, p. 345.
1. Flowers without corolla, dioecious or polygamous, axillary panicles.
  2. Leaflets ½–¾ inch long, spatulate; leaves 1½–3 inches long; Southwest . . . . *F. greggii*, Gregg Ash, p. 345.
  2. Leaflets 1–6 inches long; leaves (unless simple) over 3 inches long.
    3. Twigs 4-angled; fruit compressed, oblong wing extending to base.
      4. Leaves 8–12 inches long with 5–11 leaflets; flower with minute calyx; Eastern *F. quadrangulata*, Blue Ash, p. 353.
      4. Leaves 1½–6 inches long with 1–5 leaflets; Southwest.
        5. Leaflets 1 (rarely 2–3); fruit ½ inch long . . . .
. . . . *F. anomala*, Singleleaf Ash, p. 345.
        5. Leaflets 5 (rarely 3); fruit 1–1½ inches long.
          6. California . . . . . . *F. dipetala*, Two-petal Ash, p. 347.
          6. Arizona . . . . *F. lowellii*, Lowell Ash, p. 355.
    3. Twigs terete.
      7. Body of fruit compressed; oblong wing extending to base.
        8. Leaves 12–16 inches long; leaflets 7–11; Northeast . . . . . .
. . . . *F. nigra*, Black Ash, p. 351.
        8. Leaves 5–12 inches long; leaflets 3–7; Southeast . . . .
. . . . *F. caroliniana*, Carolina Ash, p. 351.
      7. Body of fruit nearly terete; wing not decurrent to base.
        9. Wing terminal, linear to oblanceolate; leaflets stalked.
          10. Leaves 8–12 inches long, with 7 (rarely 5 or 9) leaflets; Eastern . . . *F. americana*, White Ash, p. 347.
          10. Leaves 5–8 inches long, with 5 (rarely 7) leaflets; Texas and Oklahoma *F. texensis*, Texas Ash, p. 347.
        9. Wing decurrent to below middle of fruit body.
          11. Lateral leaflets usually sessile, 7 (rarely 3 or 5); West Coast . . . . *F. latifolia*, Oregon Ash, p. 353.
          11. Lateral leaflets stalked.
            12. Leaves 9–18 inches long, with 7–9 leaflets; Eastern.
              13. Fruit 2–3 inches long; tree of coastal or river swamps *F. profunda*, Pumpkin Ash, p. 349.
              13. Fruit 1–2½ inches long; not in deep swamps.
                14. Leaves, petioles, and twigs glabrous . . . . *F. pennsylvanica* lanceolata, Green Ash, p. 349.
                14. Leaves, petioles, and twigs hairy . . . . *F. pennsylvanica*, Red Ash, p. 349.
            12. Leaves 3–7 inches long, with 3–5 leaflets; Southwest.
              15. Fruit 1–1½ inches long . . . .
. . . . . *F. berlandieriana*, Berlandier Ash, p. 355.
              15. Fruit ¾ inch long *F. velutina*, Velvet Ash, p. 355.

*   *   *

SYTRACACEAE

Bigleaf snowbell, *Styrax grandifolia* Ait., extending from Virginia to Louisiana, resembles halesia, but differs from it in the fruit, which is a subglobose, tomentose drupe about ⅓ inch long, and the 5–7 parted corolla. Rarely reaches tree size.

*   *   *

SYMPLOCACEAE

Sweetleaf, *Symplocos tinctoria* (G.) L'Her., extending from Delaware to Florida and west to Tennessee, Arkansas, and Texas has oblong, nearly entire, thick, alternate, subpersistent leaves 5–6 inches long; small, yellow, fragrant flowers borne in dense, axillary spikes; and a dry, brown drupe about ¼ inch long. Rarely reaches tree size.

a. Flower panicle, x 1.

b. Fruit, x 1.

c. Compound leaf, x 1.

d. Twig with simple leaves and fruit, x ⅔.

OLEACEAE

SINGLELEAF ASH. DWARF ASH

Fraxinus anomala Torr.

HABIT. A shrub or small tree 18–20 feet high; crown round-topped, with contorted branches.

LEAVES. Usually single but rarely with 2–5 leaflets; broadly ovate or suborbicular; 1–2 inches long (smaller if compound); margins entire or sparingly crenate-serrate above middle; glabrous and dark green above, paler below.

FLOWERS. In short panicles; appearing with leaves; perfect or unisexual by abortion of stamens; calyx cup-shaped, minutely 4-toothed; corolla absent.

FRUIT. Obovate-oblong; ½ inch long; wing rounded or emarginate at apex, surrounding flattened seed cavity.

TWIGS. Quadrangular, slightly winged, and orange-colored at first; later round and ash-gray. Winter buds: terminal broad ovoid, ⅛–¼ inch long, covered by orange tomentum.

BARK. Thin (½ inch); dark brown slightly tinged with red; divided by shallow furrows into narrow, scaly ridges.

WOOD. Heavy; hard; close-grained; heartwood light brown; sapwood lighter colored and thick; of no importance.

SILVICAL CHARACTERS. Intolerant; in the neighborhood of streams or on dry hillsides.

* * *

FRAGRANT ASH. FLOWERING ASH

Fraxinus cuspidata Torr.

A handsome shrub or low tree with showy white flowers and small leaves; seldom a tree in the United States; Upper Sonoran zone of Texas, New Mexico, Arizona, and Mexico.

* * *

GREGG ASH. LITTLELEAF ASH

Fraxinus greggii Gray

This shrub or small tree, rarely 25 feet high, is characterized by 3–7 leaflets which are less than 1 inch long, usually entire, covered below with small, black dots, and obscurely veined; the twigs. are slender and round, and the bark is thin and separates into papery scales; it has been reported from Santa Cruz County, Arizona, western Texas, and Mexico.

a. Winter twig, x 1.
b. Leaf, x ¼.
c. Staminate flowering branchlet, x ½.
d. Staminate flower, enlarged.
e. Pistillate flowering branchlet, x ½.
f. Pistillate flower, enlarged.
g. Fruit, x 1.

WHITE ASH

TEXAS ASH

OLEACEAE

White Ash

Fraxinus americana L. (*Fraxinus biltmoreana* Beadle)

HABIT. A medium-sized tree 50–80 feet high and 2–3 feet in diameter (max. 125 by 6 feet); open, pyramidal crown.

LEAVES. 8–12 inches long; 5–9 (mostly 7) leaflets, ovate to oblong-lanceolate, 3–5 inches long, entire or obscurely toothed, dark green above and paler and usually glabrous below, with petiolules ¼–½ inch long.

FLOWERS. In loose panicles; dioecious; corolla absent; appearing with or before the leaves.

FRUIT. Lanceolate; 1–2 inches long; wing terminal or slightly decurrent along seed cavity; persistent into winter on twigs.

TWIGS. Rounded; rather stout; gray-green; lustrous; leaf scars U-shaped with deep to shallow notch. Winter buds: small, rounded, dark brown, nearly glabrous, inset in leaf scar.

BARK. Thick; gray; closely fissured with narrow ridges.

WOOD. Important; hard; heavy; strong; ring-porous; used for handles, implements, containers, etc.

SILVICAL CHARACTERS. Intermediate in tolerance; moist sites; rapid growth; the most abundant and commonly planted species.

* * *

Texas Ash

Fraxinus texensis (Gray) Sarg.

This small tree of Oklahoma and Texas is very similar to white ash, differing from it in having smaller leaves (5–8 inches long) with 5 (rarely 7) leaflets 1–3 inches long.

* * *

Two-Petal Ash

Fraxinus dipetala Hook. & Arn.

This shrubby species of central to lower California forms a small tree. It is characterized by 4-angled twigs, a two petaled corolla, 5 leaflets, and flowers which appear before the leaves from leafless, axillary buds.

[347]

RED ASH

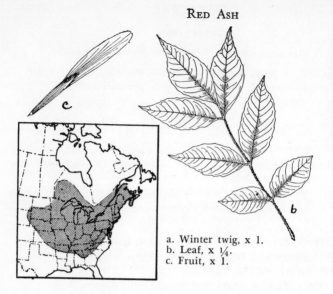

a. Winter twig, x 1.
b. Leaf, x ¼.
c. Fruit, x 1.

GREEN ASH

a. Winter twig, x 1.
b. Fruit, x 1.
c. Leaf, x ¼.

[348]

OLEACEAE

Red Ash

Fraxinus pennsylvanica Marsh.

HABIT. A small to medium-sized tree 30–50 feet high and 1–2 feet in diameter (max. 85 by 3 feet); broad, irregular crown.

LEAVES. 10–12 inches long; 7–9 leaflets, oblong-lanceolate to elliptic, 4–6 inches long, entire or finely toothed, yellow-green above, paler and silky hairy below, with petiolule ⅛–¼ inch long.

FLOWERS. In compact panicles; dioecious; corolla absent; appearing with leaves.

FRUIT. Lanceolate; 1–2½ inches long; wing extending to middle of terete, slender seed cavity; persistent through winter.

TWIGS. Rounded; rather stout; red-gray; pale-hairy; leaf scar not notched. Winter buds: small, rounded, red-brown, woolly, set above leaf scar.

BARK. Thin; brown; shallow fissures and scaly ridges.

WOOD. Important; heavy; hard; ring-porous; like white ash.

SILVICAL CHARACTERS. Intolerant; moist sites, but hardy on dry sites; rapid growth; shallow roots.

* * *

Green Ash

Fraxinus pennsylvanica var. *lanceolata* (Borkh.) Sarg.

This variety, considered a distinct species by some authors and not given variety status by others, is the most widely distributed of the ashes and second in importance to white ash. While typical specimens can be readily identified, it is sometimes impossible to distinguish certain individuals from red or white ash. Green ash differs from red ash in having:

1. Glabrous leaves, petioles, and twigs.
2. Narrower, more sharply serrate, bright green leaflets.
3. Leaf scars truncate below the bud.

* * *

Pumpkin Ash

Fraxinus profunda (Bush) Bush (*Fraxinus tomentosa* Michx.)

This unimportant species of river or coastal swamps ranges from New York to Indiana and Missouri and south. It differs from *F. pennsylvanica* in having fruits 2–3 inches long and often ¼ inch wide and a much enlarged swollen base.

BLACK ASH

a. Winter twig, x 1.
b. Fruit, x 1.
c. Leaf, x ¼.

CAROLINA ASH

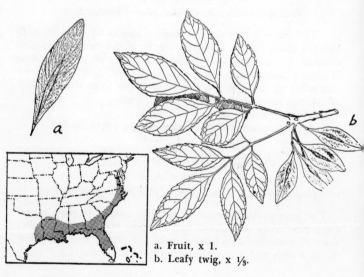

a. Fruit, x 1.
b. Leafy twig, x ⅓.

OLEACEAE

Black Ash

Fraxinus nigra Marsh.

HABIT. A medium-sized tree 40–60 feet high and 1–2 feet in diameter (max. 90 by 5½ feet); narrow, small, open crown.

LEAVES. 12–16 inches long; 7–13 leaflets, oblong to oblong-lanceolate, 3–5 inches long, finely toothed, glabrous, dark green above and paler below, sessile.

FLOWERS. In loose panicles; polygamo-dioecious; corolla and calyx absent; appearing before the leaves.

FRUIT. Oblong; 1–1¾ inches long; wing surrounding the flat, indistinct seed cavity; falling early or late.

TWIGS. Rounded; stout; gray; glabrous. Winter buds; ¼ inch long, ovoid-conical, nearly black, nearly glabrous.

BARK. Thin; gray; smooth, becoming scaly.

WOOD. Moderately important; softer and weaker than white ash.

SILVICAL CHARACTERS. Intolerant; wet sites.

* * *

Carolina Ash. Water Ash

Fraxinus caroliniana Mill. (*Fraxinus pauciflora* Nutt.)

This small, unimportant tree is found in coastal or river swamps from Virginia to Florida and west to Arkansas and Texas. It is characterized by leaves 7–12 inches long with usually 7 thin, mostly glabrous, stalked leaflets; and an oblong-obovate to elliptic fruit, frequently 3-winted, with a compressed seed cavity which is more than half the length of the wing.

BLUE ASH

a. Side and front view of fruit, x ⅔.
b. Leaf, x ½.
c. Winter twig, x ⅔.

OREGON ASH

a. Leaf, x ½.
b. Fruit, x ½.

OLEACEAE

BLUE ASH

Fraxinus quadrangulata Michx.

HABIT. A medium-sized tree 40–50 feet high and 1–2 feet in diameter (max. 120 by 3 feet); narrow, open crown.

LEAVES. 8–12 inches long; 5–11 (usually 7) leaflets, lanceolate to ovate-oblong, 3–5 inches long, coarsely toothed, thick, yellow-green above and paler below, glabrous, with short petiolules.

FLOWERS. In loose panicles; perfect; corolla absent; calyx reduced to ring; appearing before the leaves.

FRUIT. Oblong-ovate; 1–2 inches long; wing surrounding the compressed seed cavity; falling soon after maturing.

TWIGS. 4-angled and corky-winged; stout; orange-brown; red-hairy. Winter buds: small, rounded, dark red-brown, somewhat hairy.

BARK. Rather thin; gray; divided into platelike scales; often shaggy; inner bark contains material which turns blue on exposure.

WOOD. Moderately important; similar to black ash.

SILVICAL CHARACTERS. Similar to red ash; a scattered tree.

* * *

OREGON ASH

Fraxinus latifolia Benth. (*Fraxinus oregona* Nutt.)

HABIT. A medium-sized tree 60–80 feet high and 2–3 feet in diameter (max. 120 by 6 feet); narrow, compact crown.

LEAVES. 5–14 inches long; 5–7 leaflets, ovate to elliptical, 3–7 inches long, entire or finely toothed, light green above and usually hairy below, sessile or with petiolules up to ½ inch.

FLOWERS. In compact panicles; dioecious; corolla absent; appearing with the leaves.

FRUIT. Oblong to elliptic; 1–2 inches long; wing extending to below middle of slightly compressed seed cavity.

TWIGS. Round; stout; woolly; red-brown. Winter buds; ⅛–¼ inch long, conical, brown, hairy.

BARK. Thick; dark gray; deeply fissured with broad ridges.

WOOD. Of slight importance; similar to white ash.

SILVICAL CHARACTERS. Rather intolerant; moist sites; mixed stands; the variety *glabra* Rehd. has glabrous leaves and twigs.

[353]

LOWELL ASH

a. Leaves and fruit, x ⅓.

VELVET ASH

a. Fruit, x ½.
b. One form of leaf, x ⅓.
c. Twig with leaves and fruit, x ⅓.

OLEACEAE

LOWELL ASH

Fraxinus lowelli Sarg. (*Fraxinus anomala* var. *lowellii* (Sarg.) Little.)

HABIT. A small tree 20–25 feet high.

LEAVES. 3½–6 inches long, with a stout petiole; 5 (rarely 3–7) leaflets, ovate to elliptic-ovate, 2½–3 inches long, remotely and lightly serrate, yellow-green, glabrous or slightly pubescent along midrib; leaves sometimes single.

FLOWERS. In axillary panicle; corolla absent.

FRUIT. Oblong-obovate to oblong-elliptic; 1–1½ inches long; wing extending to base of compressed seed cavity.

TWIGS. Quadrangular; often winged; stout; orange-brown.

BARK. Rather thick; dark; deeply furrowed.

SILVICAL CHARACTERS. Intolerant; on dry, rocky slopes and in canyons.

* * *

VELVET ASH

Fraxinus velutina Torr. (*Fraxinus standleyi* Rehd.)

HABIT. A small, slender tree 20–50 feet high.

LEAVES. 4–5 inches long, with a broad, grooved, densely villous petiole; 3–5 leaflets; elliptic to ovate; 1–1½ inches long; finely crenate-serrulate above the middle; thick; pale green, glabrous above, tomentose below; tardily deciduous.

FLOWERS. In pubescent panicles; corolla absent.

FRUIT. Oblong-obovate to elliptic; ¾ inch long; wing shorter than and extending to below middle of terete seed cavity.

TWIGS. Rounded; slender; velvety pubescent first year.

BARK. Thin; furrowed; gray, slightly tinged with red.

SILVICAL CHARACTERS. Intolerant; in dry mountain canyons and on banks of streams; hardy.

GENERAL. *F. velutina* passes into the following varieties: 1. *coriacea* Rehd., with leathery leaves. 2. *glabra* Rehd., with glabrous leaves and branches. 3. *toumeyi* Rehd., with lanceolate, acuminate leaflets, having petioles ⅛–½ inch long.

* * *

BERLANDIER ASH

Fraxinus berlandieriana A. DC.

This small tree of southern Texas and Mexico resembles *F. velutina*, but has a longer fruit (1–1½ inches), glabrous leaves and twigs, and thin, dark green leaflets 3–4 inches long.

[355]

FRINGETREE

a. Fruit, x 1/2.
b. Twig, x 1.
c. Flowering twig, x 1/2.

SWAMP-PRIVET

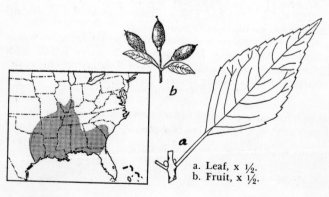

a. Leaf, x 1/2.
b. Fruit, x 1/2.

OLEACEAE

Fringetree
Chionanthus virginicus L.

HABIT. A beautiful shrub or small tree rarely 40 feet high and 1 foot in diameter; narrow, deep crown.

LEAVES. Opposite; simple; deciduous; 4–8 inches long; oval to ovate; entire; dark green above, paler and nearly glabrous below.

FLOWERS. Dioecious; showy; in drooping panicles 4–6 inches long; white, deeply divided corolla; appearing with leaves.

FRUIT. An oval, nearly black, thin-fleshed drupe ½–¾ inch long; stone thick, ⅓ inch long.

TWIGS. Rather stout; green-brown; hairy. Winter buds: terminal present, ovoid, acute, ⅛ inch long, scaly.

BARK. Thin; scaly; red-brown.

WOOD. Unimportant; heavy; hard; fine-textured.

SILVICAL CHARACTERS. Tolerant; moist to wet sites; widely planted as an ornamental.

* * *

Swamp-privet. Forestiera
Forestiera acuminata (Michx.) Poir.

A rather rare shrub or small tree distributed along streams and in swamps. It is characterized by opposite, simple, deciduous, elliptic, long-pointed, glabrous, finely toothed leaves 2½–4½ inches long and yellow-green; by minute, dioecious or polygamous flowers without a corolla and appearing before the leaves in fascicles or panicles; and an oblong, purple, thin-fleshed drupe about 1 inch long. Desert-olive foresteria, *F. phillyreoides* Torr., is a shrubby form in southern Arizona.

* * *

Devilwood
Osmanthus americanus (L.) B. & H.

This is a shrub to medium-sized tree of the Coastal Plain from Virginia to Florida and Louisiana. It is characterized by opposite, simple, persistent, oblong, thick, entire, revolute leaves 3½–5 inches long and lustrous bright green; by small, perfect or polygamous flowers in racemes or fascicles; and by an oblong, purple, thin-fleshed drupe ½–1 inch long. The tree gets its name from the wood which is hard and difficult to work or split. Bigfruit osmanthus, *O. megacarpus* Small, is limited to central Florida.

[357]

ANACAHUITA

a. Flowering branchlet, x 1/3.
b. Fruit, x 2/3.

DESERTWILLOW

a. Seed, x 2/3.
b. Flowering branchlet, x 1/3.
c. Fruit, x 1/3.
d. Leaf, x 1/3.

BORRAGINACEAE

Anacahuita

Cordia boissieri A. DC.

HABIT. An aromatic shrub or small tree 20–25 feet high and 6–8 inches in diameter; crown round-topped.

LEAVES. Alternate; simple; oval to oblong-ovate; 4–5 inches long; entire or obscurely crenulate-serrate; thick and firm; dark green above, woolly below; tardily deciduous.

FLOWERS. Regular; perfect; in cymes; calyx; corolla funnelform, 2 inches across, white with yellow spot in throat.

FRUIT. Drupaceous; ovoid; 1 inch long and ¾ inch broad; acute; lustrous, bright red-brown; enclosed by orange-brown, tomentose calyx; stone thick-walled.

TWIGS. Stout, dark gray or brown, puberlous, marked by occasional large lenticels and by elevated obcordate leaf-scars.

BARK. Thin; gray; divided into broad, flat ridges.

WOOD. Light; rather soft; close-grained; diffuse-porous.

SILVICAL CHARACTERS. Intolerant; dry limestone ridges and depressions; planted as ornamental.

* * *

BIGNONIACEAE

Desertwillow

Chilopsis linearis (Cav.) Sweet (*Chilopsis saligna* D. Don)

HABIT. A shrub or small tree rarely 20–30 feet high; trunk usually reclining; crown narrow with slender branches.

LEAVES. Opposite or scattered; simple; linear or linear-lanceolate; 5–12 inches long and ¼–⅓ inch wide; acuminate; entire margins; thin; light green; deciduous during winter.

FLOWERS. Irregular; perfect; showy; in racemes; corolla white, yellow-spotted in throat, ¾–1½ inches long.

FRUIT. Slender, elongated, thin-walled capsule, 7–12 inches long and ¼ inch thick; splitting into 2 concave valves; persistent into the winter. Seed; numerous; ⅓ inch long.

TWIGS. Slender, glabrous or densely tomentose, light brown. Winter buds: terminal absent; lateral minute, scaly.

BARK. Thin (⅛–¼ inch); dark brown; furrowed.

WOOD. Soft; not strong; close-grained; ring-porous; brown.

SILVICAL CHARACTERS. Intolerant; short-lived; banks of desert and low mountain water courses.

a. Winter twig, x 1.

b. Leaf, x ¼.

c. Panicle of flowers, x ⅜.

d. Fruit, x ½.

e. Seed, x 1.

BIGNONIACEAE

Northern Catalpa. Hardy Catalpa

* * *

Catalpa speciosa Warder

HABIT. A medium-sized tree 30–60 feet high and 1–3 feet in diameter (max. 120 by 6 feet); broad, rounded crown.

LEAVES. Opposite or whorled; simple; deciduous; 8–12 inches long; heart-shaped; entire; thick; dark green above, paler and hairy below; petioles long, stout, round.

FLOWERS. 2-lipped; perfect; showy; in open few-flowered panicles; calyx hairy; corolla white with inconspicuous yellow spots, 2½ inches across; appearing after the leaves.

FRUIT. A long, round, 2-celled, thick-walled capsule 8–20 inches long and ½ inch thick; persistent through winter. Seed: numerous, flattened, with rounded, fringed wings 1 inch long.

TWIGS. Very stout; brown; glabrous; orbicular leaf scar. Winter buds; terminal absent; lateral small, immersed in bark.

BARK. Rather thin; brown; broken into thick scales.

WOOD. Light; soft; weak; brown; durable; ring-porous; used for posts.

SILVICAL CHARACTERS. Intolerant; varied sites; fast growth; taproot; widely planted and naturalized through all but coldest portions of United States.

* * *

Southern Catalpa

Catalpa bignonioides Walt.

This smaller and more southern tree, while native from Florida to Louisiana, has been naturalized as far north as New York. It is less hardy in cold sites than northern catalpa and is distinguished from it by having flowers 1½ inches across in many-flowered, crowded panicles with glabrous calyx and corolla with many conspicuous yellow spots and by a thinner-walled fruit about ¼–⅓ inch in diameter.

* * *

Paulownia

Paulownia tomentosa (Thunb.) Sieb & Zucc.

This beautiful Chinese species has been widely cultivated in the eastern states and has become naturalized from New York to Georgia. In cold sites it winter-kills badly. It is characterized by opposite, heart-shaped, simple, deciduous leaves with entire margins, 5–8 inches long, and densely hairy on the lower surface; by perfect, 2-lipped, showy, purple flowers 1½–2 inches long, which appear before the leaves; and by a leathery, ovoid, beaked, brown capsule 1–2 inches long.

[361]

a. Flower, x 1.

b. Leaves and fruit, x ⅔.

RUBIACEAE

COMMON BUTTONBUSH

Cephalanthus occidentalis L.

HABIT. A shrub or rarely a small tree up to 50 feet high and 1–2 inches in diameter; open, spreading crown.

LEAVES. Opposite or whorled in 3's; simple; ovate, lanceolate, or elliptic; 2–7 inches long; acute or acuminate at apex; margins entire; thin; dark green and glabrous above; paler below, with yellow midrib; tardily deciduous during winter; petioles stout, grooved, glabrous, ½–¾ inch long.

FLOWERS. Regular; perfect; minute; in dense, globose heads 1–1½ inches in diameter; fragrant; calyx tube 4–5-lobed; corolla cream-white, salver-form, 4–5 lobed; stamens as many as and alternate with corolla lobes; ovary inferior, 2-celled, with protruding, threadlike style and capitate stigma.

FRUIT. Nutlike capsule; inversely pyramidal; splitting from base upwards into 2–4 closed, 1-seeded portions; in heads ⅝–¾ inch in diameter; green tinged with red, becoming dark red-brown. Seed: small, oblong, pendulous.

TWIGS. Stout; glabrous; thick pith; marked by large lenticels; opposite or in whorls of 3; light green at first, becoming red-brown. Winter buds: terminal absent; lateral minute, nearly immersed in the bark.

BARK. Thin; dark brown to nearly black; with broad, flat, superficially scaly ridges; contains tannin.

WOOD. Moderately heavy and hard; fine-grained; diffuse-porous; light red-brown; unimportant.

SILVICAL CHARACTERS. Rather tolerant; reproduction abundant; on moist sites or in dry stream beds; often forming dense thickets.

* * *

BIGNONIACEAE

TRUMPETFLOWER

Tecoma stans (L.) H. B. K.

A shrub or small tree extending through Mexico into the southern parts of Texas, New Mexico, and Arizona. Characterized by showy, bright yellow flowers; opposite, pinnately compound leaves with 5–13 leaflets; and a linear capsule, 4–8 inches long.

[363]

a. Flower, x 5.

b. Fruit, x 2.

c. Flowering branchlet, x ⅔.

CAPRIFOLIACEAE

BLUEBERRY ELDER

Sambucus glauca Nutt. (*Sambucus cerulea* Raf.)

HABIT. A shrub or small tree 30–50 feet high and 12–18 inches in diameter; compact, round-topped crown.

LEAVES. Opposite; unequally pinnately compound; petiolate; deciduous; 5–7 inches long; leaflets 5–9, ovate or narrow oblong, coarsely serrate margin, 1–6 inches long, green above, pale and glabrous to pubescent below.

FLOWERS. Regular; perfect; small (⅛ inch in diameter); in broad, terminal, long-branched corymbose cymes; corolla yellow-white, stamens 5; ovary inferior, 3–5 celled.

FRUIT. Dense clusters of small, blue, drupelike berries; ¼ inch in diameter, with sweet, juicy flesh. Seed: 3–5 1-seeded nutlets in each drupe.

TWIGS. Stout; somewhat angled; pubescent first year; red-brown; nearly encircled by large, triangular leaf-scars; thick, soft pith. Winter buds: terminal absent; lateral scaly, greenish.

BARK. Thin; dark brown, tinged with red.

WOOD. Light; soft; weak; coarse-grained; diffuse-porous; heartwood yellow tinged with brown, durable; unimportant.

SILVICAL CHARACTERS. Intolerant; short-lived; reproduction abundant but scattered; coppices freely; moist porous soils; along streams, ravines, or moist hillsides.

* * *

The key distinguishes between the seven native species:

1. Native to western North America.
   2. Cymes flat-topped; fruit blue-black, commonly glaucous.
      3. Twigs and lower surface of leaf pubescent; leaves deciduous western Arizona and California.................................
      ....*S. velutina* D. & H., **Velvet Elder**
      3. Twigs and leaves usually glabrous or nearly so.
         4. Leaves persistent; leaflets 3–5, oblong-lanceolate to ovate; western Texas to southern California......................
         ....*S. mexicana* Presl., **Mexican Elder**
         4. Leaves deciduous; leaflets 5–9, lanceolate to oblong-lanceolate...................*S. glauca*, **Blueberry Elder**
   2. Cymes pyramidal to ovoid.
      5. Fruit red; leaflets 5–9, oval, slightly pubescent below, Pacific coast from Alaska to southern California....................
      ....*S. callicarpa* Greene, **Pacific Red Elder**
      5. Fruit black; leaflets commonly 5, scurfy-puberulent or villous below; Alberta and Montana south to New Mexico and California.............*S. melanocarpa* Gray, **Black Bead Elder**
1. Native to eastern North America; usually shrubs.
   6. Leaflets usually 5, obovate to oblong; Florida to Louisiana......
   ....*S. simpsonii* Rehd., **Florida Elder**
   6. Leaflets usually 7, lanceolate to elliptic; Nova Scotia to Manitoba to Florida and Texas.........*S. canadensis* L., **American Elder**

a. Winter twig, with leaf buds
   x 1.

b. Winter twig, with flower bud
   x 1.

c. Leaf, x 3/4.

d. Flower, enlarged.

e. Fruiting branchlet, x 1/2.

CAPRIFOLIACEAE

Nannyberry

Viburnum lentago L.

HABIT. A shrub or small tree 15–30 feet high and 6–10 inches in diameter; bushy, compact, rounded crown.

LEAVES. Opposite; simple; ovate; 2–4 inches long and 1–2 inches wide; sharply serrate; thick and firm; lustrous and bright green above; yellow-green and marked with minute, black dots below; deciduous; turning orange and red in autumn.

FLOWERS. Regular; perfect; small (¼ inch in diameter); fragrant; in stout-branched, scurfy, terminal cymes 3–5 inches across, corolla tubular, 5-lobed, white; stamens 5; ovary inferior, 1-celled.

FRUIT. Few-fruited, red-stemmed clusters of small, juicy, blue-black, berry-like drupes; each drupe oval or ovoid, flattened, and covered with glaucous bloom. Seed: solitary within oval, rough, flattened nutlet.

TWIGS. Slender; light green and hairy, becoming dark red-brown. Winter buds: enclosed by one pair of valvate scales; flower buds ¾ inch long, grayish, swollen; terminal leaf bud 1 inch long, light red, narrow, and long-pointed.

BARK. Red-brown; irregularly broken into small, thick plates which are superficially scaly.

WOOD. Heavy; hard; close-grained; diffuse-porous; ill-scented; heartwood dark orange-brown; unimportant.

SILVICAL CHARACTERS. Intolerant; very hardy; an attractive small ornamental tree; endures city smoke.

* * *

Five species reach tree size:

1. Leaves entire or nearly so, dark green and lustrous.
    2. Leaves 4–6 inches long, broad oval; cymes long-stalked; Connecticut to Kentucky, south to Florida and Texas............
    .... *V. nudum* L., **Possumhaw Viburnum**
    2. Leaves ½–2 inches long, oblong to spatulate; cymes sessile; Virginia to Florida...... *V. obovatum* Walt., **Walter Viburnum**
1. Leaves sharply toothed; cymes sessile or short-stalked.
    2. Leaves lustrous above, petioles and veins red-hairy below; buds red-hairy; New Jersey to Kansas and south............
    .... *V. rufidulum* Raf., **Rusty Blackhaw**
    2. Leaves dull above, petioles and veins not hairy below; buds long and slender, scurfy or glabrous.
        3. Petioles and veins on lower leaf surface and buds red-scurfy
        .... *V. lentago* L., **Nannyberry**
        3. Petioles and veins glabrous; buds gray to brown, glabrous or scurfy; Connecticut to Michigan and Kansas and south
        .... *V. prunifolium* L., **Blackhaw**

[367]

a. Section of leaf, x 1.

b. Fruit, x 1.

c. Flower, x 2⁄3.

LILIACEAE

Soaptree Yucca. Spanish-bayonet

Yucca elata Engelm.

HABIT. A tree often 15–20 feet high and 7–8 inches in diameter with a deep, branched, underground stem; simple or branched at top; covered with pendent, persistent dead leaves.

LEAVES. Alternate; simple; 20–30 inches long and ¼–½ inch wide; thin and flat above, rounded below; glabrous; yellow-green; entire pale margins soon splitting into slender filaments; parallel-veined; persistent; stipules absent.

FLOWERS. Regular; in compound, terminal panicles, 4–6 feet high; perianth cup-shaped, white, 3½–4 inches across; stamens 6; ovary 6-sided, 3-celled; ovules numerous.

FRUIT. Erect, oblong capsule, 1½–2 inches long; 3–valved; light brown, thin and woody outside; light yellow inside; edible. Seed: numerous, black, ⅓ inch wide.

BARK. Dark brown; with thin plates; ¼ inch thick.

WOOD. Light; soft; spongy; pale brown or yellow; in concentric layers.

SILVICAL CHARACTERS. Lower Sonoran zone; intolerant; on desert plateaus; large roots used as substitute for soap.

* * *

Seven species of Yucca reach tree size:
1. Southwestern.
  2. Fruit erect, dehiscent; flower clusters long-stalked; leaves filamentose, thin, pale yellow-green......................Y.*elata-*.
  2. Fruit pendent, indehiscent; flower clusters sessile or short-stalked; leaves concave above the middle.
    3. Fruit with thin, dry flesh; leaves blue-green, serrate; southwestern Utah to California *Y. brevifolia* Engelm.; Joshua-tree
    3. Fruit with succulent flesh; leaves with no, or minute teeth.
      4. Panicle hoary-tomentose; leaves flexible, 2½–3 feet long; margins not filamentous; southern Arizona................
      ....*Y. schottii* Engelm.; Schotts Yucca
      4. Panicle glabrous or puberulous; margins filamentous.
        5. Leaves 2½–4 feet long, dark green; Texas.
          6. Leaves concave; perianth nearly free...............
          ....*Y. treculeana* Carr.; Trecul Yucca
          6. Leaves flat, perianth united into tube...............
          ....*Y. faxoniana* Sarg.; Faxon Yucca
        5. Leaves 1½–2 feet long, light yellow-green.
          7. Style elongated; western Texas to eastern Arizona....
          .... *Y. torreyi* Shaf.; Torrey Yucca
          7. Style short; southeastern Nevada, northwestern Arizona...... . *Y. mohavensis* Sarg.; Mohave Yucca
1. Southeastern Coastal Plain, North Carolina and south.
  8. Leaves sharply serrate on horny margin; fruit succulent........
  ....*Y. aloifolia* L., Aloe Yucca
  8. Leaves entire or nearly so; fruit with thin dry flesh............
  . ...*Y. gloriosa* L.; Moundilly Yucca

a. Leaf petiole, x ⅓.

b. Leaf, x 1/9.

c. Part of fruit cluster, x ⅔.

PALMAE

CALIFORNIA PALM. WASHINGTONIA

Washingtonia filifera Wendl. (*Washingtonia arizonica* Cook)
(*Washingtonia robusta* Wendl.)

HABIT. An evergreen tree 30–50 feet high and 1–2 feet in diameter; crown broad, consisting of large leaves; columnar trunk clothed with thatchlike mass of pendent dead leaves.

LEAVES. Clustered at top of stem; 3–6 feet long; fan-shaped; nearly circular; with 40–70 ribbon-like folds deeply slashed ½–⅔ of distance to base; the margins of the divisions separating into threadlike filaments; petioles 3–5 feet long, 1–3 inches wide, armed along margins with stout, hooked spines.

FLOWERS. Regular; perfect; minute; in compound clusters 8–10 feet long; appearing from axils of upper leaves; calyx tubular; corolla white, tubular; stamens 6; ovary 3-lobed and 3-celled with a single ovule in each cell.

FRUIT. Drupelike berry; ⅜ inch long; black when ripe in September; ellipsoidal; with a thin, dry, sweet pulp; produced in large quantities. Seed: ¼ inch long, ⅛ inch wide, pale chestnut-brown.

BARK. Stem with thick barklike rind; narrowly furrowed; pale cinnamon to dull red-brown.

WOOD. Light; soft; spongy and fibrous; numerous, dark orange-colored, fibro-vascular bundles; unimportant.

SILVICAL CHARACTERS. Moderately tolerant when young, becoming intolerant; reproduction plentiful; long, deep roots; alkaline soils; dry, warm mountain canyons.

GENERAL. This palm is reported from southern California and southwestern Arizona, often occurring there in large numbers. Considerable confusion exists as to the nomenclature and classification of the forms of *Washingtonia*.

* * *

CABBAGE PALMETTO

Sabal palmetto (Walt.) Lodd.

This species, of the Coastal Plain from North Carolina to Florida, forms a tree 40–90 feet high and 1–2 feet in diameter. It resembles *Washingtonia* in its fan-shaped leaves, flowers, and fruit; but can be easily distinguished by its unarmed leaf stalks. Two other species are native to the Gulf area: Louisiana palmetto, *S. louisiana* (Darby) Bom., in Louisiana and Texas and palmetto, *S. texana* (Cook) Becc., in southern Texas.

GLOSSARY

Abortive. Imperfectly or not developed; barren.

Acicular. Slenderly needle-shaped.

Accrescent. Increasing in size with age.

Achene. A dry indehiscent, 1-celled and 1-seeded fruit or carpel.

Acuminate. Gradually tapering to the apex; long-pointed.

Acute. Sharply pointed, but not drawn out.

Adnate. Descriptive of unlike organs or parts fused together.

Alternate. Scattered singly along axis; not opposite.

Ament. A scaly, bracted spike of usually unisexual flowers, frequently deciduous in one piece.

Angiosperms. Plants with seeds borne in an ovary.

Anther. The pollen-bearing part of the stamen.

Antherozoid. Male sexual cells.

Anthesis. The time when fertilization takes place or a flower expands.

Apetalous. Without petals.

Apiculate. Ending in a minute, short, pointed tip.

Apophysis. That part of a cone scale which is exposed when the cone is closed.

Appressed. Lying close and flat against.

Arborescent. Attaining the size or character of a tree.

Aril. An appendage or an outer covering of a seed, growing out from the hilum or funiculus.

Attentuate. Slenderly tapering; acuminate.

Awl-shaped. Tapering from the base to a slender and stiff point.

Axil. The upper angle formed by a leaf or branch with the stem.

Axillary. Situated in an axil.

Baccate. Berry-like; pulpy throughout.

Berry. A fleshy or pulpy fruit with immersed seeds.

Blade. The expanded portion of a leaf.

Bloom. A powdery or waxy substance easily rubbed off.

Bole. The stem of a tree.

Boss. A raised projection, usually pointed.

Bract. A modified leaf subtending a flower or belonging to an inflorescence.

Bractlet. The bract of a pedicel or ultimate flower stalk; a secondary bract.

Bud. The undeveloped state of a branch or flower cluster, with or without scales.

Bud scales. Modified leaves covering a bud.
Bundle (leaf). Strand of fibro-vascular tissue found in cross section of leaf.

Caducous. Falling off very early.
Calyx. The flower-cup or exterior part of a perianth.
Campanulate. Bell-shaped.
Canescent. Gray-pubescent and hoary.
Capsule. A dry fruit of more than one carpel which splits at maturity to release its seeds.
Carpel. A simple pistil or an element of a compound pistil.
Catkin. The same as an ament.
Caudate. Furnished with a tail or with a slender tip.
Cell. The unit of structure of living things; a cavity of an ovary or anther.
Chambered. Said of pith which is interrupted by hollow spaces.
Ciliate. Fringed with hairs on the margin.
Cone. A fruit with woody, overlapping scales.
Coniferous. Pertains to cone-bearing; or the order Coniferales.
Coppice. Growth arising from sprouts at the stump.
Cordate. Heart-shaped.
Coriaceous. Of the texture of leather.
Corolla. Inner part of the perianth, composed of petals.
Corymb. A flat-topped flower cluster, the flowers opening from the outside inward.
Crenate. Dentate with the teeth much rounded.
Crenulate. Diminutive of crenate, finely crenate.
Crown. The upper part of a tree, including the living branches with their foliage.
Cuneate. Wedge-shaped, or triangular with an acute angle downward.
Cuspidate. Tipped with a sharp, rigid point.
Cylindric. Shaped like a cylinder.
Cyme. A flat-topped flower cluster, the flowers opening from the center outward.

Deciduous. Not persistent; falling away as the leaves of a tree in autumn.
Decurrent. Running down, as of the blades of leaves extending down their petioles.
Decussate. In pairs alternately crossing at right angles.
Dehiscent. The opening of an anther or capsule by slits or valves.
Deltoid. Delta-shaped, triangular.

Dentate. Toothed, with the teeth directed outward.

Denticulate. Minutely toothed.

Diadelphous. Stamens formed into two groups through the union of their filaments.

Diaphragmed. Said of pith which is solid but with more or less regularly spaced disks of horizontally elongated cells with thickened walls.

Dimorphous. Occurring in two forms.

Dioecious. Unisexual, the staminate and pistillate flowers on different individuals.

Disk. A development of the receptacle at or around the base of the pistil.

Dissemination. The spreading abroad of ripe seeds from the parent plant.

Divergent. Spreading apart; pointing away.

Dorsal. Relating to the back or outer surface of an organ; the lower surface of a leaf.

Downy. Clothed with a coat of soft, fine hairs.

Drupaceous. Resembling or relating to a drupe.

Drupe. A stone fruit, such as a plum.

E. A latin prefix denoting that parts are missing, as eglandular, without glands.

Ellipsoidal. Of the shape of an elliptical solid.

Elliptic. Of the form of an elipse.

Emarginate. Notched at the apex.

Entire. Leaf margin without divisions, lobes or teeth.

Erose. Descriptive of an irregularly toothed or eroded margin.

Excrescences. Warty outgrowths or protuberances.

Exfoliate. To cleave or peel off in thin layers.

Exserted. Prolonged beyond the surrounding organs, as stamens from the corolla.

Falcate. Scythe- or sickle-shaped.

Fascicle. Dense cluster or bundle.

Fibro-vascular. Consisting of woody fibers and ducts.

Filament. The stalk of an anther.

Fluted. Regularly marked by alternating ridges and groovelike depressions.

Foliaceous. Leaflike in texture or appearance.

Fugacious. Falling or withering away very early.

Fulvous. Tawny; dull yellow with gray.

Funiculus. The stalk of an ovule.
Furrowed. With longitudinal channels or grooves.

Gibbous. Swollen on one side.
Glabrous. Smooth, not pubescent or hairy.
Gland. Secreting surface or structure; a protuberance having appearance of such an organ.
Glandular. Furnished with glands.
Glaucous. Covered or whitened with a bloom.
Globose. Spherical in form or nearly so.
Gymnosperms. Plants with naked seeds; i.e. not enclosed in an ovary.

Habit. The general appearance of a plant; best seen from a distance.
Habitat. The place where a plant naturally grows.
Halberd-like. Like an arrowhead, but with the basal lobes pointing outward nearly at right angles.
Hilum. The scar or place of attachment of a seed.
Hirsute. Covered with rather coarse or stiff, long hairs.
Hispid. With rigid or bristly hairs.
Hoary. Covered with a close, whitish or gray-white pubescence.
Hybrid. A cross, usually between two related species.

Imbricate. Overlapping, like shingles on a roof.
Indehiscent. Not splitting open; remaining closed.
Inferior ovary. Appearing to grow below the adnate calyx.
Inserted. Attached to or growing out of.
Intolerant. Not capable of doing well under dense forest cover.
Involucre. A circle of bracts surrounding a flower cluster.
Irregular flower. Bilaterally symmetrical; similar parts of different shapes or sizes.

Keeled. With a central ridge like the keel of a boat.

Laciniate. Cut into narrow, pointed lobes.
Lanceolate. Lance-shaped.
Lateral. Situated on the side; not at apex.
Leaflet. One of the small blades of a compound leaf.
Leaf scar. Scar left on twig by the falling of a leaf.
Legume. Fruit of the pea family; podlike and splitting open by both sutures.

Lenticel. Corky growth on young bark which admits air to the interior of a twig or branch.

Linear. Long and narrow, with parallel edges.

Lobe. A somewhat rounded division of an organ.

Lobulate. Divided into small lobes.

Lustrous. Glossy, shining.

Membranaceous. Thin and somewhat translucent.

Midrib. The central vein of a leaf or leaflet.

Monoecious. The stamens and pistils in separate flowers but borne on the same individual.

Mucro. A small and abrupt tip to a leaf.

Mucronate. Furnished with a mucro (bristle-tipped).

Naked buds. Buds without scales.

Nut. A hard and indehiscent, 1-seeded pericarp produced from a compound ovary.

Nutlet. A diminutive nut or stone.

Ob. Latin prefix signifying inversion.

Obconic. Inverted cone-shaped.

Oblanceolate. Lanceolate, with the broadest part toward the apex.

Oblong. About three times longer than broad with nearly parallel sides.

Oblique. Slanting or with unequal sides.

Obcordate. Inverted heart shape.

Obovate. Ovate with the broader end toward the apex.

Obovoid. An ovate solid with the broadest part toward the apex.

Obtuse. Blunt or rounded at apex.

Odd-pinnate leaf. Pinnate with a terminal leaflet.

Orbicular. A flat body circular in outline.

Oval. Broad elliptic, rounded at ends and about 1½ times as long as broad.

Ovary. The part of a pistil that contains the ovules.

Ovate. Shaped like the longitudinal section of an egg, with the broad end basal.

Ovoid. Solid ovate or solid oval.

Ovule. The part of the flower which after fertilization becomes the seed.

Palmate. Radiately lobed or divided, veins arising from one point.

Panicle. A loose, compound or branched flower cluster.

Papilionaceous. Butterfly-like; typical flower shape of legumes.

Pedicel. Stalk of a single flower in a compound inflorescence.

Pedicellate. Borne on a pedicel.

Peduncle. A general flower stalk supporting either a cluster of flowers or a solitary flower.

Peltate. Shield-shaped and attached by its lower surface to the central stalk.

Pendent. Hanging downward.

Pendulous. More or less hanging or declined.

Penniveined. Having the form of a feather; secondary veins arranged parallel to each other and arising from a main vein.

Perfect. Flower with both stamens and pistil.

Perianth. The calyx and corolla of a flower considered as a whole.

Persistent. Remaining attached, not falling off.

Petiolate. Having a petiole.

Petiole. Footstalk of a leaf.

Petiolule. Footstalk of a leaflet.

Pilose. Hairy, with soft and distinct hairs.

Pinnate. A compound leaf with leaflets arranged along each side of a common petiole.

Pistil. Female organ of a flower, consisting of ovary, style, and stigma.

Pistillate. Female flowers; descriptive of unisexual flowers.

Pith. The central, softer part of a stem.

Pollen. The fecundating grains borne in the anther.

Polygamo-dioecious. Flowers sometimes perfect, sometimes unisexual and dioecious.

Polygamo-monoecious. Flowers sometimes perfect and sometimes unisexual, the 2 forms borne on the same individual.

Polygamous. Flowers sometimes perfect and sometimes unisexual.

Pome. An inferior fruit of 2 or several carpels enclosed in thick flesh; an apple.

Prickle. A small spine-like growth from the bark or epidermis.

Prostrate. Lying flat on the ground.

Puberulous. Minutely pubescent.

Pubescent. Clothed with soft, short hairs.

Pungent. Terminating in a rigid, sharp point; acrid.

Pyramidal. Shaped like a pyramid.

Raceme. A simple inflorescence of stalked flowers on a more or less elongated rachis.

Racemose. In racemes; resembling racemes.

Rachis. An axis bearing leaflets, as in a compound leaf.

Receptacle. The more or less expanded portion of an axis which bears the organs of a flower or the collected flowers of a head.

Recurved. Curving downward or backward.

Reflexed. Abruptly turned downward.

Regular flower. Radially symmetrical; similar parts of same shape and size.

Remotely. Scattered, not close together.

Reniform. Kidney-shaped.

Repand. With a slightly sinuate margin.

Reticulate. Netted.

Retrosely. Directed backward or downward.

Revolute. Rolled backward, margin rolled toward the lower side.

Rhombic. Having the shape of a rhombus.

Rufous. Red-brown.

Rugose. Wrinkled.

Samara. An indehiscent, winged fruit.

Scabrous. Rough to the touch.

Scarious. Thin, dry, membranceous, not green.

Scorpioid. A form of unilateral inflorescence circinately coiled in the bud.

Scurfy. Covered with small branlike scales.

Serotinus. Late in bearing or opening.

Serrate. Toothed, the teeth pointing upward or forward.

Sessile. Without a stalk.

Sheath. A tubular envelope, or enrolled part or organ.

Shrub. A woody, bushy plant, branched at or near the base and usually less than 15 feet in height.

Sinuate. With a strong, wavy margin.

Sinus. The cleft or space between two lobes.

Spike. A simple inflorescence of sessile flowers arranged on a common, elongated axis.

Spine. A sharp, mostly woody outgrowth in the position of a leaf or stipule.

Spinescent. With short, rigid branches resembling spines.

Spinose. Furnished with spines.

Stamen. The pollen-bearing organ of the male flower.

Staminate. Male flowers; provided with stamens but without pistils.

Stellate. Star-shaped.

Sterigmata. Short, persistent leaf bases found on spruces and
   hemlocks.
Stigma. The part or surface of a pistil which receives pollen
   for the fecundation of the ovules.
Stipule. An appendage at the base of the petiole, usually one on
   each side.
Stoma. An orifice in the epidermis of a leaf used to connect in-
   ternal cavities with air.
Stomata. Plural of stoma.
Stomatiferous. Furnished with stomata.
Strobile. A cone.
Style. The attenuated portion of a pistil between the ovary
   and the stigma.
Sub. A Latin prefix denoting somewhat or slightly.
Subtend. To lie under or opposite to.
Subulate. Awl-shaped.
Succulent. Juicy; fleshy.
Superior ovary. Free from and inserted above calyx; hypogy-
   nous.
Superposed. Placed above, as one bud above another at a node.
Suture. A junction or line of dehiscence.
Syncarp. A multiple fleshy fruit.

Taproot. The primary descending root, which may be either
   very large or absent at the maturity of the tree.
Terete. Circular in traverse section.
Terminal. Situated at the end of a branch.
Ternate. In groups of three.
Thorn. A sharp woody outgrowth in the position of a lateral branch.
Tolerant. Capable of enduring shade.
Tomentose. Densely pubescent with matted wool or tomentum.
Tomentulose. Slightly pubescent with matted wool.
Torulose. Cylindric, with swollen partitions at intervals.
Tree. A plant with a woody stem, unbranched at or near base,
   and at least 8 feet in height and 2 inches in diameter.
Truncate. Ending abruptly, as if cut off at the end.
Tubercle. A small tuber or excrescence.
Turbinate. Top-shaped.
Twig. A young woody stem; more precisely the shoot of a woody
   plant representing the growth of the current season.

Umbel. A simple inflorescence of flowers with pedicels all arising
   from the same point.

Umbo. A boss or protuberance.
Undulate. With wavy surface or margin.
Unisexual. Of one sex, either staminate or pistillate.

Valvate. Leaf buds meeting at the edges, not overlapping.
Valve. One of the pieces into which a capsule splits.
Veins. Threads of fibro-vascular tissue in a leaf or other flat organ.
Ventral. Belonging to the anterior or inner face of an organ; the upper surface of a leaf.
Vernal. Appearing in the spring.
Vesicle. A little bladder or cavity.
Villose. Hairy with long and soft hairs.

Whorled. Three or more organs arranged in a circle round an axis.
Wing. A membranous or thin and dry expansion or appendage of an organ.
Woolly. Covered with long and matted or tangled hairs.

INDEX

Abies, 72
  amabilis, 83
  balsamea, 75
  bracteata, 87
  concolor, 79
  concolor lowiana, 79
  fraseri, 75
  grandis, 81
  Key to species, 73
  lasiocarpa, 77
  lasiocarpa arizonica, 77
  magnifica, 85
  magnifica shastensis, 85
  nobilis, 87
  procera, 87
  venusta, 87
Acacia amentacea, 269
  angustissima, 269
  catclaw, 269
  constricta paucispina, 269
  emoryana, 269
  farnesiana, 269
  greggii, 269
  greenbarked, 279
  millefolia, 269
  tortuosa, 269
  wrightii, 269
Acer, 294
  barbatum, 295
  circinatum, 301
  glabrum, 301
  glabrum douglasii, 301
  grandidentatum, 307
  Key to species, 295
  leucoderme, 295
  macrophyllum, 305
  negundo, 307
  negundo arizonicum, 307
  negundo californicum, 307
  negundo interius, 307
  negundo texanum, 307
  negundo violaceum, 307
  nigrum, 297
  pensylvanicum, 303
  platanoides, 295

pseudoplatanus, 295
  rubrum, 299
  saccharinum, 299
  saccharophorum, 297.
  saccharum, 297
  saccharum sinuosum, 297
  spicatum, 303
Aesculus, 308
  arguta, 309
  californica, 309
  x carnea, 308
  glabra, 311
  hippocastanum, 308
  Key to species, 309
  octandra, 311
  pavia, 309
  sylvatica, 309
Ailanthus altissima, 287
  glandulosa, 287
Alaska cedar, 105
Albizia julibrissin, 271
Alder, 156
  Arizona, 157
  European, 157
  Hazel, 157
  Mountain, 161
  Red, 159
  Seaside, 157
  Sitka, 161
  Speckled, 157
  Thinleaf, 161
  White, 157
Allthorn, 321
Almond, 259
  flowering, 256
Alnus, 156
  glutinosa, 157
  Key to species, 157
  maritima, 157
  oblongifolia, 157
  rhombifolia, 157
  rubra, 159
  rugosa, 161
  serrulata, 157
  sinuata, 161

Alnus (*continued*)
  sitchensis, 161
  tenuifolia, 161
Amelanchier alnifolia, 251
  arborea, 251
  florida, 251
  interior, 251
  laevis, 251
  sanguinea, 251
  utahensis, 251
American Hornbeam, 165
Anacahuita, 359
Apple, 247
Apricot, 259
Aralia spinosa, 323
Arborvitae, Eastern, 97
  Giant, 97
  Oriental, 97
Arbutus arizonica, 333
  menziesii, 333
  texana, 333
Ash, 342
  Berlandier, 355
  Biltmore, 347
  Black, 351
  Blue, 353
  Carolina, 351
  Dwarf, 345
  Florida, 351
  Flowering, 345
  Fragrant, 345
  Green, 349
  Gregg, 345
  Lowell, 355
  Oregon, 353
  Prickly, 285
  Pumpkin, 349
  Red, 349
  Singleleaf, 345
  Texas, 347
  Velvet, 355
  Water, 351
  White, 347
Asimina triloba, 237
Aspen, Bigtooth, 123
  Quaking, 123
Atlantic White-cedar, 105
Avocado, 239

Baldcypress, 93
  Montezuma, 93
Basswood, American, 319
  White, 319
Bay, Loblolly, 323

Bayberry, evergreen, 135
  odorless, 135
  Pacific, 135
  Southern, 135
Beech, American, 167
  Blue, 165
  Bronzeleaf, 167
  Cutleaf, 167
  European, 167
  Weeping, 167
Betula, 146
  alleghaniensis, 151
  caerulea-grandis, 149
  xeastwoodiae, 155
  fontinalis, 155
  glandulosa, 155
  Key to species, 147
  lenta, 153
  lutea, 151
  nigra, 151
  occidentalis, 155
  papyrifera, 149
  papyrifera commutata, 149
  papyrifera cordifolia, 149
  papyrifera humilis, 149
  papyrifera kenaica, 149
  papyrifera montanensis, 149
  papyrifera subcordata, 149
  pendula, 146
  pendula dalecarlica, 146
  populifolia, 153
Bigcone Douglas-fir, 63
Bigtree, 89
Birch, 146
  Blueleaf, 149
  Bog, 155
  European White, 146
  Gray, 153
  Paper, 149
  River, 151
  Sweet, 153
  Water, 155
  Weeping, 146
  Yellow, 151
  Yukon, 155
Blackgum, 327
Blackhaw, 367
  Rusty, 367
Blackthorn, 256
Bluebeech, 165
Blueblossom Ceanothus, 317
Bluewood, 317
Boxelder, 307

Broussonetia papyrifera, 227
  secundiflora, 281
Buckeye, California, 309
  Mexican, 313
  Ohio, 311
  Painted, 309
  Red, 309
  Texas, 309
  Yellow, 311
Buckthorn, California, 315
  Carolina, 315
  Cascara, 315
  European, 315
  Glossy, 315
  Hollyleaf, 315, 317
Buckwheat-tree, 293
Buffaloberry, Silver, 329
Bumelia celastrina, 339
  lanuginosa, 339
  lyciodes, 339
  tenax, 339
Burning Bush, 293
Bursera fagaroides, 287
  microphylla, 287
  simaruba, 287
Butternut, 137
Buttonbush, Common, 363

Cactaceae, 324
Cactus, Cane, 325
California-laurel, 327
California Palm, 371
Canotia holacantha, 293
Caragana arborescens, 281
Carnegiea gigantea, 325
Carpinus caroliniana, 165
Carya, 138
  alba, 143
  aquatica, 145
  cordiformis, 145
  floridana, 143
  glabra, 143
  illinoensis, 145
  Key to species, 139
  laciniosa, 141
  leiodermis, 143
  myristicaeformis, 145
  ovata, 141
  pallida, 143
  pecan, 145
  texana, 143
  tomentosa, 143
Castanea alnifolia floridana, 169
  ashei, 169

  dentata, 169
  ozarkenis, 169
  pumila, 169
Castanopis chrysophylla, 171
Catalpa bignonioides, 361
  Hardy, 361
  Northern, 361
  Southern, 361
  speciosa, 361
Ceanothus arboreus, 317
  spinosus, 317
  thyrisiflorus, 317
Celtis, 220
  douglasii, 225
  Key to species, 221
  laevigata, 225
  laevigata brevipes, 225
  lindheimeri, 223
  occidentalis, 223
  pumila georgiana, 223
  reticulata, 225
  tenuifolia, 223
Cephalanthus occidentalis, 363
Cercidium floridum, 279
  macrum, 279
  microphyllum, 279
  torreyanum, 279
Cercis canadensis, 273
  canadensis texensis, 273
  occidentalis, 273
Cereus giganteus, 325
  schottii, 324
  thurberi, 324
Cerocarpus betuloides, 255
  breviflorus, 255
  ledifolius, 255
Chamaecyparis, 98
  Key to species, 99
  lawsoniana, 103
  nootkatensis, 105
  obtusa, 103
  pisifera, 103
  thyoides, 105
Cherry, Black, 261
  Bitter, 263
  Catalina, 258
  Hollyleaf, 258
  Mahaleb, 256
  Pin, 263
  Sour, 256, 259
Chestnut, American, 169
Chilopsis linearis, 359
  saligna, 359
Chinaberry, 287

Chinkapin, Allegheny, 169
    Ashe, 169
    Florida, 169
    Golden, 171
    Ozark, 169
Chionanthus virginicus, 357
Chokecherry, Alabama, 258
    Allegheny, 257
    Beadle, 258
    Black, 261
    Common, 261
    Georgia, 258
    Southwestern, 258
    Western, 261
Cholla, 325
    Staghorn, 325
Christmasberry, 258
Cladrastis lutea, 275
Cliffrose, 258
Cliftonia monophylla, 293
Coffeetree, Kentucky, 275
Condalia obovata, 317
Coralbean, 266
Cordia boissieri, 359
Cornus alternifolia, 331
    drummondii, 331
    florida, 331
    nutallii, 331
    occidentalis, 331
Corono de Cristo, 321
Corylus cornuta, 165
    maxima, 165
Cotinus obovatus, 309
Cottonwood, Black, 127
    Eastern, 125
    Fremont, 125
    Lanceleaf, 129
    Narrowleaf, 129
    Palmer, 125
    Plains, 125
    Rio Grande, 125
    Swamp, 125
Cowania mexicana, 258
Crab Apple, Bigfruit, 245
    Biltmore, 245
    Buncombe, 245
    Dunbar, 245
    Lanceleaf, 245
    Oregon, 245
    Prairie, 245
    Siberian, 245
    Southern, 245
    Sweet, 247
Crataegus douglasii, 253

Cucumbertree, 233
    Yellow, 233
Cupressus, 98
    arizonica, 101
    bakeri, 99
    goveniana, 99
    guadalupensis, 99
    macnabiana, 99
    macrocarpa, 99
    sempervirens, 99
Cypress, Arizona, 101
    Gowen, 99
    Italian, 99
    McNab, 99
    Modoc, 99
    Monterey, 99
    Tecate, 99
    Yellow, 105
Cyrilla racemiflora, 293
    Swamp, 293

Dahoon, 291
Dalea spinosa, 266
Desert-olive foresteria, 357
Desertwillow, 359
Devils-walkingstick, 323
Devilwood, 357
Diospyros texana, 341
    virginiana, 341
Dogwood, Alternate-leaf, 331
    Flowering, 331
    Pacific, 331
    Roughleaf, 331
    Western, 331
Douglas-fir, 363

Elaeagnus angustifolia, 329
    utilis, 329
Elder, American, 365
    Arizona, 365
    Blueberry, 365
    Florida, 365
    Pacific, 365
    Velvet, 365
Elephanttree, 287
Elliottia racemosa, 333
Elm, American, 217
    Cedar, 217
    Chinese, 215
    Cork, 219
    English, 215
    Red, 219
    Rock, 219
    September, 217

Elm, American (*continued*)
  Siberian, 215
  Slippery, 219
  Water, 221
  White, 217
  Winged, 217
  Wych, 215
Erythrina crista-galli, 266
  flabelliformis, 266
  herbacea, 266
Euonymus atropurpureus, 293
  occidentalis, 293
Eysenhardtia angustifolia, 266
  polystachya, 266

Fagus grandifolia, 167
  grandifolia caroliniana, 167
  sylvatica, 167
  sylvatica atropunicea, 167
  sylvatica laciniata, 167
  sylvatica pendula, 167
Farkleberry, 337
Ficus aurea, 229
  carica, 229
  laevigata, 229
Fig, Common, 229
  Florida Strangler, 229
  Shortleaf, 229
Filbert, Giant, 165
Fir, Balsam, 75
  Bristlecone, 87
  California Red, 85
  Corkbark, 77
  Douglas, 63
  Fraser, 75
  Grand, 81
  Lowland White, 81
  Noble, 87
  Pacific Silver, 83
  Pacific White, 79
  Shasta Red, 85
  Subalpine, 77
  White, 79
Flannelbush, 321
Forestiera acuminata, 357
  phillyreoides, 357
Fraxinus, 342
  americana, 347
  anomala, 345
  berlandieriana, 355
  biltmoreana, 347
  caroliniana, 351
  cuspidata, 345
  dipetala, 347

greggii, 345
Key to species, 343
latifolia, 353
lowellii, 355
nigra, 351
oregona, 353
pauciflora, 351
pennsylvanica, 349
pennsylvanica lanceolata, 349
profunda, 349
quadrangulata, 353
standleyi, 355
texensis, 347
tomentosa, 349
velutina, 355
velutina coriacea, 355
velutina glabra, 355
velutina toumeyi, 355
Fremontia californica, 321
  mexicana, 321
Fremontodendron californicum, 321
Frijolito, 281
Fringetree, 357

Ginkgo biloba, xi
Gleditsia aquatica, 277
  x texana, 277
  triacanthos, 277
  triacanthos inermis, 277
Gordonia lasianthus, 323
Gum, Black, 327
  bumelia, 339
  elastic, 339
  Sweet, 241
Gumbo-limbo, 287
Gymnocladus dioicus, 275

Hackberry, 220, 223
  Georgia, 223
  Lindheimer, 223
  Netleaf, 225
Halesia carolina, 341
  diptera, 341
  monticola, 341
  parviflora, 341
Hamamelis virginiana, 241
Hawthorn, Black, 253
Hazelnut, 165
Hemlock, Carolina, 67
  Eastern, 67
  Mountain, 71
  Western, 69
Hercules-Club, 285
Heteromeles arbutifolia, 258

Hicoria, 138
Hickory, Bitternut, 145
    Black, 143
    Mockernut, 143
    Nutmeg, 145
    Pignut, 143
    Sand, 143
    Scrub, 143
    Shagbark, 141
    Shellbark, 141
    Swamp, 143
    Water, 145
Holly, American, 291
    English, 291
    Tawneyberry, 291
Honeylocust, 277
    Texas, 277
Hophornbeam, 163
    Eastern, 163
    Knowlton, 163
Hoptree, Common, 285
    Narrowleaf, 285
Hornbeam, American, 165
Horsechestnut, 308
Heteromeles arbutifolia, 258

Ilex aquifolium, 291
    cassine, 291
    decidua, 291
    krugiana, 291
    montana, 291
    opaca, 291
    vomitoria, 291
Incense-cedar, 95

Jerusalem-thorn, 279
Joshua Tree, 369
Juglans, 134
    californica, 134
    cinerea, 137
    hindsii, 134
    Key to species, 135
    major, 134
    microcarpa, 134
    nigra, 137
    regia, 134
    rupestris, 134
Juniper, Alligator, 113
    Ashe, 113
    California, 115
    Common, 106
    Drooping, 113
    Eastern, 109

One-seed, 111
    Pinchot, 113
    Prostrate, 106
    Rocky Mountain, 111
    Sierra, 115
    Utah, 113
    Western, 115
Juniperus, 106
    ashei, 113
    californica, 115
    communis, 106
    deppeana, 113
    flaccida, 113
    horizontalis, 106
    Key to species, 107
    monosperma, 111
    occidentalis, 115
    osteosperma, 113
    pachyphloea, 113
    pinchotii, 113
    scopulorum, 111
    silicicola, 109
    utahensis, 113
    virginiana, 109

Kalmia latifolia, 335
Kentucky Coffeetree, 275
Kidneywood, 266
Koeberlinia spinosa, 321

Larch, Eastern, 45
    European, 42
    Subalpine, 47
    Western, 47
Larix, 42
    alaskensis, 45
    decidua, 42
    Key to species, 43
    laricina, 45
    lyallii, 47
    occidentalis, 47
Laurel, California, 237
Laurelcherry, Carolina, 258
    Myrtle, 258
Leadtree, Great, 266
    Gregg, 266
    Littleleaf, 266
Leguminosae, 266
Leucaena glauca, 266
    greggii, 266
    pulverulenta, 266
    retusa, 266
Libocedrus decurrens, 95

Linden, European, 319
  Small-leaved, 319
Liquidambar styraciflua, 241
Liriodendron tulipifera, 235
Lithocarpus densiflorus, 173
Loblolly Bay, 323
Locust, Black, 283
  Clammy, 283
  Honey, 277
  Kelsey, 283
  New Mexican, 283
Logwood, 317
Lyonia ferruginea, 333
Lysiloma bahamensis, 266
  microphylla, 266

Maclura pomifera, 229
Madrone, Arizona, 333
  Pacific, 333
  Texas, 333
Magnolia, 230
  acuminata, 233
  acuminata cordata, 233
  Ashe, 231
  ashei, 231
  Bigleaf, 231
  Cucumber, 233
  Evergreen, 233
  Fraser, 231
  fraseri, 231
  grandiflora, 233
  Key to species, 231
  macrophylla, 231
  Pyramid, 231
  pyramidata, 231
  Southern, 233
  tripetala, 231
  Umbrella, 231
  virginiana, 231
Mahogany, West Indies, 287
Maidenhair tree, xi
Malus, 244
  angustifolia, 245
  baccata, 245
  coronaria, 247
  diversifolia, 245
  glabrata, 245
  ioensis, 245
  Key to species, 245
  platycarpa, 245
  pumila, 247
Maple, Bigleaf, 305
  Bigtooth, 305
  Black, 297

Chalk, 295
Douglas, 301
Florida, 295
Mountain, 303
Norway, 295
Red, 299
Rocky Mountain, 301
Silver, 299
Striped, 303
Sugar, 297
Sycamore, 295
Mazzard, 259
Melia azedarach, 287
Mescalbean, 281
Mesquite, 271
  Fremont, 271
  Screwbean, 271
Mimosa, 271
Mohavethorn, 293
Moosewood, 303
Morus alba, 227
  microphylla, 227
  nigra, 227
  rubra, 227
Mountain-ash, American, 249
  European, 249
  Showy, 249
Mountain-laurel, 335
Mountain-mahogany, Birchleaf, 255
  Curlleaf, 255
  Hairy, 255
Mulberry, Black, 227
  Paper, 227
  Red, 227
  Texas, 227
  White, 227
Myrica californica, 135
  cerifera, 135
  heterophylla, 135
  inodora, 135

Nannyberry, 367
Nutmeg, California, 117
Nyssa aquatica, 327
  ogeche, 327
  sylvatica, 327
  sylvatica biflora, 327
  ursina, 327

Oak, 174
  Arizona White, 209
  Arkansas, 178
  Bear, 176

Oak (*continued*)
  Bigelow, 175
  Black, 193
  Blackjack, 197
  Blue, 185
  Bluejack, 205
  Bur, 181
  California Black, 201
  California Live, 211
  California Scrub, 178
  California White, 187
  Canyon Live, 213
  Chapman, 175
  Chestnut, 189
  Chinkapin, 191
  Durand, 175
  Dwarf Chinkuapin, 176
  Emory, 209
  Engelmann, 178
  English, 174
  Gambel, 185
  Georgia, 177
  Interior Live, 211
  Island Live, 178
  Laurel, 205
  Live, 207
  Mexican Blue, 207
  Mohr, 175
  Myrtle, 178
  Netleaf, 179
  Northern Pin, 199
  Northern Red, 193
  Nuttall, 199
  Oregon White, 187
  Overcup, 183
  Pin, 199
  Post, 183
  Sandpaper, 175
  Scarlet, 197
  Shingle, 205
  Shumard, 195
  Silverleaf, 213
  Southern Red, 195
  Swamp Chestnut, 189
  Swamp Red, 195
  Swamp White, 191
  Toumey, 179
  Turkey, 201
  Water, 203
  Wavyleaf, 175
  White, 181
  Willow, 203
Olneya tesota, 266
Opuntia fulgida, 325

  imbricata, 325
  spinosior, 325
  versicolor, 325
Oregon-myrtle, 237
Osage-orange, 229
Osmanthus americanus, 357
  megacarpus, 357
Ostrya knowltonii, 163
  virginiana, 163
Oxydendrum arboreum, 337

Palm, California, 371
Palmetto, Cabbage, 371
  Texas, 371
Paloverde, Blue, 279
  Border, 279
  Yellow, 279
Paper-mulberry, 227
Paradise Flower, 269
Parkinsonia aculeata, 279
Paulownia tomentosa, 361
Pawpaw, 237
Pea Tree, 281
Peach, 259
Pear, 244
Pecan, 145
Persea americana, 239
  borbonia, 239
  palustris, 239
Persimmon, Common, 341
  Texas, 341
Photinia arbutifolia, 258
Picea, 48
  abies, 48
  breweriana, 59
  canadensis, 51
  engelmannii, 57
  glauca, 51
  glauca albertiana, 51
  Key to species, 49
  mariana, 53
  pungens, 61
  rubens, 55
  sitchensis, 59
Pine, 2
  Apache, 33
  Arizona, 31
  Austrian, 17
  Bishop, 41
  Bristlecone, 13
  Chihuahua, 35
  Coulter, 37
  Digger, 37
  Eastern White, 9

Pine (*continued*)
 Foxtail, 13
 Jack, 19
 Jeffrey, 33
 Knobcone, 39
 Limber, 11
 Loblolly, 25
 Lodgepole, 35
 Longleaf, 27
 Mexican Pinyon, 15
 Monterey, 39
 Norway, 17
 Parry Pinyon, 15
 Pinyon, 15
 Pitch, 21
 Pond, 21
 Ponderosa, 31
 Red, 17
 Sand, 25
 Scotch, 17
 Shore, 35
 Shortleaf, 23
 Singleleaf Pinyon, 15
 Slash, 29
 Spruce, 23
 Sugar, 7
 Table-mountain, 29
 Torrey, 41
 Virginia, 19
 Washoe, 33
 Western White, 9
 Western Yellow, 31
 Whitebark, 11
Pinus, 2
 albicaulis, 11
 apacheca, 33
 aristata, 13
 attenuata, 39
 balfouriana, 13
 banksiana, 19
 caribaea, 29
 cembroides, 15
 clausa, 25
 contorta, 35
 contorta latifolia, 35
 coulteri, 37
 echinata, 23
 edulis, 15
 elliottii, 29
 engelmannii, 33
 flexilis, 11
 flexilis reflexa, 11
 glabra, 23
 insignis, 39

 jeffreyi, 33
 Key to species, 3
 lambertiana, 7
 leiophylla chihuahuana, 35
 monophylla, 15
 monticola, 9
 muricata, 41
 murrayana, 35
 nigra, 17
 palustris, 27
 ponderosa, 31
 ponderosa arizonica, 31
 ponderosa scopulorum, 31
 pungens, 29
 quadrifolia, 15
 radiata, 39
 resinosa, 17
 rigida, 21
 sabiniana, 37
 serotina, 21
 x sondereggeri, 27
 strobiformis, 11
 strobus, 9
 sylvestris, 17
 taeda, 25
 torreyana, 41
 virginiana, 19
 washoensis, 33
Pistache, Texas, 309
Pistacia texana, 309
Planera aquatica, 221
Planertree, 221
Planetree, 243
Platanus acerifolia, 243
 occidentalis, 243
 orientalis, 243
 racemosa, 243
 wrightii, 243
Plum, American, 265
 Canada, 265
 Chickasaw, 257
 Damson, 256, 265
 Flatwoods, 257
 Garden, 256, 265
 Hortulan, 256
 Inch, 257
 Klamath, 257
 Mexican, 257
 Wildgoose, 257
Poinciana gilliesii, 266
 mexicana, 266
 Paradise, 266
Poison Ivy, 289
Poison Sumac, 289

Pondcypress, 93
Poplar, 120
    Balm-of-Gilead, 127
    Balsam, 127
    Black, 123
    Carolina, 125
    Gray, 123
    Lombardy, 123
    White, 123
Populus, 120
    x acuminata, 129
    alba, 123
    angustifolia, 129
    balsamifera, 127
    balsamifera subcordata, 127
    x canadensis, 125
    x canescens, 123
    deltoides, 125
    fremontii, 125
    fremontii wislizenii, 125
    grandidentata, 123
    heterophylla, 125
    Key to species, 121
    nigra, 123
    nigra italica, 123
    x parryi, 125
    palmeri, 125
    sargentii, 125
    tacamahacca, 127
    tremuloides, 123
    trichocarpa, 127
Port-Orford-cedar, 103
Possumhaw, 291
Prickly-ash, 285
Prosopis juliflora, 271
    odorata, 271
    pubescens, 271
Prunus, 256
    alleghanensis, 257
    americana, 265
    amygdalus, 256, 259
    angustifolia, 257
    armeniaca, 256, 259
    avium, 256, 259
    caroliniana, 258
    cerasus, 256, 259
    domestica, 256, 265
    emarginata, 263
    hortulana, 257
    ilicifolia, 258
    insititia, 256, 265
    Key to species, 257
    lyonii, 258
    mahaleb, 256

    mexicana, 257
    munsoniana, 257
    myrtifolia, 258
    nigra, 265
    pensylvanica, 263
    persica, 257, 259
    serotina, 261
    spinosa, 256
    subcordata, 257
    triloba, 256
    umbellata, 257
    virginiana, 261
    virginiana demissa, 261
    virginiana melanocarpa, 261
Pseudotsuga macrocarpa, 63
    menziesii, 63
    taxifolia, 63
    taxifolia glauca, 63
Ptelea angustifolia, 285
    trifoliata, 285
Pyrus communis, 244

Quercus, 174
    agrifolia, 211
    alba, 181
    arizonica, 209
    arkansana, 178
    bicolor, 191
    borealis, 193
    catesbaei, 201
    chapmani, 175
    chrysolepis, 213
    chrysolepis palmeri, 213
    coccinea, 197
    douglasii, 185
    dumosa, 178
    durandii, 175
    ellipsoidalis, 199
    emoryi, 209
    engelmanni, 178
    falcata, 195
    falcata pagodaefolia, 195
    gambelii, 185
    garryana, 187
    georgiana, 177
    graciliformis, 174
    gravesii, 174
    grisea, 174
    havardii, 174
    hypoleuca, 213
    hypoleucoides, 213
    ilicifolia, 176
    imbricaria, 205
    incana, 205

Quercus (*continued*)
kelloggii, 201
Key to species, 175
laceyi, 174
laevis, 201
laurifolia, 205
leptophylla, 185
lobata, 187
lyrata, 183
macrocarpa, 181
marilandica, 197
michauxii, 189
mohriana, 175
montana, 189
muehlenbergii, 191
myrtifolia, 178
nigra, 203
novomexicana, 185
nuttallii, 199
oblongifolia, 207
palustris, 199
phellos, 203
prinoides, 176
prinus, 189
pungens, 175
reticulata, 179
robur, 174
rubra, 193, 195
shumardii, 195
stellata, 183
tomentella, 178
toumeyi, 179
undulata, 175
utahensis, 185
velutina, 193
virginiana, 207
wislizenii, 211
Quininebush, 258

Redbay, 239
Redbud, California, 273
Eastern, 273
Texas, 273
Redcedar, Eastern, 109
Southern, 109
Western, 97
Redgum, 241
Redwood, 89
Rhamnus californica ursina, 315
caroliniana, 315
cathartica, 315
crocea ilicifolia, 315, 317
frangula, 315

purshiana, 315
purshiana betulaefolia, 315
Rhododendron catawbiense, 335
Great, 335
macrophyllum, 335
maximum, 335
Pacific, 335
Rosebay, 335
Rhus copallina, 289
glabra, 289
integrifolia, 289
kearneyi, 289
lanceolata, 289
laurina, 289
microphylla, 289
ovata, 289
radicans, 289
typhina, 289
vernix, 289
Robinia kelseyi, 283
neomexicana, 283
pseudoacacia, 283
viscosa, 283
Russian-olive, 329

Sabal louisiana, 371
palmetto, 371
texana, 371
Saffron-plum, 339
Saguaro, 325
Salix alba, 131
amygdoides, 133
babylonica, 131
bebbiana, 131
bonplandiana, 131
caroliniana, 131
eriocephala, 131
exigua, 131
fragilis, 131
gooddingi, 131
interior, 131
laevigata, 131
lasiandra, 131
lasioepis, 131
mackenzieana, 131
nigra, 133
scouleriana, 131
taxifolia, 131
Sambucus callicarpa, 365
canadensis, 365
glauca, 365
melanocarpa, 365
mexicana, 365

Sambucus (*continued*)
  simpsonii, 365
  velutina, 365
Sapindus drummondii, 313
  marginatus, 313
Sassafras albidum, 239
  varifolium, 239
Sequoia gigantea, 91
  sempervirens, 89
  washingtoniana, 91
  wellingtoniana, 91
Serviceberry, Allegheny, 251
  Downy, 251
  Pacific, 251
Shadbush, 251
Shepherdia argentea, 329
Siberian Pea Tree, 281
Silktree, 271
Silverbell, Carolina, 341
  Little, 341
  Mountain, 341
  Two-wing, 341
Sloe, 257
Smokethorn, 266
Smoketree, 309
Snowbell, Bigleaf, 343
Soapberry, Florida, 313
  Western, 313
Sophora affinis, 281
  secundiflora, 281
  Texas, 281
Sorbus americana, 249
  americana sitchensis, 249
  aucuparia, 249
  decora, 249
  sitchensis, 249
Sourwood, 337
Spanish-bayonet, 369
Spruce, Black, 53
  Blue, 61
  Brewer, 59
  Colorado Blue, 61
  Engelmann, 57
  Norway, 48
  Red, 55
  Sitka, 59
  Western White, 51
  White, 51
Stinking-cedar, 117
Styrax grandifolia, 343
Sugarberry, 225
Sumac, Kearney, 289
  Laurel, 289
  Littleleaf, 289

Mahogany, 289
Poison, 289
Prairie Shining, 289
Shining, 289
Smooth, 289
Staghorn, 289
Sugar, 289
Swampbay, 239
Swamp-privet, 357
Sweetbay, 231
Sweetgum, 241
Sweetleaf, Common, 343
Swietenia mahagoni, 287
Sycamore, American, 243
  Arizona, 243
  California, 243
Symplocos tinctoria, 343

Tamarack, 41
Tamarisk, 308
Tamarix gallica, 308
Tanoak, 173
Tasajo, 325
Taxodium distichum, 93
  distichum nutans, 93
  mucronatum, 93
Taxus brevifolia, 119
  floridana, 119
Tecoma stans, 363
Tesota, 267
Thuja occidentalis, 97
  orientalis, 97
  plicata, 97
Tilia americana, 319
  caroliniana, 319
  cordata, 319
  floridana, 319
  heterophylla, 319
  vulgaris, 319
Torreya californica, 117
  Florida, 117
  taxifolia, 117
Toxicodendron radicans, 289
  vernix, 289
Tree-of-Heaven, 287
Tree Sparkleberry, 337
Trumpetflower, 363
Tsuga, 64
  canadensis, 67
  caroliniana, 67
  heterophylla, 69
  Key to species, 65
  mertensiana, 71
Tuliptree, 235

Tumion californicum, 117
  taxifolium, 117
Tupelo, Bear, 327
  Black, 327
  Ogeechee, 327
  Swamp, 327
  Water, 327

Ulmus, 214
  alata, 217
  americana, 217
  carpinifolia, 215
  crassifolia, 217
  fulva, 219
  glabra, 215
  Key to species, 215
  parvifolia, 215
  procera, 215
  pumila, 215
  racemosa, 219
  rubra, 219
  serotina, 217
  thomasii, 219
Umbellularia californica, 237
Ungnadia speciosa, 313

Vaccinium arboreum, 337
Vauquelinia californica, 245
  Torrey, 245
Viburnum lentago, 367
  nudum, 367
  obovatum, 367
  Possumhaw, 367
  prunifolium, 367
  rufidulum, 367
  Walter, 367

Wahoo, 293
Walnut, Arizona, 134
  Black, 137
  California, 134
  English, 134
  Hinds, 134

Little, 134
Persian, 134
Washingtonia *arizonica*, 371
  filifera, 371
  robusta, 371
Waterelm, 221
Waterlocust, 277
Waxmyrtle, Odorless, 135
  Pacific, 135
  Southern, 135
White-cedar, Atlantic, 105
  Hinoki, 103
  Northern, 97
  Sawara, 103
  Southern, 105
Willow, Black, 133
  Crack, 131
  Desert, 359
  Peachleaf, 133
  Weeping, 131
  White, 131
Winterberry, Mountain, 291
Witch-hazel, 241

Yaupon, 291
Yellow-poplar, 235
Yellowwood, 275
Yew, Florida, 119
  Pacific, 119
Yucca aloifolia, 369
  brevifolia, 369
  elata, 369
  faxoniana, 369
  gloriosa, 369
  mohavensis, 369
  Moundlily, 369
  schottii, 369
  Soaptree, 369
  torreyi, 369
  treculeana, 369

Zanthoxylum americanum, 285
  clava-herculis, 285